GUIA VISUAL PUBLIFOLHA

PORTUGUESE

PHRASE BOOK FOR TRAVELLERS IN BRAZIL

PUBLIFOLHA

PUBLIFOLHA

www.publifolha.com.br

© 2001 Publifolha – Divisão de Publicações da Empresa Folha da Manhã S.A.
Projeto editorial e gráfico da série © 2001 Dorling Kindersley, Londres

ISBN 978-85-7402-258-1
5ª reimpressão da 3ª edição

PUBLIFOLHA

Divisão de Publicações do Grupo Folha

Al. Barão de Limeira, 401, 6º andar
CEP 01202-900, São Paulo, SP
Tel.: (11) 3224-2186/2187/2197
www.publifolha.com.br

COORDENAÇÃO DE PROJETO
PUBLIFOLHA
Assistência Editorial: Lizandra Magon de Almeida, Fabricio Waltrick
Coordenação de Produção Gráfica: Marcio Soares
Assistência de Produção Gráfica: Soraia Pauli Scarpa

PRODUÇÃO EDITORIAL
EDITORA PÁGINA VIVA
Edição e editoração eletrônica: Editora Página Viva
Consultoria e versões: Ken Dean

FOTOS DA CAPA
Caio Vilela (Rio de Janeiro), Ricardo de Vicq de Cumptich
(feijoada), Folha Imagem (escultura Os Candangos, de Bruno Giorgi, em Brasília),
Subgerência de Turismo – Geplan (boi-bumbá), Folha Imagem (garça).
A Empresa Brasileira de Correios e Telégrafos generosamente
autorizou o uso das imagens de selos.

*Este livro foi impresso em agosto de 2007
pela Prol Gráfica, sobre papel offset 90 g/m².*

CONTENTS

PREFACE

This *Portuguese Phrase Book for Travellers in Brazil* was created with the objective of helping travellers around the world, whether on business or as tourists. It includes a complete range of words and useful phrases, divided into thematic sections like Hotels, Driving, Shopping and Services, Health and so on, as well as a mini-dictionary with around 2,000 words. It offers also a manual of terms connected to brazilian cooking, with around 600 items ranging from typical dishes, ingredients and recipes, to presentation.

Typical answers to questions that you need to make during your trip to Brazil are highlighted, as well as expressions or instructions that you will probably see or hear. The introduction gives basic pronunciation tips for the language; in the main body of text the pronunciation of words and phrases is imitated with syllables in English.

The pronunciation and expressions indicated always correspond to Portuguese spoken in Brazil. The differences in relation to the Portuguese of Portugal, however, are not great and not of crucial importance, since you will be able to make yourself understood in both countries.

INTRODUCTION

PRONUNCIATION

Instead of complicated pronunciation keys, totally incompatible with the objectives of this guide, the editors have opted for so-called imitated pronunciation. All you need to do is read the pronunciation key as if the words were written in English –in this way you will have no difficulty making yourself understood. Some general information concerning Portuguese, however, may be helpful.

In the first place, it is important to note that Portuguese has a distinct division of syllables. Each syllable should be pronounced as clearly as possible, so they are reasonably distinct from each other. This is why this guide has decided to separate each unit of sound with a hyphen, in the words and phrases which might cause most difficulty to readers.

Another important point to bear in mind is the need for correct stress. Each word in Portuguese has a clearly defined tonic syllable, in most cases exactly where an English speaker would not expect to find it. This is one more reason why you should pronounce each syllable clearly, taking care to place the stress correctly. In this guide, the tonic syllables are indicated by underlining.

Finally, remember that the phonetic transcriptions presented in this guide have no scientific or academic pretensions. They were put together to meet the expectations of an English speaker who wants to be reasonably well understood in any part of Brazil. Do not be concerned if you find the same word transcribed in two different ways: the modification may correspond to different needs of expression, or simply to subtle regional differences.

NOUNS AND ARTICLES

In contrast with what happens in English, in Portuguese nouns may be of two different genders: masculine or feminine. Distinct articles correspond to these: **o** for masculine (plural **os**) and **a** for feminine (plural **as**); **um** and **uma** are the indefinite forms. Nouns ending in 'o' are masculine, and nouns ending in 'a' are feminine. For the few cases when nouns end in other letters, the best thing to do is to learn them as you go along.

USEFUL EVERYDAY PHRASES

YES, NO

Yes/No
Sim/Não
seeng/nowng

Excellent!
Ótimo!
oh-tee-moo

Don't!
Não faça isso!
nowng fah-ssa eessoo

OK
OK
oh-kay

That's fine
Está bem
ess-tah beng

That's right
É verdade/Está certo
eh vehr-dah-gee/ess-tah sair-too

GREETINGS, INTRODUCTIONS

How do you do, pleased to meet you
Prazer em conhecê-lo (a)
prah-sair ayng kon-yeh-sseh-loo (lah)

Good morning/Good evening/Good night
Bom dia/Boa tarde/Boa noite
bong dee-ah/bo-ah tahr-gee/bo-ah noych

Goodbye
Até logo/Adeus
ateh loh-goo/adeh-ooss

How are you?
Como vai?
koh-moo vah-ee

My name is ...
Meu nome é ...
mel noh-mee eh

What's your name?
Qual o seu nome?
kwal oh sel noh-mee

What's his/her name?
Qual o nome dele (a)?
kwal oh noh-mee deh-lee (lah)

May I introduce ...?
Posso apresentar-lhe ...?
poh-ssoo ah-preh-zayn-tarl-yeh

This is ... *(when introducing a man/woman)*
Este (a) é ...
esstee (ah) eh

Hello
Olá
olah

Hi!
Oi!
oy

Bye!
Adeus
adeh-ooss

See you later
Até mais tarde
ateh mah-ys tahr-gee

It's been nice meeting you
Muito prazer em conhecê-lo (a)
mooytoo prah-zehr ayng kon-yeh-sseh-loo (ah)

PLEASE, THANK YOU, APOLOGIES

Thank you
Obrigado (a)
obreegah-doo (ah)

No, thank you
Não, obrigado (a)
nowng, obreegah-doo (ah)

Yes, please
Sim, por favor
seeng, poor fah-vor

Please
Por favor
poor fah-vor

Excuse me!
Desculpe-me!
desskoolp-mee!

Sorry!
Desculpe!
desskoolp

I'm really sorry
Sinto muito!
seento mooytoo

It was/wasn't my fault!
Foi/Não foi culpa minha!
foy/nowng foy kool-pah meen-ya

WHERE, HOW, ASKING

Excuse me, please
Com licença
kon lee-ss<u>ay</u>n-sah

Can you tell me …?
Pode me dizer …?
p<u>o</u>d-mee dees<u>ai</u>r

Can I have …?
Pode me dar …?
p<u>o</u>d-mee d<u>a</u>hr

Would you like a …?
Deseja um (a) …?
de-z<u>eh</u>-jah oom (<u>oo</u>ma)

Would you like to …?
Gostaria de …?
gostr<u>ee</u>h-ya dee

Is there … here?
Há … aqui?
ah … ak<u>ee</u>

What is that?
O que é isso?
ook<u>ee</u> eh <u>ee</u>ssoo

Where can I get …?
Onde posso conseguir …?
<u>o</u>ndee p<u>o</u>h-ssoo kon-sseh-gu<u>ee</u>r

How much is it?
Quanto custa?
kw<u>a</u>ntoo k<u>oo</u>s-tah

Where is the …?
Onde está o (a) …?
<u>o</u>ndee ess-t<u>a</u>h oh (ah)

Where are the toilets, please?
Por favor, onde fica o banheiro?
poor fah-vor, ondee feekah oh ban-yey-roo

ABOUT ONESELF

I'm from …
Sou de …
soul dee

I'm … years old
Tenho … anos
ten-yu … ah-noos

I'm a … *(profession)*
Sou …
soul

I'm married/single/divorced
Sou casado (a)/solteiro (a)/divorciado (a)
soul kah-zah-doo (dah)/soul-tay-roo (rah)/dee-vor-see-ah-doo (dah)

I have … sisters/brothers/children/sons/daughters
Tenho … irmãs/irmãos/crianças/filhos/filhas
ten-yu … eer-mus/eer-mowngs/feel-yos/feel-yas

LIKES, DESLIKES, SOCIALIZING

I like/I love …
Gosto (de) …
gohstoo (dee)

I don't like …
Não gosto (de) …
nowng gohstoo (dee)

I like swimming/travelling
Gosto de nadar/viajar
gohstoo dee nah-dahr/vee-yah-jahr

I hate …
Detesto …
deh-tehs-too

Do you like …?
Gosta de …?
gohstah dee

It's delicious/awful!
É delicioso/horrível!
eh deh-lee-ssee-yo-soo/oh-ree-vel

I don't drink/smoke
Não bebo/fumo
nowng beh-boh/foo-moh

Do you mind if I smoke?
Importa-se se eu fumar?
een-pohr-tah-see see el foo-mahr

I don't eat meat or fish
Não como carne nem peixe
nowng koh-moo kar-nee nayn paysh

What would you like (to drink)?
O que deseja (beber)?
ookee deh-zeh-jah (beh-behr)

I would like a …
Gostaria de um (a) …
gostreeh-ya dee oom (ooma)

Nothing for me, thanks
Não quero nada, obrigado (a)
nowng keh-roo nah-dah, obreegah-doo (ah)

I'll get this one
Ficarei com este (a)
fee-kah-ray kon esstee (tah)

1

Cheers! (toast)
Saúde!
sah-oo-dee

I would like to …
Gostaria de …
gostreeh-ya dee

Let's go to São Paulo/to the cinema/the exhibition
Vamos a São Paulo/ao cinema/à exposição
vah-moos ah sowng pahl-loh/al see-neh-mah/ah ehs-poh-zee-sowng

Let's go swimming/for a walk
Vamos nadar/dar um passeio
vah-moos nah-dahr/dahr oom pah-ssay-yu

What's the weather like?
Como está o tempo?
koh-moo ess-tah oh tayn-poo

The weather's awful
O tempo está péssimo
oh tayn-poo ess-tah peh-ssee-moo

It's pouring down
Está chovendo muito
ess-tah shoh-vayn-doo mooytoo

It's really hot
Está muito quente
ess-tah mooytoo kayn-chee

It's sunny
Está ensolarado
ess-tah ayn-ssoh-lah-rah-doo

It's cold
Está frio
ess-tah free-yu

HELP, PROBLEMS

Can you help me?
Poderia me ajudar?
podreeh-ya mee ah-joo-dahr

I don't understand
Não compreendo
nowng kon-preh-ayn-doo

Do you speak English/German?
O (A) senhor (a) fala inglês/alemão?
oh (ah) seen-your (seen-yoh-rah) fah-la een-glehs/ah-leh-mowng

Does anyone here speak English?
Alguém aqui fala inglês?
ahl-gayn akee fah-la een-glehs

I can't speak Portuguese
Não falo português
nowng fah-loo pohr-too-guehs

I don't know
Não sei
nowng say

What's wrong?
Qual é o problema?
kwal eh oh proh-bleh-mah

Please, speak more slowly
Por favor, fale mais devagar
poor fah-vor, fah-lee mah-ys dee-vah-gahr

Please write it down for me
Por favor, escreva isso para mim
poor fah-vor, ehs-kreh-vah eessoo prah meeng

I've lost my way
Eu me perdi
el mee pehr-gee

Go away!
Vá embora!
vah ayn-boh-rah

TALKING TO RECEPTIONISTS

I have an appointment with …
Tenho uma reunião com …
ten-yu ooma reyu-nee-owng kon

I'd like to see …
Gostaria de ver …
gostree-ya dee vehr

Here's my card
Aqui está meu cartão
akee ess-tah mel kartowng

My company is …
Sou da empresa …
soul dah ayn-preh-sah

May I use your phone?
Posso usar seu telefone?
poh-soo oo-zahr sel teh-leh-foh-nee

THINGS YOU'LL SEE

aberto	open
água potável	drinking water
aluga-se	for rent
andar térreo	ground floor
banheiros	toilets
bar, lanchonete	snack bar
caixa	till, cash point
dias úteis	working days
elevador	lift, elevator

→

empurrar	push
entrada	way in, entrance
entrada grátis	admission free
entrada proibida	no admittance
estrada	road
fechado	closed
fechado para férias	closed for holiday period
feriados	public holidays
horário de funcionamento	opening hours
horário de visitas	visiting hours
informação turística	tourist information
liquidação, saldo	sale
livre	vacant, free
ocupado	busy
pintura fresca	wet paint
primeiro andar	first floor
proibido	forbidden
proibido ...	please do not ...
puxar	pull
reservado	reserved
rua	street
saída	exit, way out
saída de emergência	emergency exit
sanitários	toilets
senhoras, damas	ladies
senhores, cavalheiros	gents
vende-se	for sale

THINGS YOU'LL HEAR

aqui está!	here you are!
até logo	goodbye
até mais tarde	see you later
bem, bom	good, fine
boa viagem!	have a nice trip!
como vai/vão?	how are you?
como vão as coisas?	how are things?
como?, perdão?	pardon?
cuidado!, atenção!	look out!, attention!
de nada,	you're welcome,
não há de quê	don't mention it, please
desculpe-me	excuse me
entre!	come in!
está bem	that's right
exatamente	exactly
muito bem, obrigado (a)	very well, thank you
muito obrigado (a)	thank you very much
não compreendo	I don't understand
não por isso	don't mention it, please
não sei	I don't know
o que disse?	what did you say?
obrigado (a)	thanks
obrigado (a), igualmente	thank you, the same to you
oi!	hi!
olá!	hello!
prazer em conhecê-lo (a)	nice to meet you
sim	yes
sinto muito!	I'm so sorry!
sirva-se o (a) senhor (a)	help yourself
mesmo (a)	
verdade?	really?
– e o (a) senhor (a)?	– and you?

COLLOQUIALISMS

You may hear these: to use some of them yourself could be risky!

bem feito!	it serves you right!
cala a boca!	shut up!
cara	man, bloke
cretino, idiota	idiot, fool
cuidado!	watch out!
droga!, maldição!	damn!
duvido	hard to believe
e daí?	so what?
é horrível!	it's awful!
é mesmo?	really?
então faça como quiser!	do as you please!, please, do!
experimente!	just try!
fantástico!, maravilhoso!	brilliant!
garota	girl
graças a Deus!	thank God!
legal	nice, cool
maldito	cursed
melhor assim	so much the better
meu Deus!	my God!
mexa-se!, apresse-se!	hurry up!
não acredito!	I can't believe it!
por Deus!	by God!
que absurdo!	what an absurd!
que nojo!	it's disgusting!
saia do caminho!	get out of the way!
suma!, dê o fora!	get lost!
tomar um porre	to get sozzled
tudo bem!	that's fine!, it's OK!
vá para o inferno!	go to hell!
vai tomar banho!	get lost!
você deve estar brincando!	you must be joking!
você está louco!	you must be crazy!

DAYS, MONTHS, SEASONS

Sunday	domingo	*doh-meen-goo*
Monday	segunda-feira	*seh-goon-dah fay-ra*
Tuesday	terça-feira	*tehr-ssah fay-ra*
Wednesday	quarta-feira	*kwar-tah fay-ra*
Thursday	quinta-feira	*keen-tah fay-ra*
Friday	sexta-feira	*sehs-tah fay-ra*
Saturday	sábado	*sah-bah-doo*
January	janeiro	*jah-nay-ro*
February	fevereiro	*feh-veh-ray-ro*
March	março	*mahr-sso*
April	abril	*ah-breel*
May	maio	*mah-you*
June	junho	*joon-you*
July	julho	*jool-you*
August	agosto	*ah-gohs-to*
September	setembro	*seh-tayn-bro*
October	outubro	*oul-too-bro*
November	novembro	*noh-vayn-bro*
December	dezembro	*deh-zayn-bro*
Spring	primavera	*pree-mah-vair-rah*
Summer	verão	*veh-rowng*
Fall/Autumn	outono	*oul-toh-noo*
Winter	inverno	*een-vair-noo*
Christmas	Natal	*nah-tahl*
Christmas Eve	Noite de Natal	*noych dee nah-tahl*
Good Friday	Sexta da Paixão	*sehs-tah dah pahyshowng*
Easter	Páscoa	*pahs-kwa*
New Year	Ano-Novo	*ahno noh-voo*
New Year's Eve	Véspera de Ano-Novo	*vaispra dee ahno noh-voo*
Whitsun	Pentecostes	*payn-teh-kohs-tehs*

NUMBERS

0 zero *zairo*
1 um *oom*
2 dois *doys*
3 três *trays*
4 quatro *kwah-tro*
5 cinco *seen-ko*
6 seis *seh-ees*
7 sete *sech*
8 oito *oyto*
9 nove *nov*

10 dez *dehs*
11 onze *onzeh*
12 doze *doh-zeh*
13 treze *treh-zeh*
14 catorze *kah-tohr-zeh*
15 quinze *keen-zeh*
16 dezesseis *deh-zeh-seh-ees*
17 dezessete *deh-zeh-sech*
18 dezoito *deh-zoy-too*
19 dezenove *deh-zeh-nov*

20 vinte *veen-chee*
21 vinte e um *veen-chee oom*
22 vinte e dois *veen-chee doys*
30 trinta *treen-tah*
31 trinta e um *treen-tahy oom*
32 trinta e dois *treen-tahy doys*
40 quarenta *kwah-rayn-tah*
50 cinquenta *seen-kwayn-tah*
60 sessenta *seh-ssayn-tah*
70 setenta *seh-tayn-tah*
80 oitenta *oy-tayn-tah*
90 noventa *noh-vayn-tah*
100 cem *sayn*
110 cento e dez *sayn-toh eh dehs*
200 duzentos *doo-zayn-toos*
300 trezentos *treh-zayn-toos*
400 quatrocentos *kwa-troh-ssayn-toos*
500 quinhentos *keen-yayn-toos*
600 seiscentos *seh-ees-ssayn-toos*
700 setecentos *seh-chee-ssayn-toos*
1.000 mil *meel*
54.250 cinquenta e quatro mil duzentos e cinquenta
seen-kwayn-tah eh kwah-tro meel doo-zayn-toos eh seen-kwayn-tah
1.000.000 um milhão *oom meel-yowng*

TIME

today	hoje	*oh-jee*
yesterday	ontem	*ohn-tayn*
tomorrow	amanhã	*ah-man-yan*
the day before yesterday	anteontem	*ahn-chee-ohn-tayn*
the day after tomorrow	depois de amanhã	*dehpoys dee ah-man-yan*
this week	esta semana	*esstah seh-mah-nah*
last week	semana passada	*seh-mah-nah passah-dah*
next week	semana que vem	*seh-mah-nah kee vayn*
this morning	esta manhã	*esstah man-yan*
this afternoon	esta tarde	*esstah tahr-gee*
this evening	esta noite	*esstah noych*
tonight	hoje à noite	*oh-jee ah noych*
yesterday afternoon	ontem à tarde	*ohn-tayn ah tahr-gee*
last night	ontem à noite	*ohn-tayn ah noych*
tomorrow morning	amanhã de manhã	*ah-man-yan dee man-yan*
tomorrow night	amanhã à noite	*ah-man-yan ah noych*
in three days	daqui a três dias	*dah-kee ah trays dee-ahs*
three days ago	três dias atrás	*trays dee-ahs ah-trahs*
late	tarde	*tahr-gee*
early	cedo	*seh-doo*
soon	logo	*loh-goo*
later on	mais tarde	*mah-ys tahr-gee*
at the moment	neste momento	*nehs-teh moh-mayn-too*
a second	um segundo	*oom seh-goon-doo*
a minute	um minuto	*oom mee-noo-too*
two minutes	dois minutos	*doys mee-noo-toos*
a quarter of one hour	15 minutos	*keen-zeh mee-noo-toos*
half an hour	meia hora	*may-yah orah*
three quarters of one hour	45 minutos	*kwah-rayn-tah eh seen-ko mee-noo-toos*

one hour	uma hora	_oo_ma _o_rah
a day	um dia	oom _dee_-ah
a week	uma semana	_oo_ma seh-_mah_-nah
fortnight,	15 dias,	_kee_n-zeh dee-ahs,
two weeks	duas semanas	_doo_-ahs seh-_mah_-nahs
a month	um mês	oom m_eh_s
a year	um ano	oom _ah_no
that day	aquele dia	ah-k_eh_-leh d_ee_-ah
every day	todos os dias	t_oh_-doos ohs d_ee_-ahs
all day long	o dia todo	oh d_ee_-ah t_oh_-doo
the next day	no dia seguinte	noh d_ee_-ah seh-gu_ee_n-chee

TELLING THE TIME

It's common, in Brazil, to use the 24 hour clock to tell the time. If you choose to do so everyone will understand. It is, however, a rather formal means of expression, normally reserved for occasions when you need to be really precise. In day-to-day usage, people are much more likely to use a system which divides the day into four periods: **manhã** (or 'morning': from around 5:00 a.m. to midday), **tarde** (or 'afternoon': from midday to around 6:00 p.m., variations arising according to the time of the year), **noite** (or 'night': from around 6:00 p.m. to midnight) and **madrugada** (or 'the early hours': from around midnight to 5:00 a.m., but some people also refer to this period as **manhã**). Thus, for example, **seis da manhã** means 'six a.m.'; **quatro da tarde**, 'four p.m.'; **duas da madrugada**, 'two a.m.'; and **nove da noite**, 'nine p.m.'.

If you want to ask what the time is, you say **Que horas são?**. If it's exactly on the hour you use the word **horas** in response, as in **são cinco horas** ('it's five o'clock'). To refer to how many minutes are left to the hour, you use **para** or 'to', as in **são dez para as sete** ('it's ten to seven'; note the use of the article before the hour). To refer to how many minutes have passed the hour, you use **e** or 'and', as in **são cinco e vinte** ('it's twenty past five'). Finally, 'half' is expressed with **meia**, as in **três e meia** ('half past three').

what time is it?	que horas são?	*kee orahs sowng*
it's one o'clock	é uma hora	*eh ooma orah*
it's two/three/ four o'clock	são duas/três/quatro horas	*sowng doo-ahs/trays/ kwah-tro orahs*
ten past one	uma e dez	*ooma eh dehs*
quarter past one	uma e quinze	*ooma eh keen-zeh*
half past one	uma e meia	*ooma eh may-yah*
twenty to two	vinte para as duas	*veen-chee prahs doo-ahs*
quarter to two	quinze para as duas	*keen-zeh prahs doo-ahs*
two o'clock	duas horas	*doo-ahs orahs*
one p.m.	uma da tarde	*ooma dah tahr-gee*
half past four p.m.	quatro e meia da tarde	*kwah-tro eh may-yah dah tahr-gee*
at half past five	às cinco e meia	*ahs seen-ko eh may-yah*
at seven o'clock	às sete horas	*ahs sech orahs*
noon	meio-dia	*may-yoh dee-ah*
midnight	meia-noite	*may-yah noych*

THE CALENDAR

Portuguese differs from English in that the days of the month are expressed in cardinal numbers (see page 19). The only exception is the first day of the month, which is called **primeiro**. Between the day, which comes first, and the month, the preposition **de** ('of') is used.

May first	primeiro de maio	*pree-may-roo dee mah-you*
April second	dois de abril	*doys dee ah-breel*
June third	três de junho	*trays dee joon-you*
August fourth	quatro de agosto	*kwatro dee ah-gohs-to*
May fifth	cinco de maio	*seenko dee mah-you*
April sixth	seis de abril	*seh-ees dee ah-breel*
June seventh	sete de junho	*sech dee joon-you*
July ninth	nove de julho	*nov dee jool-you*
July twentieth	vinte de julho	*veen-chee dee jool-you*

HOTELS

In Brazil, the word 'motel' refers to establishments specifically catering for couples, normally with other intentions than that of sleeping. There is no social stigma attached to motels, however; if you don't mind the décor, they can be a useful option for spending the night (never the day). **Pousadas** are usually small, family run hotels like our 'bed-and-breakfast'. A **hotel fazenda**, literally 'farm hotel', is an establishment aimed at families, especially those with young children, situated in the countryside, with various attractions like horse riding, swimming pools, sports facilities and lots of space. They are not usually the destination of foreign tourists.

Hotels themselves are classified according to a five star system, although the level of comfort and the degree of standardization is not the same as in the US or UK. They vary from the very simple, with shared bathrooms, to luxury hotels of international standards.

The main cities, like São Paulo and Rio de Janeiro, benefit from a hotel system able to cope with demand all year round. Smaller cities, especially those popular with tourists, are often very busy, and it's advisable to book in advance.

USEFUL WORDS AND PHRASES

balcony	sacada	*sah-kah-dah*
bath (tub)	banheira	*ban-yey-rah*
bathroom	banheiro	*ban-yey-roo*
bed and breakfast	alojamento com café-da-manhã	*ah-loh-jah-mayn-too kon kah-feh dah man-yan*
bed and breakfast hotel	pousada, pensão familiar	*poul-zah-dah, pensowng fah-meel-yar*
bed	cama	*kah-mah*
bedroom	quarto	*kwar-too*
bill	conta	*kohn-tah*
breakfast	café-da-manhã	*kah-feh dah man-yan*

car park, parking lot	estacionamento	ehs-tah-seeyo-nah-maуn-too
dining room	sala de jantar	sah-lah dee jahn-tahr
dinner	jantar	jahn-tahr
double bed	cama de casal	kah-mah dee kah-zahl
double room	quarto duplo	kwar-too dooploo
full board	pensão completa	pensowng kon-pleh-tah
guesthouse	pensão	pensowng
half board	meia pensão	maу-yah pensowng
hotel	hotel	oh-tehl
key	chave	shah-vee
lift, elevator	elevador	eh-leh-vah-dohr
lobby/foyer	hall de entrada	hall dee ayn-trah-dah
lounge	saguão	sah-guowng
lunch	almoço	ahl-moh-ssoo
maid	camareira	kah-mah-raу-rah
manager	gerente	geh-raуn-tee
receipt	nota, recibo	noh-tah, reh-ssee-boo
receptionist	recepcionista	reh-ssehp-seeyo-nees-tah
reception	recepção	reh-ssehp-ssowng
restaurant	restaurante	rehs-taul-rahn-chee
room service	serviço de quarto	sehr-vee-soo dee kwar-too
room	apartamento	ah-par-tah-maуn-too
shower	chuveiro	shoo-vaу-roo
single bed	cama de solteiro	kah-mah dee soul-taу-roo
single room	quarto para uma pessoa	kwar-too prah ooma peh-soul-ah
sink, washbasin	pia	pee-ah
toilet	sanitário	sah-nee-tah-rryoo
twin room	quarto com duas camas	kwar-too kon doo-ahs kah-mahs

Do you have any vacancies?
Vocês têm vagas?
vohsaуs tayn vah-gahs

I have a reservation
Fiz uma reserva
fees ooma reh-zair-vah

I'd like a single room
Eu gostaria de um quarto para uma pessoa
el gostreeh-ya dee oom kwar-too prah ooma peh-soul-ah

I'd like a room with a bathroom/balcony
Eu gostaria de um quarto com banheiro/sacada
el gostreeh-ya dee oom kwar-too kon ban-yey-roo/sah-kah-dah

I'd like a room for one night/three nights
Eu gostaria de um quarto para uma/três noites
el gostreeh-ya dee oom kwar-too prah ooma/trays noychs

What is the charge per night?
Qual o preço por noite?
kwal oh preh-ssoo poor noych

I don't know yet how long I'll stay
Ainda não sei quanto tempo vou ficar
ah-een-dah nowng say kwantoo tayn-poo voul fee-kahr

When is breakfast/dinner?
A que horas é o café-da-manhã/jantar?
ah kee orahs eh oh kah-feh dah man-yan/jahn-tahr

Please wake me at seven o'clock
Por favor, acorde-me às 7h
poor fah-vor, ah-kord-mee ahs sech orahs

Can I have breakfast in my room?
Podem servir o café-da-manhã em meu quarto?
poh-deng sehr-veer oh kah-feh dah man-yan eng mel kwar-too

I'd like to have some laundry done
Eu gostaria de usar o serviço de lavanderia
el gostreeh-ya dee oo-zahr oh sehr-vee-ssoo dee lah-vahn-dreeh-ya

I'll be back at ten o'clock
Voltarei às 10h
voul-tah-ray ahs dehs orahs

My room number is two zero five/two hundred and five
O número do meu quarto é 205
oh noo-meh-roo doh mel kwar-too eh doo-zehn-toos eh seen-ko

I've booked a double room
Eu reservei um quarto duplo
el reh-zehr-vay oom kwar-too dooploo

I asked for a room with an en suite bathroom
Eu pedi um quarto com banheiro
el peh-gee oom kwar-too kon ban-yey-roo

There is no toilet paper in the bathroom
Não há papel higiênico no banheiro
nowng ah pah-pehl ee-gee-yeh-nee-koo noh ban-yey-roo

The window won't open
A janela não abre
ah jah-neh-lah nowng ah-bree

The lift/shower isn't working
O elevador/chuveiro não está funcionando
oh eh-leh-vah-dohr/shoo-vay-roo nowng ess-tah foong-seeyo-nahn-doo

There isn't any hot water
Não há água quente
nowng ah ahgwa kayn-chee

The socket in the bathroom doesn't work
A tomada do banheiro não funciona
ah toh-mah-dah doh ban-yey-roo nowng foong-seeyoh-nah

I'm leaving tomorrow
Vou embora amanhã
voul ayn-boh-rah ah-man-yan

When do I have to liberate the room?
A que horas devo desocupar o quarto?
ah kee orahs deh-voh deh-zoh-koo-pahr oh kwar-too

Can I have the bill, please?
Minha conta, por favor?
meen-ya kon-tah, poor fah-vor

I'll pay by credit card
Vou pagar com cartão de crédito
voul pah-gahr kon kartowng dee kreh-dee-too

I'll pay cash
Vou pagar em dinheiro
voul pah-gahr eng deen-yey-roo

Can you get me a taxi, please?
Pode me chamar um táxi, por favor?
pod-mee shah-mahr oom tahk-see, poor fah-vor

Can you recommend another hotel?
Pode me recomendar outro hotel?
pod-mee re-koh-mayn-dahr oul-tro oh-tehl

THINGS YOU'LL SEE

almoço	lunch
alojamento com café-da-manhã	bed and breakfast
andar térreo	ground floor
banheiro	bathroom
café-da-manhã	breakfast
chave	key
chuveiro	shower
conta	bill, check
elevador	lift, elevator
empurre	push
entrada	entrance, way in
escadas	stairs

→

estacionamento reservado aos hóspedes	parking reserved for hotel guests only
estacionamento	car park, parking lot
hotel	hotel
jantar	dinner
meia pensão	half board
não há vagas, lotado	no vacancies
pensão completa	full board
pensão	guesthouse
primeiro andar	first floor
puxe	pull
quarto com duas camas	twin room
quarto duplo	double room
quarto para uma pessoa	single room
reserva	reservation
saguão	lounge
saída de emergência	emergency exit

THINGS YOU'LL HEAR

Sinto muito, (o estabelecimento) está lotado
I'm sorry, we're full

Não temos mais quartos para uma pessoa/duplos
There are no single/double rooms left

Para quantas noites?
For how many nights?

Como deseja pagar?
How will you be paying?

Por favor, pague adiantado
Please pay in advance

O senhor deve liberar o quarto antes do meio-dia
You must vacate the room by midday

CAMPING

The Camping Club of Brazil has 43 camping sites in 13 states in the country and charges between US$ 10 and 15 per person. For its more than 80,000 members, however, and for any traveller who presents an international camper's card, there is a 50% discount. The Camping Club sites are usually well-kept and popular, and during the high season (January and February), depending on the location, it is sometimes difficult to get in.

There are also private camping sites. Except in terms of the price, which is usually around US$ 8 per person, it's difficult to generalize about these (they vary greatly in quality, services offered and number of spaces available). It should be borne in mind, however, that Brazil is a country the size of a continent. As a consequence, the chances of finding a camping site without planning ahead are not very good, especially for a tourist unfamiliar with the peculiarities of the population distribution of the country. Never camp beside a road: as well as being against the law, it's extremely dangerous. As to the equipment, it isn't really a problem. Good quality material can be easily found in Brazil; alternatively there are various companies which rent equipment.

USEFUL WORDS AND PHRASES

backpack, rucksack	mochila	*moh-shee-lah*
bonfire	fogueira	*foh-gay-rah*
bucket	balde	*bahl-gee*
camp cot, camp bed	cama dobrável	*kah-mah doh-brah-vel*
campsite	área de camping	*ah-reea dee camping*
caravan site	área de trailers	*ah-reea dee trailers*
charcoal	carvão	*karvowng*
cooking utensils	utensílios de cozinha	*oo-tayn-sseel-lyus dee koo-zeen-ya*
drinking water	água potável	*ahgwa poh-tah-vel*
garbage, rubbish	lixo	*leeshoo*
go camping	ir acampar	*eer ah-kahn-pahr*

ground sheet	lona impermeável	_loh_-nah een-pehr-meh-_ah_-vel
hammock	rede	_reh_-gee
hitchhike	pegar carona	peh-_gahr_ kah-_roh_-nah
rope	corda	_kohr_-dah
saucepans	panelas	pah-_neh_-lahs
sleeping bag	saco de dormir	_sahko_ dee dohr-_meer_
tent	tenda	_taynda_
tokens	fichas	_feeshas_
trailer, caravan	trailer	trailer
youth hostel	albergue da juventude	ahl-_behrg_ dah joo-vayn-_too_-gee

Can I camp here?
Posso acampar aqui?
_pohsso ah-kahn-_pahr_ ak_ee_

Can we park the trailer here?
Podemos estacionar o trailer aqui?
poh-_deh_-moos ess-tah-ssyo_nahr_ oh trailer ak_ee_

Where is the nearest campsite/caravan site?
Onde fica o camping mais próximo?
ondee feekah oh camping mah-ys pr_aw_-ssee-moo

What is the charge per night?
Qual é a taxa por noite?
kwal eh ah _tah_-shah poor noych

I only want to stay for one night
Quero ficar apenas uma noite
_kehro fee-_kahr_ ah-_peh_-nahs _oo_ma noych

How much is it for a week?
Quanto custa por uma semana?
kw_an_too k_oos_-tah poor _oo_ma seh-_mah_-nah

We're leaving tomorrow
Vamos embora amanhã
vah-moos ayn-_boh_-rah ah-man-y_an_

Where is the kitchen?
Onde fica a cozinha?
ondee feekah ah koo-zeen-ya

Can I light a fire here?
Posso acender o fogo aqui?
pohssoo ah-ssen-dehr oh foh-goo akee

Can I have some tokens for the shower?
Posso conseguir algumas fichas para o chuveiro?
pohsso kon-sseh-gueer ahl-goo-mahs feeshas pahra oh shoo-vay-roo

Where can I get …?
Onde posso conseguir …?
ondee pohssoo kon-sseh-gueer

Is there any drinking water?
Há água potável?
ah ahgwa poh-tah-vel

THINGS YOU'LL SEE

água potável	drinking water
albergue da juventude	youth hostel
área de camping ou trailers	campsite
banheiros	toilets
chuveiros	showers
cozinha	kitchen
fogueira	campfire
por pessoa	per person
proibido acampar	no camping
proibido acender o fogo	no campfires
tarifa, taxa	charge
tenda, barraca	tent
trailer	trailer, caravan

FLATS AND APARTMENTS

If you intend to spend a bit more time in Brazil and find the atmosphere of a hotel a little impersonal, or perhaps you're travelling with your family and want a bit more freedom, you might want to rent a flat or house.

Flats are furnished apartments, normally of a very high standard, which you can rent for varying periods of time, from a few weeks up to two or three years. The difference in relation to a house or ordinary apartment is in connection with the services available, similar to those of a hotel: your dishes will be washed and your flat cleaned every day. Most flats also offer bilingual receptionists, which can be a great advantage. The tourist will find flats available at present only in the big urban centres like São Paulo and Rio de Janeiro, or in some of the more popular resorts.

If you're in a region where there are no flats or if you don't want to pay for the services on offer, the best option is to rent a house. You will find all kinds of property on offer –some excellent– but the responsibility will be all yours. Try to rent a house from someone who speaks English and is used to dealing with foreign tourists.

Useful Words and Phrases

air-conditioner	ar-condicionado	_ahr kon-gee-ssyo-nah-doo_
bath (tub)	banheira	_ban-yey-rah_
bathroom	banheiro	_ban-yey-roh_
bedroom	dormitório	_dohr-mee-toh-ryu_
boiler	caldeira	_kahl-day-rah_
broken	quebrado	_keh-brah-doo_
brush	vassoura	_vah-ssoul-rah_
central heating	aquecimento central	_ah-keh-ssee-mayn-too sayn-trahl_
cleaner	arrumadeira	_ah-roo-mah-day-rah_
clogged	entupido	_ayn-too-pee-doo_
deposit	depósito	_deh-poh-zee-too_

32

dining room	sala de jantar	*sah-lah dee jahn-tahr*
door lock, lock	fechadura	*feh-sha-doo-rah*
duvet, continental quilt	edredom	*eh-dreh-dohm*
electrician	eletricista	*eh-leh-tree-ssees-tah*
electricity	eletricidade	*eh-leh-tree-ssee-dah-gee*
fawcet, tap	torneira	*tohr-nay-rah*
flush	descarga	*dehs-kahr-gah*
fridge, refrigerator	geladeira	*geh-lah-day-rah*
fusebox	caixa de fusíveis	*kahy-sha dee foo-zee-vays*
garbage can	lata de lixo	*lah-tah dee leeshoo*
gas	gás	*gahs*
grill	grelha	*grehl-ya*
heater	aquecedor	*ah-keh-sseh-dohr*
iron	ferro de passar	*feh-roh dee pah-ssahr*
ironing board	tábua de passar roupa	*tah-bwa dee pah-ssahr roul-pah*
janitor, caretaker	zelador (a)	*zeh-lah-dohr*
keys	chaves	*shah-vehs*
kitchen	cozinha	*koo-zeen-ya*
leak	vazamento	*vah-zah-mayn-too*
light	luz	*loos*
living room	sala de estar	*sah-lah dee ehs-tahr*
maid	camareira	*kah-mah-ray-rah*
oven	forno	*fohr-noo*
pillow slip	fronha	*fron-ya*
pillow	travesseiro	*trah-vee-say-roo*
pipe	cano	*kah-noo*
plumber	encanador	*ayn-kah-nah-dohr*
real estate agent, estate agent	agente imobiliário	*ah-jayn-tee ee-moh-beel-yah-ryu*
refund	reembolso	*reh-ayn-boul-soh*
sheets	lençóis	*layn-soh-ys*
shower	chuveiro	*shoo-vay-roo*
sink	pia	*pee-ah*
stopcock	registro	*reh-gees-troo*

FLATS AND APARTMENTS

stove, cooker	fogão	*foh-gowng*
swimming pool	piscina	*pee-ssee-nah*
toilet	banheiro	*ban-yey-roo*
towel	toalha	*toh-ahl-ya*
washing machine	máquina de lavar roupa	*mah-kee-nah dee lah-vahr roul-pah*
water heater	aquecedor	*ah-keh-sseh-dohr*
water	água	*ahgwa*

I'd like to rent an apartment for ... days
Eu gostaria de alugar um apartamento por ... dias
el gostreeh-ya dee ah-loo-gahr oom ah-pahr-tah-mayn-too poor ... dee-ahs

Do I have to pay a deposit?
Preciso fazer um depósito?
preh-ssee-zoo fah-zehr oom deh-poh-zee-too

Does the price include gas and electricity?
O gás e a eletricidade estão inclusos no preço?
oh gahs eh ah eh-leh-tree-ssee-dah-gee esstowng een-kloo-zoos noh preh-ssoo

Where is this item?
Onde está este item?
ondee ess-tah esstee eetayn

Please take it off the inventory
Por favor, retire-o da relação
poor fah-vor, reh-tee-ryoh dah reh-lah-ssowng

We've broken this
Quebramos isto
keh-brah-moos eesstoo

This was broken when we arrived
Isso estava quebrado quando chegamos
eessoo ess-tah-vah keh-brah-doo kwandoo sheh-gah-moos

This was missing when we arrived
Isso faltava quando chegamos
eessoo fahl-tah-vah kwandoo sheh-gah-moos

Can I have my deposit back?
Pode me devolver o depósito?
pod-mee deh-voul-vehr oh deh-poh-zee-too

Can we have an extra bed?
Pode colocar outra cama para nós?
pod koh-loh-kahr oul-trah kah-mah pahra nohs

Can we have more earthenware/cutlery?
Pode colocar mais pratos e copos/talheres para nós?
pod koh-loh-kahr mah-ys prah-tohs eh koh-pohs pahra nohs

When does the maid come?
Quando vem a camareira?
kwandoo vayn ah kah-mah-ray-rah

Where can I buy/find ...?
Onde eu posso comprar/encontrar ...?
ondee el pohssoo kon-prahr/ayn-kon-trahr

How does the water heater work?
Como funciona o aquecedor de água?
koh-moh foong-seeyoh-nah oh ah-keh-sseh-dohr dee ahgwa

Do you do ironing/baby-sitting?
Você sabe passar a ferro/tomar conta das crianças?
voh-sseh sahb pah-ssahr ah feh-roh/toh-mahr kon-tah dahs kree-yan-ssahs

Do you prepare lunch/dinner?
Você prepara o almoço/jantar?
voh-sseh preh-pah-rah oh ahl-moh-ssoo/jahn-tahr

Do we have to pay extra or is it included?
Deve-se pagar à parte ou está incluído no preço?
dehv-see pah-gahr ah pahr-chee, ow ess-tah een-kloo-ee-doo noh preh-ssoo

The shower doesn't work
O chuveiro não funciona
oh shoo-vay-roo nowng foong-seeyoh-nah

The sink is clogged
A pia está entupida
ah *pee-ah* ess-t*ah* ayn-too-*pee*-dah

The sink/toilet is leaking
A pia/privada está vazando
ah *pee*-ah/*pree*-v*ah*-dah ess-t*ah* vah-z*ah*n-doo

There's a burst pipe
Há um encanamento quebrado
ah oom ayn-kah-nah-m*ay*n-too keh-br*ah*-doo

The trash has not been collected for a week
Há uma semana não recolhem o lixo
ah *oo*ma seh-m*ah*-nah nowng reh-k*oh*l-yeng oh l*ee*shoo

There's no electricity/gas/water
Falta luz/gás/água
*fah*l-tah l*oo*s/g*ah*s/*ah*gwa

Can you mend it today?
Pode consertá-lo hoje?
pod kon-ssehr-t*ah*-loo *oh*-jee

Send the bill to ...
Mande a conta para ...
m*ah*n-gee ah k*on*-tah p*ah*ra

I'm staying at ...
Estou no ...
ess-t*oul* noh

Thank you for everything!
Obrigado (a) por tudo!
obreeg*ah*-doo (dah) por t*oo*-doh

See you again next year!
Até o próximo ano!
ah-t*eh* oh pr*aw*-see-moo *ah*no

DRIVING

If you want to rent a car in Brazil, you must have a credit card. Most companies don't accept travellers cheques or foreign currency (including the dollar); payment in the local currency (the **real**), however, may get you a discount. Avis is found only in the big cities, and doesn't offer unlimited mileage, but National (or Localiza), with representatives in various locations and in association with InterRent/Europcar in Europe, does offer unlimited mileage, as long as the reservation is made in advance. In general prices are high: it will cost you around US$ 50 a day for a small car. The minimum age to rent a car is 21. Once on the road, bear in mind that the highway network in Brazil varies greatly in all aspects. Try to plan your route carefully. Generally speaking, the South and South East regions (those economically more developed) have the best driving conditions, while roads in the Centre West, Northeast and North regions vary from the tolerable to the virtually impassable. It's worth getting as much detail in this respect as you can.

The states in the South (**Rio Grande do Sul**, **Santa Catarina** and **Paraná**) and most of the South East states (**São Paulo**, **Rio de Janeiro** and the South of the state of **Minas Gerais**) have a relatively dense road network: you can reach almost all cities, even the small ones, on asphalted roads. For the tourist, however, some caution is necessary. Although many of these roads are wide and modern, you cannot be totally confident about their state of maintenance. Moreover, the intense lorry traffic, and above all the behaviour of drivers, can be frightening for those who were not used to it. Another problem, mainly in the big cities, is car theft: if possible, always leave your car in paid parking lots –they are easy to find and the money will certainly be well spent.

The situation in the states of the Centre West (**Mato Grosso do Sul**, **Mato Grosso**, and **Goiás**) is rather different. There are some excellent, modern roads. The problem is that they are limited to connecting the few most important cities (especially linking the federal capital Brasilia to the South East region and some points of the North and Northeast). The rest of the vast region has to be content with a few main roads, mostly without a hard surface.

The North East region (**Bahia**, **Alagoas**, **Sergipe**, **Rio Grande do Norte**, **Paraíba**, **Piauí**, **Pernambuco**, **Ceará** and **Maranhão**) is served by roads in a varying state of conditions –in general, however, the maintenance is precarious. Most cities are accessible only by dirt roads, which get worse as you get closer to the **sertão** (West).

Finally in the North region (**Amazonas**, **Acre**, **Rondônia**, **Roraima**, **Amapá**, **Pará** and **Tocantins**), forget the car. Unless, of course, you love adventure and a high degree of risk –and you plan your route very carefully. The vast majority of this enormous region is covered by dense forest, totally impassable. You would only manage to reach, with any degree of safety, Belém, in the extreme East of the region.

SOME COMMON ROAD SIGNS

acenda os faróis	headlights on
alfândega	customs
área de estacionamento	parking area
área para pedestres	pedestrian precinct
atenção, cuidado	watch out, caution
cidade, centro	downtown, town centre
cruzamento perigoso	dangerous junction, cross roads
cruzamento	junction
deslizamentos	falling rocks
desvio	diversion
entrada proibida	no entry
escola	school
estacionamento com manobrista	vallet parking, car park with attendant

→

estacionamento pago	paying car park
estacionamento sem manobrista	unattended car park
estrada principal	main road
estrada secundária	secondary road
faixa para ciclistas	cycle track
filas adiante	traffic queues ahead
fim de rodovia	end of motorway
gelo na pista	ice on road
gelo	ice
informações turísticas	tourist information
mão única	one way
neblina	fog
obras	roadworks
pagar aqui	pay here
passagem proibida	no throughfare
passagem subterrânea	subway
pedágio	toll
pedestres	pedestrians
perigo	danger
pista dupla	two-lane traffic
pista escorregadia	slippery road
proibido estacionar	no parking
proibido parar	no stopping
proibido ultrapassar	no trespassing
reduzir velocidade	reduce speed
rodovia	motorway
sujeito a deslizamentos	soft verge
saída de caminhões	works exit
vala	ditch
velocidade controlada por radar	automatic speed monitor
via para veículos pesados	route for heavy vehicles
via sem saída	blind alley
zona de tráfego restrito	restricted traffic area

USEFUL WORDS AND PHRASES

automatic	câmbio automático	_kanbyo al-toh-mah-tee-koo_
brake	freio	_fray-you_
breakdown	defeito, pane	_deh-fay-too, pah-nee_
car park	estacionamento	_ehs-tah-seeo-nah-mayn-too_
car	carro	_kah-hoh_
clutch	embreagem	_ayn-breh-ah-jayn_
crossroads	cruzamento	_kroo-zah-mayn-too_
drive	dirigir	_dee-ree-geer_
driver's licence	carteira de	_kar-tay-rah dee_
	motorista	_moh-toh-rees-tah_
engine	motor	_moh-tohr_
exhaust	escapamento	_ehs-kah-pah-mayn-too_
fanbelt	correia	_koh-ray-ya_
garage	oficina mecânica	_of-see-nah meh-kah-nee-ka_
gas station,	posto de gasolina	_pohs-toh dee_
petrol station		_gah-zoh-lee-nah_
gas, petrol	gasolina	_gah-zoh-lee-nah_
gear box	caixa de câmbio	_kah-ysha dee kanbyo_
gear	marcha	_mahr-sha_
headlights	faróis	_fah-roys_
hood, bonnet	capô	_kah-poh_
license plate,	placa	_plah-kah_
numberplate		
manual	câmbio manual	_kanbyo mah-noo-ahl_
mirror	espelho	_ehs-pehl-you_
motorbike	motocicleta	_moh-toh-ssee-kleh-tah_
motorway junction	anel rodoviário	_ahnel roh-doh-vee-ah-ryu_
motorway	rodovia	_roh-doh-veeya_
rear lights	luzes traseiras	_loo-zehs trah-zay-rahs_
road	estrada	_ehs-trah-dah_
seat belt	cinto de segurança	_seentoo dee seh-goo-ran-sa_
spares	peças sobressalentes	_peh-ssahs soh-breh-ssah-layn-chees_
spark plug	vela de ignição	_vehla dee eeg-nee-ssowng_

speed limit	limite de velocidade	*lee-mee-chee dee*
		veh-loh-ssee-dah-gee
speed	velocidade	*veh-loh-ssee-dah-gee*
speedometer	velocímetro	*veh-loh-ssee-meh-troh*
steering wheel	volante	*voh-lahn-chee*
traffic lights	semáforo	*seh-mah-foh-ro*
trailer	reboque	*reh-boh-kee*
trailer, caravan	trailer	*trailer*
truck, lorry	caminhão	*kah-meen-yowng*
trunk, boot	porta-malas	*pohr-tah mah-lahs*
turn signal	seta, pisca	*seh-tah, pees-kah*
tyre	pneu	*pnehl*
van	furgão	*foor-gowng*
warning triangle	triângulo	*tree-ahn-goo-loo*
wheel	roda	*rohda*
windshield wiper,	limpador de	*leen-pah-dohr dee*
windscreen wiper	pára-brisa	*pah-rah-bree-zah*
windshield, screen	pára-brisa	*pah-rah-bree-zah*

Could you check the oil/water level, please?
Poderia verificar o nível do óleo/da água, por favor?
podreeh-ya veh-ree-fee-kahr oh neevel doh ol-you/dah ahgwa, poor fah-vor

Fill it up, please!
Completa, por favor!
kon-pleh-ta, poor fah-vor

I'd like eight gallons of four-star
Coloque 30 litros (= 8 gallons) de gasolina aditivada
koh-loh-ka treen-tah lee-trohs dee gah-zoh-lee-nah ah-dee-tee-vah-dah

Do you do repairs?
Vocês fazem consertos?
voh-ssehs fah-zayn kon-ssehr-toos

Can you repair the clutch?
Pode consertar a embreagem?
pod kon-ssehr-tahr ah ayn-breh-ah-jayn

There is something wrong with the engine
Há algo errado com o motor
ah ahl-goo eh-rah-doo kon oh moh-tohr

The engine is overheating
O motor está esquentando muito
oh moh-tohr ess-tah ehs-kayn-tahn-doo mooytoo

I need a new tyre
Preciso de um pneu novo
preh-ssee-zoo dee oom pnehl noh-voo

Can you replace this?
Pode trocar isso?
pod troh-kahr eessoo

The turn signal is not working
O pisca não está funcionando
oh pees-kah nowng ess-tah foong-sse-yo-nahn-doo

How long will it take?
Quanto tempo demora?
kwantoo tayn-poo deh-moh-rah

Where can I park?
Onde eu posso estacionar?
ondee el poh-ssoo ehs-tah-ssee-oh-nahr

I'd like to hire a car
Gostaria de alugar um carro
gostreeh-ya dee ah-loo-gahr oom kah-hoh

I'd like an automatic/a manual
Gostaria de um carro com câmbio automático/manual
gostreeh-ya dee oom kah-hoh kon kanbyo al-toh-mah-tee-koo/mah-noo-ahl

How much is it for one day?
Quanto custa por um dia?
kwantoo koos-tah por oom dee-ah

Is there a mileage charge?
Há um adicional por quilometragem?
_ah_ oom ah-dee-see-yoh-n_ah_l por kee-loh-meh-tr_ah_-jayn

When do I have to return it?
Quando devo devolvê-lo?
kw_ah_ndoo d_e_h-voh deh-voul-v_e_h-loo

Where is the nearest gas station?
Onde fica o posto de gasolina mais próximo?
ondee f_ee_kah oh p_o_hs-toh dee gah-z_o_h-l_ee_-nah m_ah_-ys pr_aw_-see-moo

How do I get to …?
Como eu vou para ...?
k_o_h-moh el voul p_ah_ra

Is this the road to …?
Esta é a estrada para ...?
_e_sstah eh ah ehs-tr_ah_-dah p_ah_ra

DIRECTIONS YOU MAY BE GIVEN

à direita	right
à esquerda	left
a primeira à direita	first on the right
a segunda à esquerda	second on the left
depois de passar o/a ...	go past the …
dobre à direita	turn right
dobre à esquerda	turn left
esquina	corner
sempre em frente	strait on

THINGS YOU'LL SEE

água	water
anel rodoviário	motorway junction

→

área de serviço	service area
aspirador de pó	vacuum cleaner
borracheiro	tyre repairs
cera para carro	car wax
desligar o motor	switch off engine
desvio	diversion
dirija devagar	drive at walking speed
empurrar	push
fila	traffic queue
gasolina comum	two or three-star gas, petrol
gasolina sem chumbo	unleaded gas, petrol
gasolina super	four-star gas, petrol
gasolina	gas, petrol
lava-rápido, lavagem automática	car wash
limpa-vidros	screen wash
oficina mecânica	garage (for repairs)
óleo diesel	diesel
óleo	oil
pedágio	motorway toll booth
posto de gasolina	gas station, service station
proibido fumar	no smoking
puxar	pull
saída	exit

THINGS YOU'LL HEAR

Quer um carro com câmbio automático ou manual?
Would you like an automatic or a manual?

Sua carteira de motorista, por favor
May I see your (driver's) licence, please?

Seu passaporte, por favor
May I see your passport, please?

TRANSPORT

Air Travel

International flights usually arrive in Brazil in São Paulo or Rio de Janeiro. Connections can easily be had from these two cities to the main destinations in the country.

Domestic flights, although relatively expensive, are of excellent quality. The news couldn't be better for the tourist: owing to the great distances within the country this will be the most frequent transport option. There are routes between all the main cities, with various flights per day. On board service is usually very good in all the Brazilian companies, of which the biggest are Varig, Vasp, TAM and Transbrasil. Together (with some joint ventures), they cover the whole of Brazil.

Prices of international flights, a little more competitive during the low season, become more expensive in the high season (from the beginning of January to the end of Carnival). When buying tickets for domestic flights, find out about discounts for couples (who may sometimes pay for just one and a half tickets), for night flights (between 10:00 p.m. and 6:00 a.m. you may find some very reasonable prices in the so called **vôos coruja**) or for reservations made up to seven days beforehand. You must be sure, however, always to confirm your reservations.

When planning your trip, consult a current timetable because flight times are often changed. The magazine Panrotas, published monthly, has all the times and prices.

Trains

Despite its vast territory, most of which is extremely suited to rail transport, Brazil is notorious for its deficiency in this type of service. The few lines which exist are mainly used for transporting cargo. There are virtually no passenger lines, and the tourist should simply take this option out of any plans.

Long Distance Buses

If you're on a tight budget, the Brazilian network of long-distance buses is definitely the best option. There are routes between all the main cities from North to South, and from these to all the smaller cities.

In most cases, long-distance buses leave from bus stations called **rodoviárias**. These **rodoviárias**, although they may be rather crowded, usually have a very good infrastructure with snack bars, shops, bathrooms, left luggage departments (**guarda-volumes**) and information desks. You can also buy your tickets easily here at the company kiosk (many, mainly in the South and Southeast, will accept credit cards). Also, if you want information concerning times and prices, it's best to go direct to each company: any other source of information would not be reliable.

There are three types of bus in Brazil. The cheapest is the **convencional**: it offers little comfort and space, and the journeys tend to be longer than necessary due to the frequent stops to pick up passengers along the route. Buses known as **executivos**, a little more expensive, have more comfortable seats (almost always reclining) and fewer stops. Even if you're travelling on a tight budget, they are probably the best option. Finally buses called **leito** –literally 'bed'– travel at night between the big cities, with a minimum number of stops, totally reclining seats (with supports for head and feet), air conditioning and other services. The majority of buses on journeys of more than 100 km (45 miles) have toilets. If you want a window seat, ask for a ticket with an odd number.

You should note that buses are usually punctual, and that it's difficult to sell on a ticket once you've bought it.

Boats

The main region where you will need to use water transport is Amazonia. Many cities there can only be reached by river, frequently in slow, badly conserved boats. Water transport will also be the only option if you want to visit some areas of the Pantanal

Wetlands. Other than this, you can find boats on the river São Francisco (North East region) or on the Atlantic Coast; it's not really, however, a practical means of transport.

IN THE CITY

Taxi charges vary from city to city. When you get in, check that the meter is on 0 and that it is fixed to **bandeira 1** (tariff 1, the cheapest). **Bandeira 2** can only be charged on Sundays, in December or between 11:00 p.m. and 6:00 a.m. Radio taxis are 50% more expensive, but very reliable.

Only São Paulo and Rio de Janeiro have an underground railway system; despite being efficient and modern, they cover a very restricted region of the city. The cheapest and most practical option, therefore, are the local buses. Fares, which are very reasonable, are almost always charged for individual journeys. The biggest difficulty is getting information; at peak times it may become difficult to use certain lines.

USEFUL WORDS AND PHRASES

adult	adulto	*ah-dool-toh*
airport bus	ônibus do aeroporto	*oh-nee-boos doh ah-air-roh-pohr-toh*
airport	aeroporto	*ah-air-roh-pohr-toh*
aisle seat	assento no corredor	*ah-ssayn-too noh koh-reh-dohr*
baggage claim	esteira de bagagens	*estay-ra dee bah-gah-jayns*
boarding card	cartão de embarque	*kartowng dee ayn-bahr-kee*
boat	barco	*bahr-koh*
booking office	venda de passagens	*vayn-dah dee pah-ssah-jayns*
bus station	estação de ônibus	*ehs-tah-ssowng dee oh-nee-boos*
bus stop	ponto de ônibus	*pon-too dee oh-nee-boos*
bus	ônibus	*oh-nee-boos*
cab, taxi	táxi	*tahk-see*

cable car	bonde elétrico	*bon-jee eh-leh-tree-koo*
check-in counter, check-in desk	balcão de registro	*bahl-kowng dee reh-gees-troo*
child	criança	*kree-yan-ssah*
city map, network map	mapa da cidade	*mah-pah dah see-dah-gee*
compartment	compartimento	*kon-pahr-tee-mayn-too*
connection	conexão	*koh-nek-ssowng*
couchette	leito	*lay-toh*
cruise	cruzeiro	*kroo-zay-roo*
customs	alfândega	*ahl-fan-deh-gah*
departure lounge, waiting room	sala de espera	*sah-lah dee ehs-peh-ra*
domestic	nacional	*nah-ssee-oh-nahl*
emergency exit	saída de emergência	*sah-ee-dah dee eh-mehr-jayns-sya*
entrance	entrada	*ehn-trah-da*
exit	saída	*sah-ee-dah*
ferryboat	balsa	*bahl-sah*
first class	primeira classe	*pree-may-rah klah-ssee*
flight number	número do vôo	*noo-meh-roh doh voh-oh*
flight	vôo	*voh-oh*
gate	portão de embarque	*portowng dee ayn-bahr-kee*
hand luggage	bagagem de mão	*bah-gah-jayn dee mown*
international	internacional	*een-tehr-nah-see-oh-nahl*
left luggage office	depósito de bagagens	*deh-poh-zee-too dee bah-gah-jayns*
lost and found, lost property office	seção de achados e perdidos	*sehssowng dee ah-shah-dohs eh pehr-gee-dohs*
luggage trolley	carrinho de bagagens	*kah-reen-you dee bah-gah-jayns*
non-smoking	não-fumantes	*nowng foo-mahn-tehs*
number five bus	ônibus número 5	*oh-nee-boos noo-meh-ro 5*
passport	passaporte	*pah-ssah-pohr-chee*
platform	plataforma	*plah-tah-fohr-mah*

railway	ferrovia	*feh-roh-veeya*
reserved seat	assento reservado	*assayn-too reh-zehr-vah-do*
restaurant car	vagão-restaurante	*vagowng rehs-tahl-ran-tee*
round-trip ticket, two way ticket, return ticket	passagem de ida e volta	*pah-ssah-jayn dee ee-dah eh vohl-ta*
second class	segunda classe	*seh-goon-dah klah-ssee*
single ticket, one way ticket	passagem só de ida	*pah-ssah-jayn soh dee ee-dah*
sleeper	vagão-leito	*vagowng lay-too*
smoking	fumantes	*foo-mahn-chees*
station	estação	*ehs-tah-ssowng*
subway, underground	metrô	*meh-troh*
terminus	estação terminal	*ehs-tah-ssown ter-mee-nahl*
ticket	tíquete	*teekech*
ticket, fare	passagem	*pah-ssah-jayn*
timetable	horário	*oh-rah-ryu*
train	trem	*trayn*
trolley bus	trólebus	*traw-leh-boos*
window seat	assento na janela	*assayn-too nah jah-neh-la*

AIR TRAVEL

I'd like a non-smoking seat, please
Um assento na seção de não-fumantes, por favor
oom assayn-too nah sehssowng dee nowng foo-mahn-chees, poor fah-vor

I'd like a window seat, please
Gostaria de um assento junto à janela, por favor
gostreeh-ya dee omm assayn-too joon-toh ah jah-neh-la, poor fah-vor

How long will the flight be delayed?
Qual o atraso do vôo para a partida?
kwal oh ah-trah-zoh doh voh-oh pahra ah par-tee-dah

Which gate for the flight to New York?
Qual o portão de embarque do vôo para Nova York?
kwal oh portowng dee ayn-bahr-kee doh voh-oh pahra noh-va york

Bus and Rail

When does the bus for São Paulo leave?
A que horas sai o ônibus para São Paulo?
ah kee orahs sah-ee oh oh-nee-boos pahra sowng pahl-loh

When does the bus from Rio de Janeiro arrive?
A que horas chega o ônibus do Rio de Janeiro?
ah kee orahs sheh-gah oh oh-nee-boos doh ree-oo dee jah-nay-roh

When is the next bus to Salvador?
A que horas sai o próximo ônibus para Salvador?
ah kee orahs sah-ee oh praw-ssee-moo oh-nee-boos pahra sahl-vah-dor

When is the first/last bus to Santos?
A que horas sai o primeiro/último ônibus para Santos?
ah kee orahs sah-ee oh pree-may-roh/ool-tee-moh oh-nee-boos prah sahn-tohs

How much is the fare to Porto Alegre?
Quanto é a passagem para Porto Alegre?
kwantoo eh ah pah-ssah-jayn pahra pohr-toh ah-leh-gree

Do I have to change/connect?
Tenho de fazer baldeação?
ten-yu dee fah-zehr bahl-gee-ah-ssowng

Does the bus stop at Ouro Preto?
O ônibus pára em Ouro Preto?
oh oh-nee-boos pahra eng oul-roh preh-toh

How long does it take to get to Natal?
Quanto tempo leva para chegar em Natal?
kwantoo tayn-poo leh-vah pahra sheh-gahr eng nah-tahl

Where can I buy a ticket?
Onde posso comprar uma passagem?
ondee poh-ssoo kon-prahr ooma pah-ssah-jayn

A single/round trip ticket to Belém
Uma passagem de ida/de ida e volta para Belém
ooma pah-ssah-jayn dee ee-dah/dee ee-dah eh vohl-ta pahra beh-layn

Could you help me get a ticket?
Pode me ajudar a comprar uma passagem?
pod-mee ah-joo-dahr ah kon-prahr ooma pah-ssah-jayn

Do I have to pay a supplement?
Tenho de pagar alguma taxa adicional?
ten-yu dee pah-gahr ahl-goo-ma tah-shah ah-dee-ssee-yo-nahl

I'd like to reserve a seat
Gostaria de reservar um assento
gostreeh-ya dee reh-zehr-vahr oom ah-ssayn-too

Is this the right bus for Florianópolis?
Este é o ônibus certo para Florianópolis?
esstee eh oh oh-nee-boos sehr-toh pahra floh-ree-ah-noh-poh-lees

Is this the right platform for the Recife bus?
Esta é a plataforma do ônibus para Recife?
esstah eh ah plah-tah-fohr-mah doh oh-nee-boos pahra reh-ssee-fee

---

REPLIES YOU MAY BE GIVEN

O próximo ônibus sai às 18h
The next bus leaves at six p.m.

Faça a baldeação em São Paulo
Change/Connect at São Paulo

O senhor tem de pagar uma taxa adicional
You must pay a supplement

Não há mais lugares (assentos) para Belo Horizonte
There are no more seats available for Belo Horizonte

Which platform for the Olinda bus?
Qual a plataforma do ônibus para Olinda?
kwal ah plah-tah-fohr-mah doh oh-nee-boos pahra oh-leen-dah

Is the bus late?
O ônibus está atrasado?
oh oh-nee-boos ess-tah ah-trah-zah-doo

Could you help me with my luggage, please?
Pode me ajudar com as malas, por favor?
pod-mee ah-joo-dahr kon ahs mah-lahs, poor fah-vor

Is this a non-smoking compartment?
Esta é uma área de não-fumantes?
esstah eh ooma ah-reh-ah dee nonwg foo-mahn-tees

Is this seat free?
Este lugar está livre?
esstee loo-gahr ess-tah lee-vreh

This seat is taken
Este lugar está ocupado
esstee loo-gahr ess-tah oh-koo-pah-doh

I have reserved this seat
Eu reservei este assento
el reh-sehr-vay esstee ah-ssayn-too

May I open/close the window?
Posso abrir/fechar a janela?
pohssoo ah-breer/feh-shahr ah jah-neh-la

When do we arrive in Cuiabá?
A que horas chegamos em Cuiabá?
a kee orahs sheh-gah-moos eng kooy-ah-bah

What station is this?
Que estação é esta?
kee ehs-tah-ssowng eh esstah

Does this bus stop in São Paulo?
Este ônibus pára em São Paulo?
esstee oh-nee-boos pahra eng sowng pahl-loh

Would you keep an eye on my things for a moment?
Pode tomar conta das minhas coisas por um momento?
pod toh-mahr kon-tah dahs meen-yas koy-zahs pohr oom moh-mayn-too

Is there a toilet on this bus?
Este ônibus tem banheiro?
esstee oh-nee-boos tayn ban-yey-roo

Local Public Transport

Where is the nearest subway station?
Onde fica a estação de metrô mais próxima?
ondee feekah ah ehs-tah-ssowng dee meh-troh mah-ys praw-ssee-mah

Where is the bus station?
Onde tem um ponto de ônibus?
ondee tayn oom pohn-too dee oh-nee-boos

Wich buses go to Copacabana?
Quais ônibus vão para Copacabana?
kwah-ees oh-nee-boos vowng pahra koh-pah-kah-bah-nah

How often do the buses to Leme run?
De quanto em quanto tempo passam os ônibus para o Leme?
dee kwantoo eng kwantoo tayn-poo pah-ssahn ohs oh-nee-boos proh leh-me

Will you let me know when we're there?
Poderia me avisar quando chegarmos?
podreeh-ya mee ah-vee-zahr kwandoo sheh-gahr-moos

Do I have to get off here?
Tenho de descer aqui?
ten-yu dee deh-ssehr akee

How do I get to Interlagos?
Como eu vou para Interlagos?
koh-moh el voul pahra een-tehr-lah-goos

I want to go to Pelourinho
Quero ir para o Pelourinho
kehro eer pahra oh peh-loul-reen-yu

Do you go near Boa Viagem?
O senhor vai passar perto de Boa Viagem?
oh seen-your vah-y pah-ssahr pehr-toh dee boh-ah vee-ah-jayn

Táxi e Barco

To the airport, please
Para o aeroporto, por favor
pahra oh ah-air-roh-pohr-toh, poor fah-vor

How much will it cost?
Quanto vai custar?
kwantoo vah-y koos-tahr

Please stop here
Pare aqui, por favor
pah-reh akee, poor fah-vor

Could you wait here for me and take me back?
Pode me esperar aqui e me levar de volta?
pod-mee ehs-peh-rahr akee eh mee leh-vahr dee vohl-ta

Where can I get the boat to Manaus?
Onde eu posso pegar um barco para Manaus?
ondee el pohssoo peh-gahr oom bahr-koh pahra mah-nahls

Things You'll See

achados e perdidos	lost and found
alarme de emergência	emergency alarm
assento reservado	reserved seat
assento	seat
atraso	delay
câmbio (de moeda)	currency exchange
cartão de embarque	boarding pass
cartão de viagem	travel card
chegadas	arrivals
comissário (a) de bordo	flight attendant/steward (ess)
controle de bagagens	baggage control
controle de passagens	ticket inspection
controle de passaportes	passport control
crianças	children
depósito de bagagens	left luggage
domingos e feriados	Sundays and public holidays
domingos	Sundays
entrada proibida	no entry
entrada	entrance, way in
estação terminal	terminus
excesso de peso	overweight
fazer baldeação	to change, to connect
ferrovia	railway
fumantes	smokers
hora local	local time
horário de vôo	flight time
horário	timetable
informações	information
lanches, sanduíches	snacks, sandwiches
livre	free
lugares em pé	standing room
máquina de emitir tíquetes	ticket machine
multa por uso indevido ...	penalty for misuse ...

→

nacional, doméstico	domestic
não pára em ...	does not stop at ...
não-fumantes	non-smokers
objetos perdidos	lost property
ocupado	engaged, reserved
para as plataformas	to the platforms
parada	stop
partidas	departures
passageiros	passengers
porto	harbour, port
proibido conversar com o motorista	do not speak to the driver
proibido debruçar-se	do not lean out
proibido fumar	no smoking
retirada de bagagens	baggage claim
rota	route
saguão	lounge
saída de emergência	emergency exit
saída	exit
sala de espera	waiting room
só sábados/domingos	Saturdays/Sundays only
somente para não-fumantes	non-smokers only
terminal de bagagens	baggage terminal
tíquete diário	day ticket
tíquete para a plataforma	platform ticket
tíquete, passagem	ticket
trem intermunicipal	long-distance train
trem rápido	fast train
vagão	carriage, car
vagão-leito	sleeper
vagão-restaurante	restaurant car
viagem curta	short journey
viagem de barco	boat trip
vôo regular	scheduled flight
vôo	flight

THINGS YOU'LL HEAR

O (A) senhor (a) tem bagagem?
Do you have any luggage?

Assento no corredor ou na janela?
Window seat or aisle seat?

Fumantes ou não-fumantes?
Smoking or non-smoking?

O (A) senhor (a) tem algo a declarar?
Do you have anything to declare?

Abra sua mala, por favor
Open your suitcase, please

Posso ver seu passaporte/sua passagem, por favor?
Can I see your passport/ticket, please?

Os passageiros com destino a São Paulo devem se dirigir para o embarque
Passengers for São Paulo are requested to board

Dirijam-se ao portão número 4, por favor
Please, proceed to gate number four

As passagens, por favor
Tickets, please

O vôo número 435 procedente de Belo Horizonte está com 30 minutos de atraso
Flight number 435 from Belo Horizonte is running thirty minutes late

O ônibus número 357 de Angra dos Reis está chegando na plataforma 2
Bus number 357 from Angra dos Reis is approaching platform 2

O ônibus número 687 para Santos partirá da plataforma 3
Bus number 687 for Santos is leaving from platform 3

EATING OUT

Brazil is a country where you will probably find the greatest variety (and creativity) in the ways of serving food in the world. If you're on a tight budget there are many different options.

Lanchonetes are establishments for quick, cheap food. You can have a sandwich or the famous **salgados**, the most popular of which are the **coxinha** (a small savoury made from shredded chicken covered in dough and deep fried), the **empada** (a small tart with butter pastry and fillings like chicken, palm heart and shrimp), the **esfiha** (a widely found Arab specialty –a round piece of dough covered with minced meat), and the **pão de queijo** (literally cheesebread).

In establishments which sell food **por quilo** (by weight), you'll find a buffet with a great variety of dishes; you take a plate and help yourself to as much as you want. Then the plate is weighed and you pay the corresponding amount. A **bufê** operates on the same principle: the only difference is that it's a fixed price, giving you the right to help yourself to as much as you want, as many times as you want. The **almoço comercial** (commercial lunch) or **prato feito** (ready made dish) is widely available in establishments which prepare large quantities of a different dish each day (Wednesday, for example, is traditionally the day of **feijoada**).

Rodízios are a little different. There are cheap ones and more sophisticated ones. You pay a fixed price, and as well as a **bufê** of salads, pasta and other dishes, you are served at the table by an army of waiters who pass by non-stop, with as much as you can eat of all kinds of varieties of meat, including different cuts of beef, pork, chicken, wild boar and others.

The tourist in search of something more conventional will have no problems either. Traditional style restaurants abound, and in the big cities you'll find a great variety of different cuisines, of all quality and prices. In general, beef is much cheaper than in the US or Europe, and portions tend to be larger. The normal tip is 10% on top of the bill, unless the menu (or the bill itself) explicitly states that service is included.

Useful Words and Phrases

bar	bar	*bahr*
beer	cerveja	*sehr-veh-jah*
bill	conta	*kon-tah*
bottle	garrafa	*gah-hah-fah*
bread	pão	*powng*
butter	manteiga	*mahn-tay-gah*
café	café	*kah-feh*
cake	bolo	*boh-loh*
children's portion	porção para criança	*pohr-ssowng pahra kree-yahn-ssah*
coffee	café	*kah-feh*
cup	xícara	*shee-kah-rah*
dessert	sobremesa	*soh-breh-meh-zah*
fork	garfo	*gahr-foh*
gallon	galão	*gah-lowng*
glass	copo	*koh-poh*
half a gallon	meio galão	*may-oh gah-lowng*
knife	faca	*fah-kah*
litre	litro	*lee-troh*
main course	prato principal	*prah-to preen-ssee-pahl*
menu	cardápio, menu	*kahr-dah-peeo, meh-noo*
milk	leite	*laych*
napkin, serviette	guardanapo	*guahr-dah-nah-poh*
pepper	pimenta	*pee-mayn-tah*
pitcher, carafe	jarra	*jah-hah*
plate, dish	prato	*prah-toh*
pound	libra	*lee-brah*
receipt	recibo	*reh-ssee-boh*
restaurant	restaurante	*rehs-taul-rahn-chee*
salt	sal	*sahl*
sandwich	sanduíche	*sahn-doo-ee-sheh*
snack	refeição ligeira, lanche	*reh-fay-ssowng lee-jay-ra, lahn-sheh*
soup	sopa	*soh-pah*

spoon	colher	*kohl-yehr*
starter	entrada, antepasto	*ayn-trah-da,* *ahn-teh-pahs-toh*
sugar	açúcar	*ah-ssoo-kahr*
table	mesa	*meh-zah*
tea	chá	*shah*
teaspoon	colher de chá	*kohl-yehr dee shah*
tip	gorjeta	*gohr-jeh-tah*
towel	toalha	*toh-ahl-yah*
waiter	garçom	*gahr-ssohn*
waitress	garçonete	*gahr-ssoh-neh-chee*
water	água	*ahgwa*
wine list	carta de vinhos	*kahr-tah dee veen-yos*
wine	vinho	*veen-yo*

A table for one/two/three, please
Uma mesa para uma/duas/três pessoa (s), por favor
ooma meh-za prah ooma/doo-as/trays peh-ssoh-ah (s), poor fah-vor

Can I see the menu/wine list?
Posso ver o cardápio/a carta de vinhos?
pohssoo vehr oh karh-dah-peeo/ah kahr-tah dee veen-yos

What would you recommend?
O que o senhor sugere?
oh kee oh seen-yohr soo-jeh-ree

I'd like …
Eu gostaria de …
el gostreeh-ya dee

Just an espresso/cappuccino/caffè latte, please
Só um expresso/cappuccino/café com leite, por favor
soh oom ehs-preh-sso/kah-poo-chee-noh/kah-feh kon laych, poor fah-vor

I only want a snack
Só quero um lanche
soh keh-roh oom lahn-sheh

Is there a set menu?
Há um menu do dia?
ah oom meh-noo doh dee-ah

Can we try a local speciality?
Poderíamos experimentar uma especialidade local?
podreeh-ah-moos ehs-peh-ree-mehn-tahr ooma ehs-peh-ssee-yah-lee-dah-gee loh-kahl

A bottle of house red, please
Uma garrafa de vinho tinto da casa, por favor
ooma gah-hah-fah dee veen-yo teen-toh dah kah-zah, poor fah-vor

Do you have any vegetarian dishes?
Vocês têm algum prato vegetariano?
voh-ssehs tayn ahl-goon prah-toh veh-jeh-tah-ree-ah-noo

Could we have some water?
Poderia nos trazer água, por favor?
podreeh-ya nohs trah-zehr ahgwa, poor fah-vor

Is there a children's menu?
Há um cardápio para crianças?
ah oom kahr-dah-peeo pahra kree-yahn-ssahs

Waiter/Waitress!
Garçom/garçonete!
gahr-ssohn/gahr-ssoh-neh-chee

We didn't order this!
Não pedimos isto!
nowng peh-dee-moos eesstoo

You've forgotten to bring my dessert
O senhor se esqueceu de trazer a sobremesa
oh seen-yohr see ehs-keh-ssehl dee trah-zehr ah soh-breh-meh-zah

May we have some more …?
Poderia nos trazer mais ...?
podreeh-ya nohs trah-zehr mah-ys

Can I have another knife/spoon?
Pode trazer outra faca/colher?
pod trah-zehr oul-trah fah-kah/kohl-yehr

Can we have the bill, please?
Pode nos trazer a conta, por favor?
pod nohs trah-zehr ah kon-tah, poor fah-vor

Could I have a receipt, please?
Poderia me dar um recibo, por favor?
podreeh-ya mee dahr oom reh-ssee-boh, poor fah-vor

Can we pay separately?
Podemos pagar separadamente?
poh-deh-moos pah-gahr seh-pah-rah-dah-mayn-chee

That was very good, thank you
Estava ótimo, obrigado (a)
ehs-tah-vah oh-tee-moo, obreegah-doo

> ## THINGS YOU'LL HEAR
>
> **É para comer aqui ou é para viagem?**
> For here or to go?
>
> **Bom apetite!**
> Enjoy your meal!
>
> **O que deseja (m) beber?**
> What would you like to drink?
>
> **Vocês comeram bem?**
> Did you enjoy your meal?

MENU GUIDE

"à bolonhesa"	with meat sauce
"à milanesa"	fried covering for fillet steaks, made from beaten eggs and flour
abacate	avocado
abacaxi	pineapple
abóbora	pumpkin, squash
abobrinha	courgette, zucchini
açafrão	saffron
acarajé	fried bean paste ball, served with shrimp and chilli pepper
acelga	chard
acompanhamentos	side dishes
açúcar	sugar
açúcar mascavo	brown sugar
água	water
água-de-coco	coconut water
água de torneira	tap water
água mineral	mineral water
água mineral com gás	sparkling mineral water
água mineral sem gás	still mineral water
aguardente (de cana)	see *cachaça*
aipo	celery
alcachofra	artichoke
alcaparra	caper
alecrim	rosemary
alface	lettuce
algodão-doce	candy-floss
alho	garlic
alho-poró	leek
ambrosia	sweet made from eggs and milk, cooked in a sugar syrup
ameixa seca	prune
ameixas	plums
ameixas cozidas	stewed prunes
amêndoa	almond
amendoim	peanut
amora	mulberry
anchovas em azeite	anchovies in oil

MENU GUIDE

anéis de lula à doré	squid rings in batter
antepastos	starters
"ao ponto"	medium
aperitivo	aperitif
apimentado	spicy, hot
arenque	herring
arraia	skate
arroz	rice
arroz-doce	dessert made with rice, milk, sugar and served with cinnamon
arroz selvagem	wild rice
arroz-de-carreteiro	typical rice dish from the South of Brazil, with shredded or chopped sun-dried beef, sausage, garlic, onion, tomato, parsley and chives
asparago	asparagus
assados (carnes assadas)	roast meats
atum	tuna, tuna fish
avelãs	hazelnuts
aves domésticas	poultry
azeite	olive oil
azeite-de-dendê	oil extracted from the fruit of a palm tree from the Brazilian Northeast, used in dishes typical of Bahia
azeitona	olive
baba-de-moça	sweet made from suggar syrup, coconut milk and egg yolks
bacalhau	cod, cod fish
bacalhau salgado	dried cod
bala de coco	sweet made from sugar and grated coconut
balas, doces	candies
banana	banana
bananada	sweet made from banana
barra de cereal	cereal bar
batata	potato
batata chips	potato chips
batata-inglesa	baked potato
batatas assadas	roast potatoes
batatas fritas	french fries

batida	a cocktail traditionally made from *cachaça* (nowadays also from vodka), fruit or fruit juice, sugar and ice
baunilha	vanilla
bauru	toasted cheese, tomato and ham sandwich (sometimes roast beef is used instead of ham)
bebidas	drinks
beijinho	sweet made from sugar, eggs and coconut
beirute	sandwich made with pitta bread, filled with made-to-order selection of chicken, fillet steak or roast beef, lettuce, tomato, cheese and egg
bem-passado	well done
berinjela	aubergine, eggplant
beterraba	beet
bife de filé mignon	sirloin steak
bife grelhado	grilled steak
bife rolê	beef roll
biscoito amanteigado seco	shortbread
biscoitos amanteigados	butter cookies
bisteca de boi	T-bone steak
bobó de camarão	typical baked dish from Bahia, made with shrimp, coconut milk, *dendê* oil and creamed manioc
bolinho de bacalhau	deep-fried balls of cod, wheat flour and eggs
bolinhos de fubá	hush puppies
bolo branco com baunilha	angel's food cake
bolo de cenoura	cake made with carrot instead of wheat flour
bolo de fubá	cake made with cornmeal flour
bolo de queijo (cheese cake)	cheese cake
bolo de sorvete	ice cream tart
bolos	cakes
bomba de chocolate	chocolate puff
bomba de creme	cream puff
bombom	chocolate sweets, with all kinds of fillings

brigadeiro	round sweet made from condensed milk, butter and chocolate, covered with granulated chocolate
brócolis	broccoli
brownies	brownies
caça	game
cação	sea fish (can be served fried, baked, boiled or grilled)
cachaça	high alcohol content rum, made from cereals, root vegetables and fruit
caesar salad	caesar salad
café	coffee
café com leite	coffee with milk, white coffee, café latte
café descafeinado	decaffeinated coffee
café expresso	strong espresso coffee
caipirinha	cocktail made from *cachaça*, lime and sugar
cajuzinho	sweet made from peanut paste, the shape of a cashew nut
caldeirada de peixe	fish stew (with various types of fish and shellfish)
caldo de carne	beef stock
caldo de carne (em cubinhos)	stock cubes
caldo de peixe	clear fish soup
camafeu	sweet made from nut paste, covered with icing sugar
camarão	shrimp
camarões marinados	potted shrimps
canela	cinnamon
canja (de galinha)	rich chicken soup, with rice and vegetables
canjica	corn cooked in milk, with sugar, served with cinnamon
cappuccino	cappuccino
caranguejo	crab
"cardápio do dia"	set menu
carne	meat
carne bovina	beef
carne maturada	aged beef
carne moída	ground beef
carne-seca	see *carne-de-sol*

carne-de-sol	salted beef in slabs, also called *jabá* or *carne-seca*
carneiro	lamb
carolina	a kind of light bun, served hot with a filling of condensed milk or chocolate
carpaccio	carpaccio
caruru	dish from Bahia, made with okra, dried prawns, *dendê* oil and chilli pepper
castanha portuguesa	chestnut
catupiri	typical Brazilian cream cheese, used as filling in many recipes (the same as *requeijão*)
cebola	onion
cenoura	carrot
cereja	cherry
cerveja	beer
cerveja clara	light beer, lager
cerveja grande	large beer
cerveja pequena	small beer
cerveja preta	dark beer
chá	tea
chá com leite	tea and milk
chá com limão	lemon tea
chá de camomila	camomile tea
chá gelado	iced tea
chantilly	cream
chicória	endive, chicory
chilli	chilli pepper
chocolate	chocolate
chocolate quente	hot chocolate
chuchu	chayote
chucrute	sauerkraut
churrasco	barbecue
clara (de ovo)	egg white
coalhada	curd
cocada	sweet made from sugar and coarsely grated coconut
coco	coconut
codorna	quail
coelho	rabbit
coelho assado	roast rabbit

cogumelo	mushroom
"comida para viagem"	takeaway
"comida por quilo"	self-service food: salads, hot dishes and desserts, paid for by weight
comida vegetariana	veggie food
condimento	spice
conhaque	brandy
cookies	cookies
coquetel de camarão	shrimp cocktail
coquetel de lagosta	lobster cocktail
cordeiro assado	roast lamb
costela de porco	pork ribs
costeleta de boi	beef entrecôte
costeleta de cordeiro	lamb chop
costeleta de porco	pork chop
costeleta de vitela	veal chop
couve	collard greens, kale
couve-de-bruxelas	Brussels sprouts
couve-flor	cauliflower
coxinha	deep fried dough in the shape of a chicken drumstick, made from wheat flour, butter and eggs, with shredded chicken filling
creme de leite	cream
creme de leite azedo	sour cream
creme de limão	lemon curd
creme de milho	cooked sweet corn, served in a white sauce
creme de papaia	papaya beaten with milk and served with a cup of *cassis* poured over the top
croquetes	croquettes
crouton	crouton
cural	type of caramel pudding made from grated cooked sweet corn
curry	curry
cuscuz	steamed savoury dish in the shape of a cake, made with corn flour, vegetables, fish and shrimp
damasco	apricot
degustação	tasting
degustação de vinhos	wine tasting

delicado	jelly beans
dietético (diet)	diet
dobradinha	stew made from tripe, with beans, sausage and tomatoes
doces	sweets
donut	donut
empadinha	small savoury tart, made with butter pastry and various fillings, such as palm heart, chicken and shrimp
enguia	eel
entradas	appetizers, starters
erva-doce	fennel
ervilha	pea
escabeche de cavalinha	soused mackerel
esfiha	round piece of dough covered with minced meat (arab specialty)
espaguete à bolonhesa	spaghetti and meat sauce
espaguete com vôngole	spaghetti vongole
espinafre	spinach
expresso	espresso
estragão	tarragon
faisão	pheasant
farinha	flour
fatia (de pão)	loaf
feijão	beans
feijoada	stew made with black beans, dried pork and beef
fígado	liver
figo	fig
filé à parmegiana	fillet steak *à milanesa* (see *"à milanesa"*) covered with mozzarella cheese and tomatoes (or ham)
filé alho e óleo	fillet steak with oil and garlic
filé de carne de porco	pork steak
filé de frango (frito)	fried chicken
filé de peixe à doré	fish fillet passed in beaten egg and flour and fried
filé de peixe-espada	swordfish steak
fios de ovos	sweet made from egg yolks and sugar syrup
flã	flan

MENU GUIDE

floresta negra	black forest: chocolate cake made with cherries, cream and chocolate flakes
foundue de queijo	cheese fondue
framboesa	raspberry
frango	chicken
frango à passarinho	deep fried small chicken pieces
frios	cold meats
frozen yogurt	frozen yogurt
fruta	fruit
fruta flambada	fruit flambé
frutos-do-mar	seafood
galeto	small chicken, usually roasted
galinha ao molho pardo	chicken cooked in a blood sauce
ganso	goose
gelatina	dessert made with jelly powdered and hot water, wich solidifies in the refrigerator; jelly-O
geléia	jam, jelly
gema (de ovo)	yolk
gengibre	ginger
goiaba	guava
gordura (de origem) animal	animal fat
grão-de-bico	chickpea
grapefruit	grapefruit
guaraná	typical Brazilian soft drink, made from a fruit from the Amazon
guisado de carne	meat stew
hambúrguer	hamburger
iogurte	yogurt
isca de filé	small pieces of fillet steak
jerimu	squash
lagosta	lobster
lagostins	king prawns
laranja	orange
lebre	hare
legumes	pulses, vegetables
legumes cozidos	vegetable medley
leite	milk
leite de coco	coconut milk extracted from ripe coconut and used in cooking
leite desnatado	skim milk

leite integral	whole milk
lentilha	lentil
licor de cerejas	cherry brandy
licor digestivo	digestive liqueur
light	light
limão	lemon
língua	tongue
linguado	sole
linguado grelhado ou frito	dover sole
linguiça	sausage
linguiça calabresa	seasoned pork sausage
lombo	tenderloin
louro	bay leaves
lula	squid
lula recheada	stuffed squid
lulas fritas	fried squid
maçã	apple
maçã-do-amor	whole caramelised apple
macarrão	noodles
macarrão com queijo	macaroni and cheese
magro (alimento)	low fat
maionese	mayonnaise
malpassado	rare
manga	mango
manjar-branco	blancmange: sweet made with milk, coconut and served with prunes
manjericão	basil
manjuba	small fish deep fried whole (usually served as an aperitif)
manteiga	butter
maracujá	passion fruit
maria-mole	sweet made from jelly, egg white, sugar and coconut
marzipã	marzipan
massas	pasta
medalhão de filé	thick cut fillet steak
melancia	watermelon
melão	melon
menta, hortelã	mint
mexilhões	mussels
milho	corn

MENU GUIDE

milho verde	cooked sweet corn
milkshake de chocolate	chocolate milkshake
milkshake de frutas	fruit milkshake
milkshake de morango	strawberry milkshake
misto-quente	toasted ham and cheese sandwich
molho	sauce
molho bechamel	white sauce
molho branco	cream sauce, white sauce
molho de alcaparra	caper sauce
molho de chilli	chilli sauce
molho de soja	soy sauce
molho de tomate	tomato sauce
molho inglês	worcestershire sauce
molho mostarda	mustard sauce
molho tártaro	tartar sauce
molho vinagrete	vinaigrette dressing: vinegar, salt, olive oil, tomatoes, onion, parsley and chives, all finely chopped and mixed
moqueca de peixe	Bahian fish stew, with *dendê* oil
morango com chantilly	strawberry with cream
morcela	black pudding
mortadela	well seasoned sausage with caracteristic flavour, popular in sandwichs
mostarda	mustard
musse de café	coffee custard dessert
musse de chocolate	chocolate mousse
nabo	turnip
nata	cream
nhoque	pasta made from wheat flour, potatoes and eggs, rolled into small balls
noz	walnut
noz-moscada	nutmeg
nugá	nougat
óleo	oil
olho-de-sogra	sweet made from sugar, eggs and coconut, served inside an open prune
omelete	omelet, omellete
omelete de presunto	ham omelette
omelete de queijo	cheese omelette
orégano	oregano

ostra	oyster
ovo	egg
ovo pochê	poached egg
ovo quente	poached egg
ovos cozidos	boiled eggs, hard-boiled eggs
ovos mexidos	scrambled eggs
paçoca doce	stuffing made with crushed, roasted peanuts with sugar and manioc flour
panqueca	pancake: made with wheat flour, butter, milk and a pinch of salt (or sugar), and desired filling
pão	bread
pão com manteiga	roll and butter
pão de batata	potato bread
pão de centeio	rye bread
pão de mel	sweet made from wheat flour, sugar, honey, cinnamon and nutmeg, covered with chocolate
pão de queijo	small round savoury made from tapioca flour, vegetable oil and cheese, baked in the oven
pão francês	bread roll of 50 grams, sold in any street corner bakery
pão integral	whole wheat bread, wholemeal bread
pão na chapa	any type of bread grilled on a hotplate, with or without butter
pão sírio	pitta bread
papo-de-anjo	sweet made from beaten egg yolks, baked in small trays and then immediately immersed in hot syrup
"para viagem"	"to go"
pastel	wheat flour pastry cut in a square shape, with savoury fillings (such as meat, cheese and palm heart), then deep fried or baked
pastel doce	the same as *pastel*, but with sweet filling
pastrame	pastrami
patê de fígado	liver pâté
patês	spreads
pato	duck

pato com laranja	duck in orange sauce
peito de frango	chicken breast
peixe	fish
peixe defumado	smoked fish
peixe frito	fried fish
peixe grelhado	grilled fish
peixe-espada	swordfish
pepino	cucumber
pêra	pear
perca	perch
perna de carneiro assada com molho de hortelã	roast leg of lamb with mint sauce
pernil	leg of pork, usually roasted
peru	turkey
peru assado	roast turkey
peru recheado	stuffed turkey
pescada	typical sea fish found along the Brazilian coast
pescada-branca	Brazilian fresh water fish
pêssego	peach
picante	spicy, hot
pimenta	pepper
pimenta-do-reino	black pepper
pimentão	sweet pepper
pimentão verde	green pepper
pinga	see *cachaça*
pingado	a 250 ml cup of coffee and milk, served in any bakery or bar
pintado	fresh water fish
pipoca	pop corn
pitu	fresh water shrimp
pizza calabresa	pizza with sausage (see *linguiça calabresa*)
pizza de frango com catupiri	pizza with chicken and Brazilian processed cheese
pizza margherita	pizza with mozzarella, tomatoes and basil
pizza mozzarella	plain pizza
pizza portuguesa	pizza with ham, onion and eggs
polvo	octopus
porco	pork

prato do dia"	home made dish of the day
prato feito"	known as PF, it's a dish usually featuring rice, beans, steak, egg and salad
prato principal"	main course, main dish
resunto cozido	cooked ham
pretzel	pretzel
pudim	flan
pudim de leite	caramel pudding: condensed milk, dairy milk and eggs
purê de batata	mashed potatoes
queijo	cheese
queijo prato	american cheese
queijo-de-minas	fresh white cheese of variable consistency
queijo gorgonzola	blue cheese
queijo gruyère	Gruyère cheese
queijo parmesão	parmesan cheese
queijo ralado	grated cheese
queijo tipo cheddar	cheddar cheese
quentão	typical drink at June festivals, made of *cachaça*, ginger, cloves, cinnamon and sugar
quiabo	okra
quibe	deep fried savoury made of minced meat, flour, onion, salt and mint
quindão	same as *quindim*, but bigger
quindim	sweet made of egg yolk, sugar and coconut
rabada	braised oxtail
rabanete	radish
rapadura	sweet made of sugar cane, typical in Northeast of Brazil
refrigerante	soft drink
relish de pepino	cucumber relish
repolho	cabbage
requeijão	cream cheese
ricota	cottage cheese
risoles	Portuguese style savouries, fried or baked, made of wheat flour, with various types of filling

risoto	dish made with Italian rice and various other elements, like shrimp, chicken, vegetables and cheese
rocambole	swiss roll
rocambole recheado com creme de limão	swiss roll with lemon-curd filling
rodelas de cebola	onion rings
rodízio	type of restaurant where the customer is served at the table with as much food (specially meat) as he or she can eat
rondelli	rolled pasta filled with cheese, ham etc., served with various sauces (white sauce, rosé, tomato and others)
rosbife	roast beef
sagu	dessert made of starch, in a variety of flavours
sal	salt
salada	salad
salada completa	green salad, tomato, carrot, palm heart, potato, onion, olives, ham and cheese
salada de alface	lettuce salad
salada de batata	potato salad
salada de frango	chicken salad
salada de frutas	fruit salad
salada de frutos-do-mar	seafood salad
salada de tomate	tomato salad
salada mista	mixed salad: green salad, tomato, carrot and onion
salada verde	mixed green salad
salada waldorf	waldorf salad
salame	salami
salmão	salmon
salmão defumado	smoked salmon
salsão	celery
salsinha	parsley
sálvia	sage
sanduíche	sandwich
sardinha	sardine
sashimi	sashimi

seco	dry
sem gordura	fat free
serviço	cover charge
"serviço incluído"	service charge included
"serviço não incluído"	not including service charge
sobremesas	desserts
sonho	doughnut
sopa	soup
sopa de mexilhões	mussel soup
sopa de ostra	oyster stew
sopa de tomate	tomato soup
sopa de verduras	vegetable soup
sorbet de café	iced coffee
sortido, variado	assorted
sorvete	ice-cream
sorvete com chantilly	ice-cream with cream
sorvete de creme	vanilla ice-cream
sorvete de fruta	fruit-flavoured ice-cream
suco de laranja	orange juice
suco de maçã	apple juice
suco de pêssego	peach juice
suco de tomate	tomato juice
suflê	soufflé
suflê de queijo	cheese soufflé
sukiyaki	sukiyaki
sushi	sushi
suspiro	sweet made from egg white and sugar
tacacá	kind of porridge made from tapioca seasoned with tucupi (see *tucupi*) and chilli pepper, typical in the North of Brazil
taco	taco
tainha	mullet
tâmara	date
tangerina	mandarin
tempero	spice
têmpura	tempura
tomate	tomato
tomates recheados	stuffed tomatoes
torrada	toast
torta	pie

torta de camarão	shrimp pie
torta de chocolate	chocolate tart
torta de frango	chicken pie
torta de frutas	fruit tart
torta de limão	key lime pie
torta de maçã	apple pie
torta de maçã de massa folhada	apfelstrudel
torta de nozes	walnut tart
torta de queijo	cheese pie
torta de ricota	cheese cake
torta de rim	kidney pie
torta salgada	savoury flan
tortilha	tortilla
tripa	tripe
trufas	truffles
truta	trout
truta defumada	smoked trout
tucupi	seasoning and sauce made from the juice of grated manioc
tutu de feijão	cooked beans mashed with corn flour or manioc flour
uísque	whisky, scotch
uva	grape
uva-passa	raisin
vatapá	typical dish from Bahia, made with fish or chicken, coconut milk, *dendê* oil, fresh and dried shrimp, highly seasoned, and dashed with chilli pepper
verduras	vegetables
vinagre	vinegar
vinho	wine
vinho branco	white wine
vinho de mesa	table wine
vinho espumante	sparkling wine
vinho rosé	rosé wine
vinho tinto	red wine
vitela	veal
vitela assada	roast veal
waffle	waffle
xícara	cup

SHOPPING AND SERVICES

Until a short time ago, it was traditional throughout Brazil for shops and commercial establishments to remain open from 8:00 a.m. to 6:00 p.m. (Monday to Friday) and from 8:00 a.m. to 1:00 p.m. (Saturday). Shopping on Sunday? No way. In recent years, however, this situation has been changing, with a distinct tendency towards flexibility in shopping hours.

Today, the majority of shops stay open until 7:00 or 8:00 p.m. (to compensate, they may open only at 9:00 or 10:00 a.m.), Monday to Friday. On Saturdays, they will close sometime between 1:00 and 6:00 p.m. Some establishments also open on Sunday, normally in the afternoon.

In the **shopping centers**, commonly found in the big urban centres, the tourist will find modern shopping complexes, services and entertainment open from 10:00 a.m. to 10:00 p.m. (Monday to Saturday) and from 12:00 a.m. to 7:00 p.m. (Sunday). Prices, however, tend to be more expensive.

It's worth noting that shopping hours are the same all year round (summer or winter), and no establishment will close during the lunch hour.

Don't try to buy things with traveller's cheques, cheques from foreign banks or foreign currency: they will not be accepted anywhere. The main international credit cards, however, are more and more widely accepted, especially in the urban centres. Any shop in São Paulo or Rio, for example, will accept them.

To buy medicine, you should look for the **farmácias** or **drogarias**. The majority sell a wide range of cosmetics and personal hygiene products as well as medicine. Their opening hours very greatly; normally, however, you don't need to look very far to find one which stays open 24 hours, including Sundays and holidays. In terms of the sale of medicine, the legislation and supervision in Brazil is surprisingly relaxed: you will rarely be asked for a prescription.

Petrol stations also vary in terms of opening times. Many operate at night, and you will rarely have problems when you need to fill up. There is no system of self-service: a **frentista** will attend you and fill the tank. If you wish, he can check the water and oil —or wash the windscreen. It's common, but not obligatory, to leave a tip of US$ 1 or 2.

USEFUL WORDS AND PHRASES

amount	quantia, total a pagar	kwan-_tee_a toh-_tahl_ ah pah-_gahr_
antique shop	loja de antiguidades	_lohja_ dee ahn-tee-gwee-_dah_-dehs
audio equipment	equipamento de som	eh-kee-pah-_mayn_-too dee sohn
bakery, baker's	padaria	pah-dah-_ree_ya
barber shop	barbeiro	bahr-_bay_-roo
bookshop	livraria	lee-vrah-_ree_ya
boutique	butique	boo-_tee_-keh
brand	marca	_mahr_-kah
butcher's	açougue	ah-ss_oul_-gueh
buy	comprar	kon-_prahr_
cake shop, con-fectioner's shop	confeitaria	kon-_fay_-tah-_ree_ya
camera shop	loja de material fotográfico	_lohja_ dee mah-teh-ree-_ahl_ foh-toh-_grah_-fee-ko
camping equipment	equipamentos de camping	eh-kee-pah-_mayn_-toos dee camping
carrier bag	sacola de compras	sah-_koh_-la dee kon-prahs
cash desk, till	caixa	_kah_-ee-shah
cheap	barato	bah-r_ah_-toh
china	porcelana	pohr-sseh-_lah_-nah
cost	custar	koost_ahr_
craft shop	loja de artesanato	_lohja_ dee ar-teh-sah-_nah_-too
customer	cliente, freguês	klee-_aynch_, freh-gu_eh_s
department store	loja de departamentos	_lohja_ dee deh-pahr-tah-_mayn_-toos

discount	desconto	dehs-kohn-too
dry cleaner's	lavanderia a seco	lah-vahn-dreeya ah seh-ko
	tinturaria	teen-too-rah-reeya
electrical goods	loja de	lohja dee eh-leh-troh-
store	eletrodomésticos	doh-mehs-tee-koos
expensive	caro	kah-ro
fish market,	peixaria	pay-shah-reeya
fishmonger's		
florist's	floricultura	floh-ree-kool-too-rah
food store	armazém	ahr-mah-zayn
fruit stand	banca de frutas	bahn-ka dee froo-tahs
gift shop	loja de presentes	lohja dee preh-zayn-tees
goods	mercadoria,	mehr-kah-doh-reeya
	produto	proh-doo-toh
greengrocer's	quitanda	kee-tahn-dah
grocery store	mercearia	mehr-sseh-ah-reeya
model	modelo	moh-deh-loo
hairdresser	cabeleireiro	kah-beh-lay-ray-roo
hardware shop	loja de ferragens	lohja dee feh-rah-jayns
hypermarket	hipermercado	eeper-mehr-kah-doh
jeweler's	joalheria	joh-ahl-yeh-reeya
ladies' wear	roupas femininas	roul-pahs feh-mee-nee-nahs
market	mercado, feira	mehr-kah-doh, fay-ra
menswear	roupas masculinas	roul-pahs mahs-koo-lee-nahs
newsstand	banca de jornal	bahn-ka dee jor-nahl
optician's	óptica	oh-tee-kah
pharmacy,	farmácia,	fahr-mah-sseea
drugstore	drogaria	droh-gah-reeya
price	preço	preh-sso
receipt	recibo, nota	reh-see-boo, noh-tah
record shop	loja de discos	lohja dee dees-kohs
sale	liquidação	lee-kwee-dah-ssowng
salesman	vendedor (a)	vayn-deh-dohr (doh-ra)
shoe shop	sapataria	sah-pah-tah-reeya

shop	loja	*lohja*
size	tamanho	*tah-mahn-yo*
souvenir shop	loja de suvenires	*lohja dee soo-veh-neers*
sports equipment	equipamentos esportivos	*eh-kee-pah-mayn-toos ehs-por-tee-vohs*
sportswear	trajes esportivos	*trah-jehs ehs-por-tee-vohs*
stationer's (shop)	papelaria	*pah-peh-lah-reeya*
supermarket	supermercado	*sooper-mehr-kah-doh*
tailor's	alfaiataria	*ahl-fah-yah-tah-reeya*
tobacco shop	tabacaria	*tah-bah-kah-reeya*
toyshop	loja de brinquedos	*lohja dee breen-keh-dohs*
travel agency	agência de viagens	*ah-jayn-ssyah dee vee-yah-jayns*
vegetables	verduras, legumes	*vehr-doo-ras, leh-goo-mehs*

Excuse me, where is/where are …?
Por favor, onde fica/ficam …?
poor fah-vor, ondee feekah/feekahn

Where is there a … (shop) around here?
Onde há uma (loja de) … aqui perto?
ondee ah ooma (lohja dee) … akee pehr-to

Where is the … department?
Onde fica a seção de …?
ondee feekah ah seh-ssowng dee

Where is the main shopping area?
Onde fica o centro comercial?
ondee feekah oh sehn-tro koh-mehr-see-yahl

Is there a supermarket here?
Há algum supermercado aqui?
ah ahl-goon sooper-mehr-kah-doh akee

I'd like …
Eu gostaria de …
el gostreeh-ya dee

Do you have …?
Vocês têm ...?
voh-ssehs tayn

How much is this?
Quanto custa isto?
kwantoo koos-tah eesstoo

Where do I pay?
Onde eu pago?
ondee el pah-goh

Do you take credit cards?
Vocês aceitam cartão de crédito?
voh-ssehs ah-ssay-tahn kartowng dee kreh-dee-too

I think perhaps you've short-changed me
Acho que você me deu troco a menos
ah-shoh kee voh-sseh mee del troh-koh ah meh-nohs

Can I have a receipt/a bag, please?
Pode me dar um recibo/uma sacola, por favor?
pod-mee dahr oom reh-ssee-boh/ooma sah-koh-lah, poor fah-vor

I'm just looking
Só estou olhando
soh ehs-toul ohl-yahn-doo

I'll come back later
Eu volto mais tarde
el vohl-toh mah-ys tahr-gee

Do you have any more of these?
Vocês têm mais destes?
voh-sseh tayn mah-ys dehs-tees

Don't you have anything cheaper?
Não há algo mais barato?
nowng ah ahl-goh mah-ys bah-rah-too

Do you have anything larger/smaller?
Vocês têm algo maior/menor?
voh-ssehs tayn ahl-goh mah-yohr/meh-nohr

Can I try it/them on?
Posso experimentar?
pohssoo ehs-peh-ree-mehn-tahr

Does it come in other colours?
Há também em outras cores?
ah tahn-bayn eng oul-trahs koh-rehs

Could you gift-wrap it for me?
Você pode embrulhar para presente?
voh-sseh pod ayn-brool-yahr pahra preh-zehn-chee

I'd like to exchange this, it's faulty
Eu gostaria de trocar isto, porque tem um defeito
el gostreeh-ya dee troh-kahr eesstoo, por-keh tayn oom deh-fay-too

I'm afraid I don't have the receipt
Sinto muito, mas não tenho o recibo
seento mooytoo, mahs nowng tayn-yu oh reh-ssee-boo

Can I have a refund?
Vocês podem me devolver o dinheiro?
voh-ssehs poh-dayn mee deh-voul-vehr oh deen-yey-roo

My camera isn't working
Minha câmera não está funcionando
meen-ya kah-meh-rah nowng ess-tah foong-ssee-yoh-nahn-doo

I want a thirty six exposure colour film, a hundred ISO
Quero um filme colorido de 36 poses, de 100 ISO
kehro oom feel-meh koh-loh-ree-doh dee 36 poh-zehs, dee 100 ah-zahs

I'd like to develop this film
Eu gostaria de revelar este filme
el gostreeh-ya dee reh-veh-lahr esstee feel-meh

Glossy prints
Cópias em papel brilhante
koh-peeas eng pah-pehl breel-yahn-chee

One-hour service, please
Revelação em uma hora, por favor
reh-veh-lah-ssowng eng ooma orah, poor fah-vor

Where can I get this mended?
Onde posso consertar isto?
ondee pohssoo kon-ssehr-tahr eesstoo

Can you fix this?
Você pode consertar isto para mim?
voh-sseh pod kon-ssehr-tahr eesstoo pahra meeng

I'd like this skirt/these pants dry-cleaned
Eu gostaria de lavar esta saia/estas calças
el gostreeh-ya dee lah-vahr esstah sah-yah/esstahs kahl-ssahs

When will it/they be ready?
Quando ficará pronto?
kwandoo fee-kah-rah prohn-too

I'd like to make an appointment
Eu gostaria de marcar uma hora
el gostreeh-ya dee mahr-kahr ooma orah

I want a hair cut and blow dry
Eu gostaria de cortar o cabelo e fazer escova
el gostreeh-ya dee kohr-tahr oh kah-beh-loh eh fah-zehr ehs-koh-vah

With conditioner/No conditioner
Com condicionador/Sem condicionador
kon kon-dee-see-yoh-nah-dohr/sayn kon-dee-see-yoh-nah-dohr

Just a trim, please
Apenas apare-o um pouco, por favor
ah-peh-nahs ah-pah-reh-oh oom poul-koh, poor fah-vor

Not too much off!
Não corte demais!
nowng kohr-chee dee-mah-ys

When does the market open?
Quando o mercado abre?
kwandoo oh mehr-kah-doh ah-breh

What's the price per pound (per kilo)?
Quanto é o preço por quilo?
kwantoo eh oh preh-sso por kee-loh

Could you write that down?
Você pode escrever isso?
voh-sseh pod ehs-kreh-vehr eessoo

That's too much! I'll pay …
É muito caro! Eu dou …
eh mooytoo kah-ro! el doul

Could I have a discount?
Pode me dar um desconto?
pod mee dahr oom dehs-kohn-too

That's fine, I'll take it.
Está bem, vou levar.
ess-tah bayn, voul leh-vahr.

I'll have a piece of that cheese
Quero um pedaço deste queijo
kehro oom peh-dah-ssoh dehs-tee kay-joh

About a pound (kilo)/two pounds (kilos)
Cerca de um quilo/dois quilos
sehr-kah dee oom kee-loh/doys kee-lohs

Half a pound (kilo)/A pound (kilo) of apples, please
Meio quilo/Um quilo de maçãs, por favor
may-yoh kee-loh/oom kee-loh dee mah-ssahns, poor fah-vor

Half a pound (kilo) of that cheese, please
Meio quilo daquele queijo, por favor
may-yoh kee-loh dah-keh-leh kay-joh, poor fah-vor

May I taste it?
Posso experimentar?
pohssoo ehs-peh-ree-mehn-tahr

That's very nice, I'll take some
Está muito bom; vou levar um pouco
ess-tah mooytoo boun; voul leh-vahr oom poul-koh

It isn't what I wanted
Não é o que eu queria
nowng eh oh kee el keh-reeya

Things You'll See

açougue	butcher's
agência de viagens	travel agency
alfaiataria	tailor's
alta qualidade	high quality
andar superior	upper floor
aparar	trim
barbeiro	barber shop
bebidas alcoólicas	spirits, liquors
brinquedos	toys
cabeleireiro (a)	hair stylist
cabeleireiro (a)	hairdresser
calçados	shoes
com desconto	reduced
confeitaria	cake shop
corte de cabelo	hair cut
doceria	confectionery, cakes
dúzia	dozen
eletrodomésticos	electrical appliances

→

empurrar	push
entrada	way in
experimentar	try on
faça-você-mesmo	DIY (do it yourself)
fazer escova no cabelo	blow dry
floricultura	flower shop
fresco	fresh
legumes e verduras	vegetables
liquidação	sales
livraria	bookshop, bookstore
loja	store
loja de departamentos	department store
luzes (no cabelo)	highlights
material de escritório	office supplies
mercearia, supermercado	grocery
moda	fashion
não se trocam mercadorias sem o recibo (a nota)	goods are not exchanged without a receipt
não toque	do not touch
caixa	cash desk, till
padaria	bakery
pagar no caixa	pay at the desk
papelaria	stationer's
peixaria	fish market, fishmonger's
permanente (no cabelo)	perm (hair)
por favor, use um carrinho, uma cesta	please take a trolley, basket
preço	price
puxar	pull
revistas	magazines
roupas femininas	ladies' clothing
roupas masculinas	men's clothing
saída	exit, way out
secador de cabelo	hairdryer
seção, departamento	department
tabacaria	tobacco shop

THINGS YOU'LL HEAR

Posso ajudá-lo (a)?
Can I help you?

Está sendo atendido?
Are you being served?

Deseja pagar com cartão de crédito?
Do you want to pay with a credit card?

O (A) senhor (a) tem trocado/moedas?
Do you have any change?

Lamento, não temos mais deste artigo
I'm sorry, we're out of stock

Isto é tudo que temos
This is all we have

Pague no caixa, por favor
Please, pay at the till

Deseja algo mais?
Will there be anything else?

Quanto/Quantos o (a) senhor (a) gostaria?
How much/many would you like?

Como deseja isso?
How would you like it?

SPORT

Brazilians love sports, and without doubt, the national sport of Brazil is football (soccer). At any time of year, the main teams (veritable national institutions, like Corinthians of São Paulo or Flamengo of Rio) meet each other in various championships, with a subtle hierarchy of charm and importance.

There are games at the weekend and during the week, and the local newspapers always publish the main results on the front page. Depending on the importance of a game, it may well be the headline. Conversations concerning football take up a considerable part of men's free time, and it's an inexhaustible theme among a group of friends, in the bar, at university, or at work. All Brazilians have their lifelong favourite team, which they follow faithfully, irrespective of their position in the championship. The state capitals have as many as four or five important clubs. Normally, the fans throughout the state are divided between the clubs in the capital, because the local teams rarely have any tradition.

A tourist wanting to go to the stadium to see a game might find it quite a complicated adventure. By European or American standards, the championships are surprisingly badly organized. Tickets are never sold much beforehand: they start to be sold three days before the game (if as much as that), at only one or two sales points. Enormous queues are formed therefore, often chaotic. On the day of the game, more problems. Huge queues, crowds, lack of information and violence have all discouraged even the local fans from turning up.

Another sport greatly appreciated by Brazilians is Formula 1. Brazilian drivers have won eight F1 world championships (Emerson Fittipaldi twice; Nelson Piquet and Ayrton Senna three times each). The popularity of Motor Racing, however, dropped off considerably after the tragic death of national hero Ayrton Senna.

On the other hand, tennis –which used to be a sport restricted to the elite– has been growing in popularity after the success of Gustavo Kuerten, or 'Guga', who reached the top of the world rankings at the end of the year 2000.

USEFUL WORDS AND PHRASES

alpinism	alpinismo	*ahl-pee-nees-moo*
athletics	atletismo	*ah-tleh-tees-moo*
ball	bola	*boh-lah*
baseball	beisebol	*bay-zee-bohl*
basketball	basquete	*bahs-keh-chee*
bicycle, bike	bicicleta	*bee-ssee-kleh-tah*
boat	barco	*bahr-koh*
bowling	boliche	*boh-lee-sheh*
canoe	canoa	*kah-noh-ah*
canoeing	canoagem	*ka-noh-ah-jayn*
cycling	ciclismo	*see-klees-moo*
dive	mergulhar	*mehr-gool-yar*
diving board	trampolim	*trahn-poh-leen*
diving mask	máscara de	*mahs-kah-rah dee*
	mergulho	*mehr-gool-yoh*
diving	mergulho	*mehr-gool-yoh*
fishing rod	vara de pescar	*vah-rah dee pehs-kahr*
fishing	pesca	*pehs-kah*
flippers	pés-de-pato	*pehs dee pah-toh*
football	futebol americano	*foo-teh-bohl ah-meh-ree-kah-noo*
game	jogo	*joh-goh*
go cycling, biking	andar de bicicleta	*ahn-dahr dee bee-ssee-kleh-tah*
goggles	óculos de mergulho	*oh-koo-lohs dee mehr-gool-yoh*
golf course	campo de golfe	*kahn-poh dee gohl-fee*
gymnastics	ginástica	*gee-nahs-tee-kah*
hang-gliding	asa-delta	*ah-zah dehl-tah*
harpoon	arpão	*ahr-powng*
horse riding	equitação	*eh-kee-tah-ssowng*
hunting	caça	*kah-ssah*
ice skating	patinação no gelo	*pah-tee-nah-ssowng noh geh-loh*

ice-hockey	hóquei sobre gelo	hoh-kay sohbre geh-loh
life jacket	colete salva-vidas	koh-leh-chee
		sahl-va vee-das
oxygen bottles	garrafas de oxigênio	gah-rah-fahs dee
		ohk-see-geh-neeo
pedal boat	pedalinho	peh-dah-leen-yo
play golf	jogar golfe	joh-gahr gohl-fee
pool, swimming pool	piscina	pee-ssee-nah
racket	raquete	rah-keh-chee
ride a horse	cavalgar	kah-vahl-gahr
rock climbing	montanhismo	mohn-tan-ees-moo
saddle	sela	seh-lah
sail	vela	veh-lah
sailing	velejar	veh-leh-jahr
shooting range	tiro ao alvo	tee-roh aul ahl-voh
skate	patinar	pah-tee-nahr
skating rink	pista de patinação	pees-tah dee
		pah-tee-nah-ssowng
ski trail	pista de esqui	pees-tah dee ehs-kee
ski	esquiar	ehs-kee-ahr
skydiving	pára-quedismo	pah-rah-keh-dees-moo
soccer game,	partida de futebol	pahr-tee-dah dee
football match		foo-teh-bohl
soccer	futebol	foo-teh-bohl
sport	esporte	ehs-pohr-chee
sports centre	centro esportivo	sayn-tro ehs-pohr-tee-vo
stadium	estádio	ees-tah-deeo
surf	surfe	soorfee
surfboard	prancha de surfe	pran-shah dee soorfee
swim	nadar	nah-dahr
swimming	natação	nah-tah-ssowng
team	time, equipe	chee-meh, eh-kee-peh
tennis	tênis	teh-nees
tennis court	quadra de tênis	kwa-dra dee teh-nees
underwater fishing	pesca submarina	pehs-kah
		soo-bee-mah-ree-na

volleyball	voleibol	voh-lay-bohl
water-skiing	esqui aquático	ehs-kee ah-kwa-tee-koh
wet suit	traje isotérmico	trah-jeh ee-zoh-tehr-mee-koh
wood, driver	taco de golfe	tah-koh dee gohl-fee

How do I get to the beach?
Como eu faço para chegar à praia?
koh-moh el fahssoo pahra sheh-gahr ah prah-eea

How deep is the water here?
Qual a profundidade da água aqui?
kwal ah proh-foon-dee-dah-gee dah ahgwa akee

Is there an indoor/outdoor pool here?
Há uma piscina coberta/ao ar livre aqui?
ah ooma pee-ssee-nah koh-behr-tah/aul ahr lee-vreh akee

Is it dangerous to swim here?
É perigoso nadar aqui?
eh peh-ree-goh-zoh nah-dahr akee

Can I fish here?
Posso pescar aqui?
pohssoo pehs-kahr akee

Do I need a licence?
Preciso de uma licença?
preh-ssee-zoh dee ooma lee-ssayn-ssa

Is there a golf course near here?
Há algum campo de golfe aqui perto?
ah ahl-goon kahn-poh dee gohl-fee akee pehr-toh

Do I have to be a member?
Eu preciso ser sócio?
el preh-ssee-zoh sehr soh-sseeo

Where can I rent ...?
Onde eu posso alugar ...?
ondee el pohssoo ah-loo-gahr

I would like to rent a bike
Eu gostaria de alugar uma bicicleta
el gostreeh-ya dee ah-loo-gahr ooma bee-ssee-kleh-tah

How much does it cost per hour/day?
Quanto custa por hora/por dia?
kwantoo koos-ta por orah/por dee-ah

How does it work?
Como isso funciona?
koh-moh eessoo foong-seeyoh-na

When does the lift start?
A que horas abrem os teleféricos?
ah kee orahs ah-brayn ohs teh-leh-feh-ree-koos

Where are the nursery slopes?
Onde são as pistas para principiantes?
ondee sowng ahs pees-tahs pahra preen-see-pee-ahn-chees

Where could I watch a soccer game?
Onde eu poderia assistir a uma partida de futebol?
ondee el podreeh-ya ah-ssees-cheer ah ooma pahr-tee-dah dee foo-teh-bohl

I would like to take tennis/diving lessons
Eu gostaria de ter aulas de tênis/mergulho
el gostreeh-ya dee tehr aul-lahs dee teh-nees/mehr-gool-yoh

There's something wrong with this bicycle
Há alguma coisa errada com esta bicicleta
ah ahl-goo-mah koyh-zah eh-rah-dah kon ess-tah bee-ssee-kleh-tah

I haven't played this before
Nunca joguei isso antes
noon-kah joh-gay eessoo ahn-chees

Let's go skating/swimming
Vamos patinar/nadar
vah-moos pah-tee-nahr/nah-dahr

What's the score?
Qual é o placar?
kwal eh oh plah-kahr

Who won?
Quem ganhou?
kayn gahn-youl

THINGS YOU'LL SEE

acesso à praia	to the beach
aluguel de barcos	boat renting
aluguel de bicicletas	bike, cycle renting
aluguel de equipamento	equipment renting
aluguel de esquis	ski renting
aluguel de guarda-sol	sunshade renting
bondinho	cable car
ciclovia	bike, cycle path
correnteza perigosa	dangerous currents
entrada particular	private entrance
para o teleférico	to the chair lift
pedestres	pedestrians
perigo	danger
piscina ao ar livre	open-air swimming pool
piscina coberta	indoor swimming pool
prepare-se para descer	get ready to alight
proibida a entrada	no admittance
proibido acender fogo	no fires
proibido entrar na água	no bathing
proibido mergulhar	no diving
proibido passar	no trespassing
proibido pescar	no fishing
proibido balançar	no swinging
pronto-socorro	first aid
salva-vidas	lifeguard
trampolim	diving board, ski jump

THE POST OFFICE AND BANKS

To send a postcard or a standard letter to the United States costs US$ 0.33; to Europe, US$ 0.39; to Australia and South Africa, US$ 0.44. There are many post offices, where you can buy stamps (occasionally, you will find them for sale at newspaper kiosks). If you already have stamps, it will be even easier and without queues: you can easily find a post box in the street to post your letter.

In general the post system works very well. Airmail tends to take from four to seven days to reach the United States or England, and it's rare for a letter not to reach its destination. If you really feel insecure, registered letters (with insurance) are absolutely safe, and a good option. The same can be said for telegrams.

If you want to send packages you should also go to a post office. There you can buy cardboard boxes in three different sizes. When your package is ready, the post office employee will seal it and weigh it; although it's not common, don't forget that they have the right to inspect the contents.

Banks are open from 10:00 a.m. to 4:00 p.m. (with small variations in smaller cities), from Monday to Friday. In most of these, a tourist can change dollars or traveller's cheques (a passport is necessary for the latter).

It's not easy to change money anywhere else in the city, even in the biggest urban centres. However, if you need money on a Saturday, for example, you can go to a 24 hour electronic cash machine. There are many in any large or medium-sized city, and almost all operate with international credit cards.

The Brazilian currency is the **real** (plural **reais**), which has been in circulation since 1994. Since then, inflation has been kept under control (around 4% a year), and the exchange rate has suffered just one major fall, at the beginning of 1999. Today one **real** is worth approximately US$ 0.37, with a slight downward tendency. Values in **reais** are indicated by the symbol **R$**. There are notes of R$ 1, R$ 5, R$ 10, R$ 50 and R$ 100. The **real** is divided into units called **centavos**, and there are coins of R$ 0.01, R$ 0.05, R$ 0.10, R$ 0.25 and R$ 0.50. It's important to note that, in Brazil, the **centavos** are separated from the main value in **reais** by a comma. The decimal point is used to separate blocks of three digits in larger numbers. So to represent five thousand **reais**, you need to write **R$ 5.000,00**.

USEFUL WORDS AND PHRASES

airmail	via aérea	veea ah-_air_-reea
bank	banco	b_ah_n-koh
banknote	nota	n_oh_-tah
cash	dinheiro	deen-y_ey_-roo
cash dispenser	caixa eletrônico	k_ah_-ysha eh-leh-tr_oh_-nee-coh
change	trocar	troh-k_ah_r
check book, cheque book	talão de cheques	tah-l_ow_ng dee sh_eh_-kees
check, cheque	cheque	sh_eh_-kee
collection	coleta postal	koh-l_eh_-tah pohs-t_ah_l
counter	balcão	bahl-k_ow_ng
credit card	cartão de crédito	kart_ow_ng dee kr_eh_-dee-toh
customs form	formulário de alfândega	fohr-moo-l_ah_-reeo dee ahl-f_ah_n-deh-ga
delivery	entrega	ayn-tr_eh_-gah
deposit	depósito	deh-p_oh_-zee-toh
dollar	dólar	d_oh_-lahr
envelope	envelope	ayn-veh-l_oh_-peh
exchange rate	taxa de câmbio	t_ah_-shah dee k_a_nbyo
fax machine	aparelho de fax	ah-pah-r_eh_l-yo dee fax
fax	enviar por fax	ayn-vee-_ah_r por fax
form	formulário	fohr-moo-l_ah_-reeo
international money order	vale postal internacional	v_ah_-leh pohs-t_ah_l een-ter-nah-ssee-yo-n_ah_l
letter	carta	k_ah_r-tah
mail	correio	koh-r_ay_-oh

97

THE POST OFFICE AND BANKS

mailbox, postbox	caixa de correio	*kah-yshah dee koh-ray-oh*
money order	vale postal	*vah-leh pohs-tahl*
package, parcel	pacote	*pah-koh-chee*
post office	agência dos Correios	*ah-jayn-sseea dohs koh-ray-ohs*
post, mail	postar	*pohs-tahr*
postcard	cartão-postal	*kartowng pohs-tahl*
postman	carteiro	*kahr-tay-roh*
pound sterling	libra esterlina	*lee-bra ehs-tehr-lee-na*
registered letter	carta registrada	*kahr-tah reh-gees-trah-dah*
stamp	selo	*seh-loh*
surface mail	correio comum	*koh-ray-oh koh-moon*
telegram	telegrama	*teh-leh-grah-mah*
withdraw	retirar, sacar	*sah-kahr, reh-tee-rahr*
withdrawal	saque, retirada	*sah-keh, reh-tee-rah-da*
zipcode, postcode	código postal (CEP)	*koh-dee-goo pohs-tahl*

How much is a postcard to England?
Quanto custa enviar um cartão para a Inglaterra?
kwantoo koos-tah ayn-vee-ahr oom kartowng pahra ah een-glah-teh-rah

I would like three fifty-cent stamps
Gostaria de três selos de 50 centavos
gostreeh-ya dee trays seh-lohs dee 50 sayn-tah-vohs

I want to register this letter
Quero mandar esta carta registrada
kehro mahn-dahr esstah kahr-tah reh-gees-trah-dah

I want to send this parcel to Australia
Quero mandar este pacote para a Austrália
kehro mahn-dahr esstee pah-koh-chee pahra ah auls-trahl-ya

How long does the post to the USA take?
Quanto tempo leva o correio para os Estados Unidos?
kwantoo tayn-poo leh-vah oh koh-ray-oh pahra ohs ehs-tah-dohs oo-nee-dohs

Where can I post this?
Onde posso postar isto?
_ondee p_ohssoo pohs-t_ahr __eestoo

Is there any mail for me?
Há alguma correspondência para mim?
_ah ahl-g_oo-mah koh-rehs-pon-d_ayn_-seea p_ahra meeng

I'd like to send a telegram/a fax
Eu gostaria de enviar um telegrama/um fax
el gostr_eeh_-ya dee ayn-vee-_ahr oom teh-leh-gr_ah-mah/oom fax

This is to go airmail
Quero que isso vá por via aérea
k_ehro kee __eesoo v_ah por v_eea ah-_air-reea

I'd like to change this into ten 'reais' notes
Gostaria de trocar por notas de dez reais
gostr_eeh_-ya dee troh-k_ahr por n_oh-tahs dee dehs reh-_ah-ys

Can I cash these traveller's cheques?
Posso trocar estes traveller's cheques?
p_ohssoo troh-k_ahr __eestees traveller's cheques

What is the exchange rate for the dollar?
Qual é a cotação do dólar?
kwal eh ah koh-tah-ss_owng doh d_oh-lahr

Can I draw cash using this credit card?
Posso sacar dinheiro com este cartão de crédito?
p_ohssoo sah-k_ahr deen-y_ey_-roo kon __estee kart_owng dee kr_eh-dee-too

I'd like it in ten 'reais' notes
Eu queria em notas de dez reais
el kr_eeh_-ya eng n_oh-tahs dee dehs reh-_ah-ys

Could you give me smaller notes?
Poderia me dar notas de menor valor?
podr_eeh_-ya mee d_ahr n_oh-tahs dee meh-n_ohr vah-l_ohr

THINGS YOU'LL SEE

assinatura	signature
balcão de pacotes	parcels counter
câmbio	currency exchange
carta com valor declarado	insured mail
carta registrada	registered mail, letter
cartão-postal	postcard
código postal	zipcode, postcode
conta corrente	checking account, current account
correio aéreo, via aérea	airmail
correio expresso	express
correio, correspondência	mail
crédito	credit
depósito	deposit
destinatário	addressee
destino	destination
endereço	address
enviar dinheiro	send money
horário de funcionamento	opening hours
moeda corrente	currency
pacote	package
postagem para o exterior	postage abroad
postagem	postage
preencher	to fill in
remetente	sender
retirada	withdrawal
saque	withdrawal
selo	stamp
tarifa para postagem interna	inland postage
tarifa	charge, rate
taxa de câmbio	exchange rate
trocar dinheiro	change money

USING THE TELEPHONE

Even in the smaller cities, it's not difficult to find public telephones in the street. Until a short time ago, they all looked the same, in the form of large orange shells called **orelhões** (big ears). Today, although the name remains, there are various different types of phone box, very few of which are closed cabins (be prepared to compete with cars and lorries to make yourself heard.)

Some of these public telephones operate with **fichas** (tokens, always one unit) and the modern ones with **cartões** (telephone cards, with a varying number of units). Each unit allows three minutes of local conversation or proportionally less time for longer distances. A card with 10 units costs US$ 0.55; with ninety, US$ 1.10.

Brazil has a direct dialling system (DDD) which connects all its municipalities. Currently, after the privatisation of the 90's, you need to choose one of many local operators: you dial 0, the number of the operator (2 digits), city code and the telephone number (for collect calls add a 9 before the first 0). The two national operators are Embratel (21) and Intelig (23).

Brazil is also connected to many countries around the world by direct dialling (DDI). For international calls, you have two options: you can use an operator from the country you are calling or a Brazilian operator. In the first case dial 00080 and the number of the operator. These are the main ones: **USA** 10 (AT&T), 12 (MCI), 16 (Sprint), 11 (Worldcom); **UK** 44; **Australia** 61; **Argentina** 54; **Uruguay** 59; **Germany** 49; **Italy** 39; **France** 33. If you prefer a Brazilian operator, dial 00, followed by the number of the operator and the country code (the same as the list above, with the exception of the U.S.A., which is 1). International collect calls can be obtained with the help of the operator: dial 107 and ask for the **telefonista internacional**. Brazilian charges vary according to the time of the call; the highest can reach US$ 2.96 per minute to Europe and US$ 1,10 to the USA.

The mobile phone system is also highly developed in Brazil. At the airports in São Paulo and Rio, you will find no difficulty in renting a mobile phone. Another interesting option for the traveller is to buy a pay-as-you-go, or **pré-pago**.

USEFUL WORDS AND PHRASES

busy	ocupado	oh-koo-pah-doh
call (v.)	telefonar	teh-leh-foh-nahr
call (n.)	telefonema	teh-leh-foh-neh-mah
cardphone	telefone	teh-leh-foh-neh
	de cartão	dee kartowng
code	código,	koh-dee-goo,
	prefixo	preh-feek-soh
collect call,	chamada a cobrar	shah-mah-dah
reverse charge call		ah koh-brahr
dial	discar	dees-kahr
dialling tone	sinal de discagem	see-nahl dee
		dees-kah-jayn
extension	ramal	rah-mahl
information	informação	een-fohr-mah-ssowng
international call	chamada	shah-mah-dah een-ter-
	internacional	nah-ssee-yoh-nahl
number	número	noo-meh-roh
operator	telefonista	teh-leh-foh-nees-tah
payphone	telefone público	teh-leh-foh-neh
		poo-blee-koh
phonecard	cartão telefônico	kartowng
		teh-leh-foh-nee-ko
telephone booth	cabine telefônica	kah-bee-neh
		teh-leh-foh-nee-ka
telephone directory	lista telefônica	leesta teh-leh-foh-nee-ka
telephone	telefone	teh-leh-foh-neh
wrong number	número errado	noo-meh-roh eh-rah-do

Where is the nearest phone booth?
Onde fica a cabine telefônica mais próxima?
ondee feekah ah kah-bee-neh teh-leh-foh-nee-ka mah-ys praw-ssee-mah

Is there a telephone directory?
Há uma lista telefônica?
ah ooma leesta teh-leh-foh-nee-ka

I would like the directory for São Paulo
Eu gostaria de ver a lista telefônica de São Paulo
el gostreeh-ya dee vehr ah leesta teh-leh-foh-nee-ka de sowng pahl-loh

Can I call abroad from here?
Posso ligar daqui para o exterior?
pohssoo lee-gahr dakee pahra oh ehs-teh-ree-yohr

I would like to make a collect call
Quero que seja a cobrar
kehro kee seh-jah ah koh-brahr

I would like a number in Rio de Janeiro
Quero um número no Rio de Janeiro
kehro oom noo-meh-roh noh reeyo dee jah-nay-roo

Can you give me an outside line?
Você pode me dar uma linha externa?
voh-sseh pod-mee dahr ooma leen-ya ehs-tehr-nah

How do I get an outside line?
Como posso conseguir uma linha externa?
koh-moh pohssoo kon-sseh-gueehr ooma leen-ya ehs-tehr-nah

Hello, this is Ana speaking
Alô, aqui quem fala é Ana
aloh, akee kayn fah-lah eh ah-na

Is that Mark?
É o Mark?
eh oh mahr-kee

Speaking
Sou eu/pode falar
soul el/pod fah-lahr

I would like to speak to Paula
Eu gostaria de falar com a Paula
el gostreeh-ya dee fah-lahr kon ah pahl-lah

Extension 34, please
Ramal 34, por favor
rah-mahl treen-tahy kwah-tro, poor fah-vor

Please tell him/her Marina called
Por favor, diga-lhe que Marina ligou
poor fah-vor, deegahl-yeh kee mah-ree-nah lee-goul

Ask him/her to call me back, please
Diga-lhe que me telefone, por favor
deegahl-yeh kee mee teh-leh-foh-neh, poor fah-vor

My number is 75 35 22
Meu número é 75 35 22
mel noo-meh-roh eh sech seen-ko, trays seenko, doys doys

Do you know where he/she is?
Você sabe onde ele/ela está?
voh-sseh sah-beh ondee eh-leh/eh-lah ess-tah

When will he/she be back?
Quando ele/ela estará de volta?
kwandoo eh-leh/eh-lah ehs-tah-rah dee vohl-tah

Could you leave him/her a message?
Posso deixar um recado para ele/ela?
pohssoo day-shahr oom reh-kah-doh pahra eh-leh/eh-lah

I'll call back later
Voltarei a ligar mais tarde
voul-tah-ray ah lee-gahr mah-ys tahr-gee

Sorry, I've got the wrong number
Desculpe, foi engano
dehskoolp, foy ehn-gah-noh

You've got the wrong number
Você discou o número errado
voh-sseh dees-koul oh noo-meh-roh eh-rah-doh

THE ALPHABET

a	*ah*	h	*ah-gah*	o	*aw*	v	*veh*
b	*beh*	i	*ee*	p	*peh*	w	*dah-blee-oo*
c	*seh*	j	*joh-tah*	q	*keh*	x	*shees*
d	*deh*	k	*kah*	r	*eh-hee*	y	*eep-ssoo-lohn*
e	*eh*	l	*eh-lee*	s	*eh-ssee*	z	*zeh*
f	*eh-fee*	m	*eh-mee*	t	*teh*		
g	*geh*	n	*eh-nee*	u	*oo*		

THINGS YOU'LL HEAR

Alô
Hello

Sou eu/Pode falar
Speaking

Com quem deseja falar?
Who would you like to speak to?

O (A) senhor (a) discou o número errado
You've got the wrong number

Quem fala?
Who's calling?

Espere um momento, por favor
Hold in line, please/Hold on, please

Sinto muito, ele/ela não está
I'm sorry, he/she's not in

Posso ligar mais tarde?
Can I call back later?

Qual é o seu número?
What is your number?

→

Ele/Ela voltará às ... horas
He/She'll be back at ... o'clock

Ligue de novo amanhã, por favor
Please, call again tomorrow

Direi a ele/ela que o (a) senhor (a) ligou
I'll tell him/her you called

THINGS YOU'LL SEE

aparelho	telephone
cabine telefônica	telephone booth
cartão telefônico	phonecard
central telefônica, telefonista	local exchange, operator
chamada interurbana	long-distance call
chamada local	local call
chamada	call
código	code
discagem direta	direct dialling
discar o número	dial the number
erguer	to lift
fichas telefônicas	telephone tokens
fone	receiver
inserir moedas	insert coins
levantar o fone	hang up
lista telefônica	telephone directory
moeda	coin
não funciona	faults service, out of order
número	number
números úteis	useful numbers
Páginas Amarelas	Yellow Pages
prefixo	code
serviço gratuito	free service
sinal de discagem	tone
telefone	phone

EMERGENCIES

In Brazil there are two distinct police forces. The **polícia militar**, known as the **PM**, is a police body linked to the army, subject to military rules and hierarchy. It has, in each state of the Federation, its own organizational structure. The **polícia civil** (or **guarda civil**) is in turn a civilian police body, subject to the Town Hall of each municipality. It's clear that both these police forces should act together to prevent crime and ensure public peace. Unfortunately for Brazilian citizens, however, the responsibilities of each one are not very clearly defined, which has sometimes caused serious misunderstandings between the two commands.

Generally speaking, the **PM** is responsible for emergencies and any kind of activity which demands greater strength of concentrated action. The **polícia civil** is responsible for more systematic and constant activities, including crime investigation, record keeping etc.

In an emergency situation, like a robbery, a threat of violence with an aggressor still on the scene, and other more dangerous situations, you should call the **PM**, on **190**. In situations where the greatest danger has already passed, like the reporting of a robbery, it's more effective to call directly to the **polícia civil**, on **147**. If you are in doubt, it's probably a better idea to call **190**. (Both numbers operate throughout the country, free of charge from public call boxes).

Two other important emergency numbers, valid throughout Brazil, are **192** (ambulance service or **pronto-socorro**) and **193** (the Fire Brigade or **bombeiros**). These calls are also free from public call boxes.

The Brazilian fire brigade, linked to the **PM**, has a tradition of excellence. The same cannot be said, unfortunately, of the ambulance service. Often overworked, the quality of service varies greatly from place to place.

If you drive on a highway, check if there's an emergency service: many roads now have emergency telephones every 2 km (1.25 miles).

USEFUL WORDS AND PHRASES

accident	acidente	*ah-ssee-dayn-chee*
ambulance	ambulância	*ahn-boo-lahn-sseea*
assault	agredir	*ah-greh-deer*
break down	danificar	*dah-nee-fee-kahr*
breakdown	avaria, defeito	*ah-vah-reeya, deh-fay-too*
burglar	assaltante	*ah-ssahl-tahn-chee*
burglary	furto	*foor-toh*
crash (v.)	batida	*bah-tee-dah*
crash (n.)	colidir, bater	*koh-lee-geer, bah-tehr*
emergency room, casualty department	pronto-socorro	*prohn-too soh-koh-roh*
emergency	emergência	*eh-mehr-jayns-sseea*
fire department	corpo de bombeiros	*kohr-poh dee bohn-bay-roos*
fire	fogo, incêndio	*foh-goh, een-ssayn-deeo*
flood	inundação	*ee-noon-dah-ssowng*
Help!	Socorro!	*soh-koh-roh*
injured	ferido	*feh-ree-doh*
lose	perder	*pehr-dehr*
pickpocket	batedor de carteiras	*bah-teh-dohr dee kahr-tay-rahs*
police station	delegacia de polícia	*deh-leh-gah-sseeya dee poh-lee-sseea*
police	polícia	*poh-lee-sseea*
policeman	policial	*poh-lee-ssee-ahl*
rob	furtar	*foor-tahr*
steal	roubar	*roul-bahr*
theft	roubo	*roul-boh*
thief	ladrão	*lah-drowng*
tow	rebocar	*reh-boh-kahr*

Help!
Socorro
soh-koh-roh

Look out!
Cuidado!
kooy-dah-doh

Stop!
Pare!
pah-reh

This is an emergency!
Esta é uma emergência!
esstah eh ooma eh-mehr-jayns-sseea

Get an ambulance!
Chame uma ambulância!
shah-meh ooma ahn-boo-lahn-sseea

Hurry up!
Depressa!
deh-preh-ssah

Please send an ambulance to ...
Por favor, mande uma ambulância para ...
poor fah-vor, mahn-deh ooma ahn-boo-lahn-sseea pahra

Please come to ...
Por favor, venha a ...
poor fah-vor, vayn-ya ah

My address is ...
Meu endereço é ...
mel ayn-deh-reh-ssoh eh

We've had a break-in
Ladrões entraram na casa
lah-droh-ayns ayn-trah-rahn nah kah-zah

There's a fire at ...
Há um incêndio em ...
ah oom een-ssayn-deeo eng

Someone's been injured
Há uma pessoa ferida
ah ooma peh-ssoh-ah feh-ree-dah

Someone's been knocked down
Uma pessoa foi atropelada
ooma peh-ssoh-ah foy ah-troh-peh-lah-dah

He/She is fainted
Ele/Ela desmaiou/está inconsciente
eh-leh/eh-lah dehs-mah-youl/ess-tah een-kon-ssee-ayn-chee

My passport/car has been stolen
Roubaram meu passaporte/meu carro
roul-bah-rahn mel pah-ssah-pohr-chee/mel kah-hoh

I've lost my traveller's cheques
Perdi meus traveller's cheques
pehr-gee mels traveller's cheques

I want to report a stolen credit card
Quero informar o roubo de um cartão de crédito
kehro een-fohr-mahr oh roul-boh dee oom kartowng dee kreh-dee-toh

It was stolen from my room
Ele foi roubado do meu quarto
eh-leh foy roul-bah-doh doh mel kwar-toh

I lost it in the park/at the station
Eu o perdi no parque/na estação
el oh pehr-gee noh pahr-kee/nah ehs-tah-ssowng

My luggage has gone missing
Minha bagagem se extraviou
meen-ya bah-gah-jayn see ehs-trah-vee-oul

Has my luggage been found yet?
Minha bagagem já apareceu?
meen-ya bah-gah-jayn jah ah-pah-reh-ssehl

I've crashed my car
Eu bati o meu carro
el bah-chee oh mel kah-hoh

My car's been broken into
Alguém forçou meu carro
ahl-gayn fohr-ssoul mel kah-hoh

The plate number is ...
O número da placa é ...
oh noo-meh-roh dah plah-kah eh

I've been mugged
Eu fui agredido (a)
el foo-ee ah-greh-gee-doh

My son's missing/got lost
Meu filho sumiu/se perdeu
mel feel-yoh soo-mee-yoo/see pehr-dehl

He/She has blond/brown hair
Seu cabelo é loiro/castanho
sel kah-beh-loh eh loy-roh

He's/She's ... years old
Ele/Ela tem ... anos
eh-leh/eh-lah tayn ... ah-nohs

I've locked myself out
Fiquei trancado (a) do lado de fora
fee-kay trahn-kah-doh (ah) doh lah-doh dee foh-rah

He/She is drowning!
Ele/Ela está se afogando!
eh-leh/eh-lah ess-tah see ah-foh-gahn-doh

He/She can't swim!
Ele/Ela não sabe nadar!
eh-leh/eh-lah nowng sah-beh nah-dahr

Things You'll See

ambulância	ambulance
corpo de bombeiros	fire department
delegacia de polícia	police station
farmácia de plantão	all-night pharmacy, late-night chemist's
hospital	hospital
números de emergência	emergency phone numbers
polícia de trânsito	traffic police
polícia militar, polícia civil	police
primeiros socorros	first aid
resgate de estrada	breakdown service
resgate	rescue
serviço de emergência	emergency service
telefone	telephone

Things You'll Hear

Qual é seu endereço, por favor?
What is your address, please?

Onde você está?
Where are you?

Pode descrevê-lo (a)?
Can you describe it/him/her?

HEALTH

If you are travelling to large urban centres like São Paulo and Rio, there is no real need to worry about tropical diseases or epidemics. If you're visiting poorer regions –especially in the North, North-east and Centre West–, it's worth taking some precautions. It's difficult, however, to generalize, owing to the size of Brazil and its variety of climates and living conditions. For more details, consult the health authorities of your country before departure.

In general, the public health system in Brazil is of poor quality and the tourist shouldn't rely on it. There are, however, excellent private hospitals. As these are expensive, the ideal thing to do is take out travel insurance, or check to see if your health plan has international coverage. Check also whether your credit card offers this type of service.

You can easily find in Brazil almost all the medicines produced by international laboratories (in a **farmácia** or **drogaria**), even without a prescription. Its better, however, to take sufficient quantities of whatever medicine you need regularly with you. If you feel ill, don't make the mistake of asking advice from a pharmacist: many –though not all– are not equipped to make well-informed diagnoses.

USEFUL WORDS AND PHRASES

accident	acidente	ah-ssee-dayn-chee
allergic	alérgico	ah-lair-gee-koh
ambulance	ambulância	ahn-boo-lahn-sseea
anemic, anaemic	anêmico	ah-neh-mee-koh
appendicitis	apendicite	ah-payn-dee-ssee-chee
appendix	apêndice	ah-payn-dee-sseh
arm	braço	brah-ssoh
aspirin	aspirina	ahs-pee-ree-nah
asthma	asma	ahs-mah
backache	dor nas costas	dohr nahs kohs-tahs
bite	mordida	mohr-gee-dah
bladder	bexiga	beh-shee-gah

blister	vesícula	*veh-zee-koo-lah*
blood donor	doador de sangue	*doh-ah-dohr dee sahn-gueh*
blood type	tipo sanguíneo	*chee-poh sahn-guee-neh-oh*
blood	sangue	*sahn-gueh*
bone	osso	*oh-ssoh*
burn	queimadura	*kay-mah-doo-rah*
cancer	câncer	*kahn-ssehr*
cast, plaster of Paris	gesso	*geh-ssoh*
chest	peito	*pay-toh*
chickenpox	catapora	*kah-tah-poh-rah*
cold	resfriado	*rehs-free-ah-doh*
concussion	concussão cerebral	*kon-koo-ssowng seh-reh-brahl*
constipation	prisão de ventre	*pree-zowng dee vayn-tree*
contact lenses	lentes de contato	*lehn-chees dee kon-tah-too*
cough	tosse	*toh-sseh*
cut	corte	*kohr-chee*
dentist	dentista	*dayn-tees-tah*
diabetes	diabetes	*dee-ah-beh-chees*
diarrhoea	diarréia	*dee-ah-reh-eea*
doctor	médico	*meh-gee-koh*
earache	dor de ouvido	*dohr dee oul-vee-doh*
fever	febre	*feh-breh*
filling	obturação	*ohb-too-rah-ssowng*
first aid	primeiros socorros	*pree-may-roos soh-koh-rohs*
flu	gripe	*gree-peh*
fracture	fratura	*frah-too-rah*
German measles	rubéola	*roo-behl-lah*
haemorrhage	hemorragia	*eh-moh-rah-geeya*
hand	mão	*mowng*
head	cabeça	*kah-beh-ssah*

headache	dor de cabeça	*dohr dee kah-beh-ssah*
heart attack	infarte	*een-fahr-chee*
heart	coração	*koh-rah-ssowng*
high, low-pressure	pressão alta, baixa	*preh-ssowng ahl-tah, bah-ysha*
hospital	hospital	*ohs-pee-tahl*
hypertensive	hipertenso	*ee-pehr-tayn-ssoo*
ill	doente	*doh-aynch*
indigestion	indigestão	*een-dee-gehs-towng*
injection, shot	injeção	*een-geh-ssowng*
itch	coceira	*koh-ssay-rah*
kidney	rim	*heen*
leg	perna	*pehr-nah*
liver	fígado	*fee-gah-doh*
lungs	pulmões	*pool-moh-ayns*
measles	sarampo	*sah-rahn-poo*
medicine	remédio	*reh-meh-deeo*
migraine	enxaqueca	*ayn-shah-keh-kah*
mumps	caxumba	*kah-shoon-bah*
nausea	náusea	*nahl-zeh-ah*
nurse	enfermeiro (a)	*ayn-fehr-may-roh (ah)*
operation	operação	*oh-peh-rah-ssowng*
ophthalmologist	oftalmologista	*of-tahl-moh-loh-gees-tah*
pain	dor	*dohr*
painkiller	analgésico	*ah-nahl-geh-zee-koh*
penicillin	penicilina	*peh-nee-ssee-lee-nah*
pharmacist, chemist	farmacêutico	*fahr-mah-ssehl-tee-koh*
pneumonia	pneumonia	*pee-nehl-moh-neeya*
pregnant	grávida	*grah-vee-dah*
prescription	receita	*reh-ssay-tah*
rheumatism	reumatismo	*rehl-mah-tees-moo*
scratch	arranhão	*ah-hahn-yowng*
smallpox	varíola	*vah-reel-lah*
sore throat	dor de garganta	*dohr dee gahr-gahn-tah*
sprain	torção	*tohr-ssowng*
sting	picada	*pee-kah-dah*

stomach	estômago	*ehs-toh-mah-goh*
temperature	temperatura	*tayn-peh-rah-too-rah*
tonsils	amídalas	*ah-mee-dah-lahs*
toothache	dor de dente	*dohr dee daynch*
travel sickness	enjôo	*ayn-joh-oh*
ulcer	úlcera	*ool-sseh-rah*
vaccination	vacinação	*vah-ssee-nah-ssowng*
vomit, throw up	vomitar	*voh-mee-tahr*
whooping cough	coqueluche	*koh-keh-loo-sheh*

I have a pain in …
Sinto dor no (a) …
seen-toh dohr noh (ah)

I do not feel well
Não me sinto bem
nowng mee seen-toh bayn

I feel dizzy
Sinto-me fraco/tonto
seen-toh-mee frah-koh/toun-too

I feel sick
Sinto náuseas/Estou enjoado
seen-toh nahl-zeh-ahs/ehs-toul ayn-joh-ah-doh

It hurts here
Me dói aqui
mee doy akee

It's a sharp/dull pain
É uma dor aguda/leve
eh ooma dohr ah-goo-dah/leh-veh

It hurts all the time
É uma dor constante
eh ooma dohr kons-tahn-chee

It only hurts now and then
Só dói de vez em quando
soh doy dee vehs ayn kwandoo

It hurts when you touch it
Dói quando é tocado
doy kwandoo eh toh-kah-doo

It hurts more at night
Dói mais à noite
doy mah-ys ah noych

It stings/burns
Arde
ahr-gee

It aches
Dói
doy

I have fever
Estou com febre
hs-toul kon feh-breh

I need a prescription for …
Preciso de uma receita para …
preh-ssee-zoh dee ooma reh-ssay-tah pahra

I normally take …
Normalmente eu tomo …
nohr-mahl-mayn-chee el toh-moo

I'm allergic to …
Sou alérgico (a) a …
oul ah-lair-gee-koh (ah) ah

Do you have anything for …?
O senhor tem algo para …
oh seen-your tayn ahl-goo pahra

Do I need a prescription for …?
Eu preciso de uma receita para …?
el preh-ss<u>ee</u>-zoo dee <u>oo</u>ma reh-ss<u>ay</u>-tah p<u>a</u>hra

I have lost a filling
Perdi uma obturação
pehr-g<u>ee</u> <u>oo</u>ma ohb-too-rah-ss<u>ow</u>ng

Will he/she be all right?
Ele/Ela vai ficar bem?
<u>e</u>h-leh/<u>e</u>h-lah v<u>a</u>h-ee fee-k<u>a</u>hr bayn

Will he/she need an operation?
Ele/Ela vai precisar de uma operação?
<u>e</u>h-leh/<u>e</u>h-lah v<u>a</u>h-ee preh-ssee-z<u>a</u>hr dee <u>oo</u>ma oh-peh-rah-ss<u>ow</u>ng

How is he/she?
Como ele/ela está?
k<u>o</u>h-moh <u>e</u>h-leh/<u>e</u>h-lah ess-t<u>a</u>h

THINGS YOU'LL SEE

ala (de hospital)	ward
ambulância	ambulance
cirurgia	surgery
cirurgião	surgeon
dermatologista	dermatologist
enfermaria	infirmary
especialista	specialist
farmácia de plantão	all-night pharmacy, late-night chemist's
ginecologista	gynaecologist
horário de visitas	visiting hours
hospital	hospital
internado	inpatient
médico de plantão	doctor on duty
médico	doctor

→

oculista	optician
oftalmologista	ophthalmologist
otorrinolaringologista	ear, nose and throat specialist
pronto-socorro	first aid, casualty ward
sala de espera	waiting room
sala de operações	surgery room, operating theatre

THINGS YOU'LL HEAR

Para tomar com água
With water

Mastigue-os
Chew them

Uma/duas/três vezes por dia
Once/twice/three times a day

Ao se deitar
At bedtime

Pela manhã
In the morning

O que o (a) senhor (a) toma normalmente?
What do you normally take?

O (A) senhor (a) deveria consultar um médico
I think you should see a doctor

Lamento, não temos/vendemos isso
I'm sorry, we don't have/sell that

Para isto é necessário uma receita médica
You need a prescription for that

CONVERSION TABLES

Women's dresses and suits

USA	6	8	10	12	14	16	18
UK	10	12	14	16	18	20	22
Brazil	40	42	44	46	48	50	52

Women's shoes

USA	6	6.5	7	7.5	8	8.5
UK	4.5	5	5.5	6	6.5	7
Brazil	36	37	38	38.5	39	40

Men's suits and coats

USA	36	38	40	42	44
UK	36	38	40	42	44
Brazil	46	48	50	52	54

Men's shirts

USA	14	14.5	15	15.5	16
UK	36	37	38	39	40
Brazil	36	37	38	39	40

Men's shoes

USA	5.5	6.5	7.5	8.5	9.5
UK	37-38	39	40	41	42
Brazil	37-38	39	40	41	42

Distances

miles	0.62	1.24	1.86	2.43	3.11	3.73	4.35	6.21
miles or km	1	2	3	4	5	6	7	10
km	1.61	3.22	4.83	6.44	8.05	9.66	11.27	16.10

Weights

pounds	2.20	4.41	6.61	8.82	11.02	13.23	19.84	22.04
pounds or kg	1	2	3	4	5	6	9	10
kg	0.45	0.91	1.36	1.81	2.27	2.72	4.08	4.53

Temperature

°Celsius	-10	0	5	10	20	30	36.9	40
°Fahrenheit	14	32	41	50	68	77	98.4	104

MINI-DICTIONARY

This mini-dictionary has all the expressions found in each section of this book, and also a selection of the main vocabulary items necessary for you to communicate in Portuguese. When there are differences in the vocabulary between British and American English, two separate entries have been made, one for each form. Thus, the reader will find in the list both 'downtown' and 'town centre'.

A

a, an um (a)
about acerca, sobre
above acima
accelerator acelerador
accident acidente
accommodation acomodação
ache dor
  headache dor de cabeça
  toothache dor de dente
  sore throat dor de garganta
  earache dor de ouvido
  backache dor nas costas
address endereço
addressee destinatário
adhesive adesivo (a)
admission free entrada grátis
adult adulto (a)
after depois
  the day after tomorrow depois
  de amanhã
after all afinal
afternoon tarde
aftershave após-barba
again novamente
against contra
age idade
agency agência

travel agency agência de viagens
travel agent agente de viagens
aid ajuda
Aids Aids
air ar
air-conditioner ar-condicionado
airplane avião
airport aeroporto
alarm clock despertador
alcohol álcool
all todo (a/os/as), tudo
  I want all the books Eu quero
  todos os livros
  I want it all Eu quero tudo
allergic alérgico (a)
almost quase
alone sozinho (a)
alpinism alpinismo
already já
also, too também
always sempre
ambulance ambulância
America América
American americano (a)
among entre, em meio a
amount quantia
ancient antigo (a)
and e

121

anemic anêmico (a)
angle canto, ângulo
ankle tornozelo
another outro (a)
to answer responder
antique antigo (a)
antiseptic anti-séptico
any algum (a/uns/as), qualquer
  is there any chance há alguma chance
  any of them qualquer um deles
apart à parte
apéritif aperitivo
appartment apartamento
appendicitis apendicite
appendix apêndice
appetite apetite
apple maçã
apricot damasco
April abril
area área
  parking area área de estacionamento
  service area área de serviço
arm braço
arrival chegada
to arrive chegar
art arte
artist artista
as tão
  as much as, as many as tanto (a/os/as) quanto (a/os/as)
  as soon as possible assim que possível
  as well as assim como
ashtray cinzeiro
aside à parte
to ask perguntar
aspirin aspirina
to assault agredir
asthma asma
at a, no (a/os/as)
  at midnight à meia-noite
  at the cinema no cinema
athletics atletismo
122

attention atenção
attic sótão
attractive atraente
audio equipment equipamento de som
August agosto
aunt tia
Australia Austrália
Australian australiano (a)
automatic automático (a)
automatic (car) câmbio automático
Autumn outono
awful horrível
axe machado

B

baby bebê
back (adv.) atrás
back (n.) costas
backpack mochila
bacon bacon
bad mau (má)
bag bolsa
baggage bagagem
  baggage claim retirada de bagagens
  baggage control controle de bagagens
  baggage terminal terminal de bagagens
baker padeiro
bakery, baker's padaria
balcony sacada
ball bola
banana banana
band banda musical
bandage bandagem
bank banco
banknote nota
bar bar
barbecue churrasco
barber shop barbeiro
baseball beisebol
basement porão
basket cesta

basketball basquete
bath banho
bathroom banheiro
bathtub banheira
battery pilha
to be ser, estar
  I am a doctor eu sou um médico
  I am here eu estou aqui
  he/she/it is ele (a) é/está
  you are você (s) é (são)/ está (ão)
  we are nós somos/estamos
  they are eles (as) são/estão
beach praia
beans feijão
beard barba
beautiful belo (a)
because porque
bed cama
  camp bed cama dobrável
  double bed cama de casal
  single bed cama de solteiro
bed and breakfast pousada,
  alojamento com café-da-manhã
bedroom quarto, dormitório
  double room quarto duplo
  single room quarto para uma pessoa
  twin room quarto com duas camas
beef bife
beer cerveja
before antes
to begin começar, iniciar
beginner principiante
beginning início, começo
behind atrás
beige bege
Belgian belga
Belgium Bélgica
to believe acreditar
bell campainha, sino
below abaixo, embaixo
bench banco
better melhor
  the best o melhor
between entre

beverage bebida
beyond além
bicycle, bike bicicleta
  bike, cycle renting aluguel de
  bicicletas
  bike path, cycle path ciclovia
  biking, cycling ciclismo
  go cycling, biking andar de
  bicicleta
big grande
bill conta
bird ave
birthday aniversário
biscuit biscoito
to bite morder
bite mordida
bitter amargo (a)
black preto (a)
bladder bexiga
blade lâmina
blanket cobertor
blind cego (a)
blister vesícula
blond, blonde loiro (a)
blood sangue
  blood donor doador de sangue
  blood type tipo sanguíneo
blouse blusa
blue azul
boat barco, balsa
  boat renting aluguel de barcos
  pedal boat pedalinho
body corpo
to boil ferver
boiler caldeira
bone osso
bonfire fogueira
book livro
booking-office bilheteria
bookshop, bookstore livraria
boot bota
border fronteira
to be born nascer
  I was born in eu nasci em

123

boss chefe
bottle garrafa
boutique butique
bowling boliche
box caixa
  fusebox caixa de fusíveis
  gear box caixa de câmbio
  mailbox, postbox caixa de correio
boy menino
brassière, bra sutiã
bracelet bracelete, pulseira
brake freio
brand marca
Brazil Brasil
Brazilian brasileiro (a)
bread pão
breakdown avaria, defeito
breakdown service resgate de estrada
breakfast café-da-manhã
to breathe respirar
breathing respiração
bride, bridegroom noivo (a)
bridge ponte
brilliant! fantástico!, maravilhoso!
British britânico (a)
broken quebrado (a)
brooch broche
brother irmão
brown marrom
brush escova, vassoura
  hairbrush escova de cabelo
  toothbrush escova de dentes
bubble bolha
bucket balde
building edifício
bulb lâmpada
burglar assaltante
burglary furto
to burn queimar
burn queimadura
  sunburn queimadura de sol

124

bus ônibus
  airport bus ônibus do aeroporto
  bus stop ponto de ônibus
  trolley bus trólebus
business negócios
busy, reserved ocupado (a)
but mas, porém
butcher's açougue
butter manteiga
buttock nádega
button botão
to buy comprar
by por
  written by escrito por

C

cab táxi
cabbage couve
cable car bonde elétrico, bondinho
café café
cake torta, bolo
to call *(telephone)* telefonar, chamar
call *(telephone)* telefonema, chamada
  collect call, reverse charge call chamada a cobrar
  international call chamada internacional
  local call chamada local
  long-distance call chamada interurbana
camera câmera fotográfica
to camp acampar
camping equipment equipamentos de camping
campsite área de camping
to can poder
  can I use your phone? posso usar seu telefone?
can lata
can-opener abridor de latas
Canada Canadá
Canadian canadense
to cancel cancelar

cancer câncer
candle vela
canoe canoa
canoeing canoagem
cap boné, tampinha de garrafa
car carro
  car park estacionamento
  car wash lava-rápido
  car wax cera para carro
caravan site área de trailers
carburettor carburador
card cartão
  boarding card cartão de embarque
  credit card cartão de crédito
  phonecard cartão de telefone
  travel card cartão de viagem
carriage vagão
carrier bag sacola de compras
carrot cenoura
to carry levar, carregar
cash dispenser caixa eletrônico
cash desk caixa
casserole caçarola
cast *(plaster of Paris)* gesso
castle castelo
casualty department pronto-socorro
cat gato
cathedral catedral
cauliflower couve-flor
cave gruta
cavern caverna
ceiling teto
cemetery cemitério
center centro
  sports centre centro esportivo
century século
chair cadeira
  wheelchair cadeira-de-rodas
chair lift teleférico
to change mudar, trocar
change troco
channel canal
charcoal carvão
charge tarifa

cheap barato (a)
check book, cheque book talão de cheques
check conta
checking account conta corrente
check, cheque cheque
cheerio adeus, até logo, tchau, olá
cheers! saúde!
cheese queijo
chemist farmacêutico (a)
chemist's drogaria, farmácia
cherry cereja
chest *(cupboard)* armário
chest peito, tórax
chicken frango
chickenpox catapora
chief chefe
child criança
chin queixo
china porcelana
chocolate chocolate
Christmas Natal
church igreja
cigar charuto
cigarette cigarro
cinema cinema
city map mapa da cidade
class classe
clean limpo (a)
cleaner *(maid)* arrumadeira
clear claro (a)
clock relógio
clogged entupido (a)
to close fechar
closed fechado (a)
cloth pano
clothe roupa
  ladies' clothing, ladies' wear roupas femininas
  men's clothing, menswear roupas masculinas
  underwear roupas íntimas
clubs *(cards)* paus
clutch embreagem

coat casaco
cockroach barata
code prefixo, código
coffee café
cognac conhaque
coin moeda
cold (adj.) frio (a)
  it's cold está frio
cold (n.) resfriado
collar gola, colarinho
collection coleta postal
color, colour cor
to comb pentear
comb pente
to come vir
comfortable confortável
common comum
company empresa
compartment compartimento
computer computador
concert concerto
concussion concussão cerebral
conditioner condicionador de cabelo
condom camisinha
confectioner's shop confeitaria
confectionery doceria
congratulations parabéns
connection conexão
constipation prisão de ventre
consulate consulado
contact lenses lentes de contato
continental quilt edredom
contraceptive anticoncepcional
to cook cozinhar
cook cozinheiro (a)
  cooking utensil utensílio de
  cozinha
cooker fogão
cork rolha
corkscrew saca-rolhas
corn calo
corner canto, esquina
corridor corredor
cosmetics cosméticos

to cost custar
cotton algodão
couchette leito
cough tosse
counter balcão
  check-in counter balcão de
  check-in
  parcels counter balcão de pacotes
country país
couple par
cover tampa
crab caranguejo
cramp cãimbra
to crash colidir, bater
crash batida
crawler lane pista para veículos
  pesados
crazy louco (a)
cream creme
credit crédito
cross-country skiing esqui cross-
  country
crossed line linha cruzada
crossroads cruzamento
cruise cruzeiro
crutch muleta
to cry chorar
cucumber pepino (alimento)
cuff link abotoadura
cuff punho (da camisa)
cup xícara
cupboard armário
currency moeda (corrente)
currency exchange câmbio de moeda
current account conta corrente
curtain cortina
customer cliente, freguês (esa)
customs alfândega
to cut cortar
cut corte
cycle path, bike path ciclovia
cycle renting, bike renting aluguel
  de bicicletas
cycling, biking ciclismo

D

to dance dançar
danger perigo
dangerous currents correnteza
  perigosa
dangerous perigoso (a)
dark escuro (a)
daughter filha
day dia
  all day long o dia todo
  every day todos os dias
  in three days daqui a três dias
  working days dias úteis
deaf surdo (a)
dear querido (a)
death morte
December dezembro
deck of cards baralho
deep fundo (a), profundo (a)
delay atraso
delicious delicioso (a)
to deliver entregar
delivery entrega
dentist dentista
to deny negar
deodorant desodorante
department seção, departamento
departure partida (de avião, trem)
to deposit depositar
depression depressão
depth profundidade
dermatologist dermatologista
dessert sobremesa
destination destino
to develop desenvolver
diabetes diabetes
to dial discar, teclar
  dial the number discar o número
diamond diamante
diamonds (cards) ouros
diapers fraldas descartáveis
diarrhoea diarréia
dictionary dicionário
to die morrer

diesel óleo diesel
different diferente
difficult difícil
dinner jantar
direct dialling discagem direta
dirty sujo (a)
discount desconto
district prefeitura
dish prato
ditch vala
to dive mergulhar
diversion desvio
diving board trampolim
diving mask máscara de mergulho
diving mergulho
divorced divorciado (a)
to do fazer
doctor médico (a)
  doctor on duty médico de plantão
dog cachorro
doll boneca
dollar dólar
domestic nacional, doméstico (a)
door porta
  door lock fechadura
doorkeeper porteiro
down abaixo, em baixo
downtown centro da cidade
dozen dúzia
drain descarga
dress vestido
dressing molho
to drink tomar, beber
drink bebida
to drive dirigir
  drive at walking speed dirigir em
  baixa velocidade
driver motorista
driver's licence carteira de habilitação
drugstore drogaria, farmácia
dry cleaner's lavanderia (a seco),
  tinturaria
dry seco (a)
during durante

dustbin lata de lixo
duvet edredom

E

each cada, todo (a)
  each day, each time todo dia, toda vez
  each of you cada um de vocês
ear orelha, ouvido
ear, nose and throat specialist otorrinolaringologista
early cedo
earrings brincos
earth Terra
East leste
Easter Páscoa
easy fácil
to eat comer
edge ponta
egg ovo
eight oito
eighteen dezoito
eighty oitenta
either ... or ou ... ou
elastic elástico
elbow cotovelo
electrical appliances eletrodomésticos
electrician eletricista
electricity eletricidade
elevator elevador
eleven onze
embassy embaixada
embroidery bordado
emergency emergência
  emergency alarm alarme de emergência
  emergency phone numbers números de emergência
  emergency service serviço de emergência
emergency room pronto-socorro
empty vazio (a)
end fim
engine motor

England Inglaterra
Englishman/Englishwoman inglês (esa)
enough bastante
to enter, to come in entrar
  come in! entre!
entrance entrada
  no admittance, no entry entrada proibida
  private entrance entrada particular
envelope envelope
eraser borracha
error erro
escalator escada rolante
estate agent agente imobiliário
evening, night noite
  this evening esta noite
  tonight hoje à noite
every cada
exactly exatamente
example exemplo
excellent excelente, ótimo (a)
exchange rate taxa de câmbio
excursion excursão
exhaust cano de escapamento
exhibition exposição
exit saída
  emergency exit saída de emergência
  works exit saída de caminhões
expensive caro (a)
extension ramal
eye olho
eyebrow sobrancelha
eyelash máscara rímel

F

fabric, cloth tecido
face rosto
facility facilidade
to faint desmaiar
Fall outono
falling rocks deslizamentos

false falso (a)
false teeth dentadura
family família
fanbelt correia do ventilador
far longe
fare passagem, bilhete
farm fazenda
farmer fazendeiro (a)
fashion moda
fast rápido (a)
fat (adj.) gordo (a)
fat (n.) gordura
father pai
fawcet torneira
fax fax
fax machine aparelho de fax
February fevereiro
to feel sentir
ferryboat ferryboat
fever febre
  hayfever febre do feno
few poucos (as)
field campo
fifteen quinze
fifty cinquenta
figo figo
to fill in preencher
filling *(teeth)* obturação
film filme
finally enfim
find achar
fine bem
finger dedo
fire department corpo de bombeiros
fire fogo, incêndio
fireplace lareira
first aid primeiros-socorros
first primeiro (a)
  first class primeira classe
  first floor primeiro andar
to fish pescar
fish peixe
fish market peixaria
fishmonger's peixaria

fishing pesca
fishing rod vara de pescar
five cinco
flag bandeira
flashlight, torch lanterna
flat chato (a), achatado (a)
flavour, taste sabor
flight attendant steward (ess)
  comissário (a) de bordo
flight vôo
  flight number número do vôo
  scheduled flight vôo regular
flipper pé-de-pato
flood inundação
floor andar
  first floor primeiro andar
  ground floor andar térreo
  upper floor andar superior
floor, pavement piso
flour farinha
flower flor
flower shop floricultura
flu gripe
to fly voar
fly mosca
foam espuma
fog neblina
food alimento, comida
food store armazém
foot pé
football futebol americano
for para
  for me para mim
forbidden proibido (a)
foreigner estrangeiro (a)
forest floresta
forget esquecer
fork garfo
form formulário
  customs form formulário da
  alfândega
forty quarenta
four quatro
fourteen catorze

fourth quarto (a)
fracture fratura
France França
free grátis
Frenchman/Frenchwoman francês (esa)
fresh fresco (a)
Friday sexta-feira
fridge geladeira
friend amigo (a)
friendly amigável
fridge geladeira
fringe, bangs *(hair)* franja
from de
frontier fronteira
fruit fruta
fruit stand banca de frutas
to fry fritar
frying-pan frigideira
full cheio (a)
funny divertido (a)
furniture mobília
furrier peleteria
fuse fusível

G

gallon galão
game jogo
garage garagem, oficina mecânica
garbage can lata de lixo
garbage lixo
garden jardim
garlic alho
gas gás
gas station, petrol station posto de gasolina
gas, petrol gasolina
  two or three-star gas/petrol gasolina comum
  four-star gas/petrol gasolina aditivada
gate portão de embarque
gathering reunião, agrupamento
gear lever alavanca de câmbio

gear marcha
gentleman senhor, cavalheiro
German alemão (ã)
German measles rubéola
Germany Alemanha
to get out, to get off sair
gift presente
gin gim
ginger gengibre
girl menina
to give dar
glass vidro
glasses óculos
gloves luvas
glue cola
to go ir
  go away! vá embora!
  go for a walk passear
to go down, to come down descer
to go up, to come up subir
goggles óculos de mergulho
gold ouro
golf course campo de golfe
good bom (boa)
  good morning bom dia
  good afternoon boa tarde
  good night, good evening boa noite
Good Friday Sexta da Paixão
goodbye adeus, até logo, tchau
goods mercadoria, produto
government governo
grandfather/grandmother avô (ó)
grandparents os avós
grandson/granddaughter neto (a)
grape uva
Great Britain Grã-Bretanha
green verde
greengrocer's quitanda
grey cinza
grill grelha
grocery, grocery store mercearia
ground sheet lona impermeável
group grupo

guarantee garantia
to guarantee, to warrant garantir
guesthouse estalagem, pensão
guide guia
gymnastics ginástica
gynaecologist ginecologista

H

had tinha, tinham, tínhamos
  I/he had eu/ele tinha
  you had você tinha, vocês tinham
  we had nós tínhamos
  they had eles tinham
haemorrhage hemorragia
hair cabelo
hairdresser, hair stylist cabeleireiro (a)
hairdryer secador de cabelo
half meio (a)
  half an hour meia hora
  half board meia pensão
  half-litre meio litro
hamburger hambúrguer
hammer martelo
hammock rede
hand mão
handicapped deficiente físico
handkerchief lenço
handle maçaneta
hang-gliding asa-delta
hanger, rack, peg cabide
hangover ressaca
happy feliz
harbour, port porto
hard duro (a)
harpoon arpão submarino
hat chapéu
to hate detestar
  I hat eu detesto
to have ter
  I have eu tenho
  he/she has ele (a) tem
  you have você tem, vocês têm
  we have nós temos
  they have eles têm

head cabeça
headlights faróis
health saúde
heart attack infarto
heart coração
hearts (cards) copas
heat calor
heater aquecedor
  water heater aquecedor de água
heating aquecimento central
heaven céu, paraíso
heavy pesado (a)
heel (body) calcanhar
heel (shoes) salto
height altura
hello oi, olá
to help ajudar
  can you help me? pode me ajudar?
help ajuda, socorro
here aqui
  here's my card aqui está meu
  cartão
  here you are! aqui está!
hi oi
high alto (a)
  high/low-pressure pressão
  alta/baixa
  high quality alta qualidade
highway rodovia
hiring aluguel
his/her/hers/its dele (a)
history história
to hitchhike pegar carona
hobby passatempo
hole furo
holidays feriados
home lar
homosexual homossexual
honest honesto (a)
honey mel
honeymoon lua-de-mel
hood (car) capô
horn buzina
horse riding equitação

hospital hospital
hot quente
hotel hotel
hour hora
  opening hours horário de
  funcionamento
  visiting hours horário de visitas
house casa
how como
  how are you? como vai/vão?
  how are things? como vão as
  coisas?
how many quantos
  how many of these? quantos
  destes?
how much quanto
  how much is it? quanto custa?
however contudo, porém
hunger fome
hunting caça
hurry pressa
husband marido
hut barraca
hypermarket hipermercado
hypertensive hipertenso (a)

I

I eu
ice gelo
ice-cream sorvete
ice skating patinação no gelo
ice-hockey hóquei sobre o gelo
if se
ignition ignição
ill doente
immediately imediatamente
impossible impossível
in front em frente
in front of diante de
in order to/ that a fim de
in, within dentro
in-patient internado (a)
indigestion indigestão
infection infecção

infirmary enfermaria
information informações
  tourist information informação
  turística
to initiate começar, iniciar
injection injeção
injured ferido (a)
injury ferimento
inn hospedaria
insect inseto
to insert inserir
  insert coins inserir moedas
insomnia insônia
intelligent, clever inteligente
interesting interessante
international internacional
interpreter intérprete
invitation convite
Ireland Irlanda
Irishman/Irishwoman irlandês (esa)
to iron passar roupa
iron (element) ferro
iron (utensil) ferro de passar
ironing board tábua de passar roupa
island ilha
Italian italiano (a)
Italy Itália
itch coceira

J

janitor zelador (a)
January janeiro
jelly geléia
jeweler's joalheria
juice suco
July julho
to jump pular
junction cruzamento
June junho

K

keep manter
key chave
kidney rim

kilogram, kilo quilo
kilometre quilômetro
kind amável
kitchen cozinha
knee joelho
knife faca
to know conhecer, saber
  I know you eu conheço você
  I know how to eu sei como

L

label rótulo
lady senhora, dama
lake lago
lampshade abajur
to land aterrissar
land terra
large grande
last último (a)
last name sobrenome
late tarde
to laugh rir
laxative laxante
lazy preguiçoso (a)
leaf folha
leak vazamento
to learn aprender
leather couro
left *(direction)* esquerdo (a)
  to the left à esquerda
left luggage office depósito de
  bagagens
leg perna
lemon limão
lemonade limonada
lenght comprimento
less menos
  least o menos
to let deixar, permitir
letter carta
  registered letter carta registrada
lever alavanca
library biblioteca
license licensa

license plate placa
lid tampa
life insurance seguro de vida
life jacket colete salva-vidas
life vida
lifeguard salva-vidas
to lift erguer, levantar
lift elevador
light (adj.) leve
light (n.) luz
lighter isqueiro
to like gostar
  do you like ...? você gosta de ...?
  I don't like não gosto de
  I like gosto de
limit limite
  speed limit limite de velocidade
lip lábio
lipstick batom
liqueur licor
liquors bebidas alcoólicas
list lista
to listen ouvir
litre litro
little pouco
to live viver
liver fígado
lobster lagosta
local time hora local
lock fechadura
lodging place hospedaria
long longo (a)
to look olhar
lorry caminhão
to lose perder
lounge saguão, sala de espera
to love amar
love amor
luck sorte
luggage bagagem
  hand luggage bagagem de mão
lump nódulo
lunch almoço
lungs pulmões

M

machine máquina
mad louco (a)
magazine revista
mail correspondência
mail office agência do Correio
  airmail correio aéreo
  surface mail correio comum
to make fazer
make-up maquiagem
man homem
manager gerente
manual câmbio manual
many muitos (as)
map mapa
March março
margarine margarina
market mercado, feira
  indoor market mercado coberto
marmalade geléia
marriage casamento
married casado (a)
match fósforo
mattress colchão
mature maduro (a)
to may poder
  may I introduce ...? posso
  apresentar-lhe ...?
May maio
maybe talvez
meal refeição
measles sarampo
meat carne
mechanic mecânico
medicine remédio
meeting, reunion encontro, reunião
menu cardápio
message mensagem, recado
midnight meia-noite
migraine enxaqueca
mile milha
milk leite
million milhão
mint hortelã
134

minute minuto
mirror espelho
miss (n.) senhorita
mist neblina
mistake erro
model modelo
moment momento
  at the moment neste momento
Monday segunda-feira
money dinheiro
money order vale postal
monkey-wrench chave inglesa
montain montanha
month mês
monument monumento
moon lua
more mais
  the most o mais
morning manhã
mosquito mosquito
mother mãe
motion movimento
motorbike motocicleta
motorboat lancha
motorway auto-estrada
moustache bigode
mouth boca
to move mover
movie filme
  movie theater cinema
much muito (a)
mulberry amora
mumps caxumba
museum museu
mushroom cogumelo
music música
musical instrument instrumento
  musical
musician músico
to must dever
mustard mostarda
my, mine meu (minha/meus/minhas)
  my name is meu nome é
  this book is mine este livro é meu

N

nail unha
nail polish esmalte de unhas
name nome
  what's your name? qual o seu
  nome?
napkin guardanapo
narrow estreito (a)
nausea náusea
near perto, próximo (a)
necessary necessário
neck pescoço
necklace colar
to need necessitar, precisar
needle agulha
neither nem
  neither ... nor nem ... nem
nephew sobrinho
network map mapa da cidade
never nunca
new novo (a)
New Year's Eve Véspera de Ano-
  Novo
news notícias
newspaper jornal
newsstand banca de jornais
next seguinte
  the next day no dia seguinte
next to próximo a
nice simpático (a)
niece sobrinha
night noite
night-club boate
nightdress camisola
nine nove
nineteen dezenove
ninety noventa
no não
  no, thank you não, obrigado (a)
no vacancies lotado (a)
nobody ninguém
noisy barulhento (a)
none nenhum (a)
noon meio-dia

North norte
nose nariz
note (n.) nota
nothing nada
  for nothing por nada
November novembro
now agora
  until now, up to now até agora
number número
  useful numbers números úteis
  wrong number número errado
nurse enfermeiro (a)
nut noz
nutmeg noz-moscada

O

occasionally ocasionalmente
October outubro
of de
office escritório
office supplies material de escritório
often freqüentemente
oil óleo
old antigo (a), velho (a)
olive azeitona
olive oil azeite
on sobre, em
one um
one hundred cem
one way *(traffic)* mão única
onion cebola
only somente
to open abrir
opened aberto (a)
operation operação
operator telefonista
ophthalmologist oculista, oftalmolo-
  gista
optician oculista
optician's óptica
or ou
orange laranja
order pedido
ordinary comum

organ órgão
our nosso (a, os, as)
out, outside fora
oven forno
oyster ostra

P

pack of cards baralho
package pacote
padlock cadeado
page página
pain dor
painkiller analgésico
to paint pintar
paintbrush pincel
palace palácio
pale pálido (a)
panties calcinha
pants calças
paper papel
  toilet paper papel higiênico
  wrapping paper papel de embrulho
  writing paper papel de carta
parasol guarda-sol
parcel pacote
parents pais
to park estacionar
parking lot estacionamento
parsley salsa
part parte
party festa
to pass passar
passenger passageiro (a)
passport passaporte
passport control controle de passaportes
pastas massas
pastime passatempo
path caminho
patrolman patrulheiro
to pay pagar
  pay at the desk pagar no caixa
  pay cash pagar em dinheiro
  pay here pagar aqui

pea ervilha
peach pêssego
peanut amendoim
pear pêra
pearl pérola
pedestrian pedestre
peg cabide
pen caneta
  felt tip pen caneta hidrográfica
  fountain pen caneta-tinteiro
pencil lápis
pencil sharpener apontador de lápis
penicillin penicilina
penknife canivete
pension pensão
  full board pensão completa
people gente
pepper pimenta
perfect perfeito (a)
perfume perfume
perhaps talvez
perm *(hair)* permanente
person pessoa
petrol *(see also gas)* gasolina
petrol station posto de gasolina
pharmacist farmacêutico (a)
pharmacy drogaria, farmácia
  all/late-night pharmacy farmácia de plantão
to photograph fotografar
photograph, photo fotografia
photographer fotógrafo (a)
pickpocket batedor de carteira
picnic piquenique
picture fotografia
piece peça, pedaço
pig porco
pile pilha
pill pílula
pillow travesseiro
pillow slip fronha de travesseiro
pilot piloto
pin alfinete
  safety pin alfinete de segurança

pineapple abacaxi
pink cor-de-rosa
pipe *(plumber)* cano
pitcher, carafe jarra
place local, lugar
plane avião
plant planta
plaster esparadrapo
plaster of Paris gesso
plastic plástico
plate prato
platform plataforma
to play *(music)* tocar
to play *(sports, games)* jogar
play *(theatre)* peça de teatro
please por favor
plumber encanador
pneumonia pneumonia
pocket bolso
police polícia
police station delegacia de polícia
policeman, policewoman policial
pomade pomada
pool, swimming pool piscina
  indoor swimming pool piscina
  coberta
  open-air swimming pool piscina
  ao ar livre
poor pobre
pork porco
Portuguese português (esa)
possible possível
to post postar
post office agência dos Correios
postage postagem
  postage abroad, international
  postage postagem para o exterior
postcard cartão-postal
postcode código postal
postman carteiro
postpone adiar
potato batata
poultry aves domésticas
pound libra

pound sterling libra esterlina
powder pó, talco
pray rezar
prefer preferir
pregnant grávida
prescription receita
pretty bonito (a)
price preço
priest padre
private privado (a)
problem problema
prohibitted proibido (a)
public público (a)
public holiday feriado
pull puxar
pullover suéter, malha, pulôver
puncture furo
purple roxo (a)
purse bolsa, carteira (de dinheiro)
to push empurrar
to put colocar, pôr
pyjamas pijama

Q
quality qualidade
question pergunta, questão

R
racket raquete
radish rabanete
railway ferrovia
rain chuva
raincoat capa de chuva
raspberry framboesa
rat rato
rate tarifa
  postage rates tarifas postais
razor blade lâmina de barbear
to read ler
ready pronto (a)
real estate agent
  agente imobiliário
rear lights *(car)* luzes traseiras
receipt recibo, nota

receiver *(phone)* aparelho de telefone
reception recepção
receptionist recepcionista
recipe receita
to recover recuperar
red vermelho (a)
refrigerator, fridge geladeira
refund reembolso
to relax relaxar
to remain sobrar
to remember lembrar
to remind lembrar
to rent alugar
  for rent aluga-se
renting aluguel
rescue resgate
reservation reserva
to reserve reservar
reserved reservado (a)
respiration respiração
to rest descansar
restaurant restaurante
restricted traffic area zona de tráfego restrito
to return retornar
rheumatism reumatismo
rice arroz
rich rico (a)
to ride a horse cavalgar
right certo (a)
right *(direction)* direito (a)
  to the right à direita
ring anel
to rise subir, levantar
river rio
road estrada
  main road estrada principal
  secondary road estrada secundária
roadworks obras (na estrada)
to rob furtar
rock climbing montanhismo
roof telhado

room sala
  departure lounge, waiting room sala de espera
  dining room sala de jantar
  living room sala de estar
  surgery room, operating theatre sala de operações
rope corda
route rota
to row remar
row fila
rubbish lixo
rucksack mochila
rug tapete
rugby rúgbi
rule regra
to run correr

S
sad triste
saddle sela
safety segurança
to sail velejar
salad salada
to sale vender
sale liquidação, saldo
salesman/saleswoman vendedor (a)
salt sal
same mesmo (a)
sand areia
sandal sandália
sandwich sanduíche
Saturday sábado
sauce molho
saucepan panela
sausage salsicha
to say dizer
  What did you say? O que você disse?
school escola
scissors tesoura
scratch arranhão
scream grito
to scream gritar

138

screen wash limpa-vidros
screwdriver chave de fenda
sea mar
seafood frutos-do-mar
to search procurar
seat assento
  aisle seat assento no corredor
  reserved seat assento reservado
  seat belt cinto de segurança
  window seat assento na janela
second (*time*) segundo
second (*order*) segundo (a)
  second class segunda classe
secret (**adj.**) secreto (a)
security segurança.
sedative sedativo, pílula para dormir
to see ver
  see you later até mais tarde
to seem parecer
seldom raramente
to send enviar
  send money enviar dinheiro
sender remetente
separated separado (a)
September setembro
serious sério (a)
to serve servir
service serviço
  free service serviço gratuito
  room service serviço de quarto
seven sete
seventeen dezessete
seventy setenta
several muitos (as), vários (as)
sew coser (costurar)
shallow raso (a)
shampoo xampu
to shave barbear
sheet (*paper*) folha (de papel)
sheet (*bed*) lençol
shell concha
ship navio
shirt camisa
shoe sapato

shoe polish graxa de sapato
shoe repair shop conserto de sapatos
shoe shop sapataria
shooting range tiro-ao-alvo
shop, store loja
  antique shop loja de antiguidades
  camera shop loja de material
  fotográfico
  craft shop loja de artesanato
  department store loja de departa-
  mentos
  electrical goods store loja de
  eletrodomésticos
  gift shop loja de presentes
  record shop loja de discos, CDs
  souvenir shop loja de suvenires
  toyshop loja de brinquedos
short baixo (a), curto (a)
shorts shorts
shoulder ombro
to shout gritar
shovel pá
shower chuveiro
shrimp camarão
side lado
sidewalk calçada
signature assinatura
silent silencioso (a)
silk seda
silver prata
simple simples
since desde
to sing cantar
single solteiro (a)
sink, washbasin pia
sister irmã
six seis
sixteen dezesseis
sixty sessenta
size tamanho
to skate patinar
skates patins
skating rink pista de patinação
to ski esquiar

ski esqui
ski trail pista de esqui
skin pele
skirt saia
sky céu
skydiving pára-quedismo
slang gíria
to sleep dormir
sleep sono
sleeping bag saco de dormir
sleeping dormindo, adormecido (a)
  he is sleeping ele está dormindo
slippers chinelos
slippery road pista escorregadia
slow lento (a)
small pequeno (a)
smallpox varíola
smell cheiro, odor
to smile sorrir
to smoke fumar
  do you mind if I smoke?
  importa-se se eu fumar?
smoke fumaça
smoker fumante
  non-smoker não-fumante
snack lanche
snack bar lanchonete
snorkel respirador, snorkel
snow neve
so então, tão
  so small tão pequeno
  so ... então ...
soap sabonete
soccer futebol
soccer game partida de futebol
socket tomada elétrica
socks meias
  pantie-hose meia-calça
soft drink refrigerante
some algum (a)
somebody alguém
someone alguém
something algo
sometimes às vezes

somewhere em algum lugar
son filho
song canto, canção
soon logo
sorry! desculpe!
sound som
soup sopa
South sul
souvenir suvenir
spades *(cards)* espadas
Spain Espanha
Spanish espanhol (a)
spares peças sobressalentes
spark plug vela de ignição
speak falar
  I can't speak Portuguese não falo
  português
  speak more slowly, please
  fale mais devagar, por favor
specialist especialista
speed velocidade
speedometer velocímetro
spice, seasoning tempero
spider aranha
spirits bebidas alcoólicas
splinter farpa
spoon colher
sport esporte
sports equipment equipamentos
  esportivos
sportswear traje esportivo
Spring primavera
square *(public place)* praça
square *(shape)* quadrado
stadium estádio
stairs escadas
stamp selo
stapler grampeador
star estrela
to start começar, iniciar
starter antepasto, entrada
station estação
  bus station estação de ônibus
  terminus estação terminal

stationer's *(shop)* papelaria
statue estátua
to steal roubar
steering wheel volante
steward (ess) comissário (a) de
   bordo
stew-pan caçarola
sticker adesivo
still ainda
sting picada, ferroada
stomach estômago
to stop parar
   stop! pare!
stop parada
stopcock registro (hidráulico)
store *(see also shop)* loja
storm tempestade
stove fogão
strawberry morango
street rua
string barbante
stroller carrinho de bebê
strong forte
student estudante
suburb subúrbio
subway metrô
such tão
to suffer sofrer
sugar açúcar
suit *(clothes)* terno
suitcase mala, pasta
Summer verão
sun sol
Sunday domingo
sunglasses óculos de sol
sunny ensolarado (a)
sunshade guarda-sol
suntan lotion bronzeador
supermarket supermercado
surf surfe
surfboard prancha de surfe
surgeon cirurgião
surgery cirurgia
surname sobrenome

sweater suéter, malha, pulôver
sweet doce
sweet pepper pimentão
swim nadar
swimming natação
synagogue sinagoga

T

T-shirt camiseta
table mesa
table lamp abajur
tailor's alfaiataria
to take tomar, pegar
to talk conversar
tall alto (a)
tangerine tangerina
tanned bronzeado (a)
   to get a (sun) tan bronzear-se
tap torneira
taste, flavour gosto
taxi táxi
tea chá
team equipe, time
teaspoon colher de chá
telegram telegrama
telephone, phone telefone
   cardphone telefone com uso de
   cartão
   payphone telefone público
   telephone booth
   cabine telefônica
   telephone directory
   lista telefônica
television televisão
to tell contar, dizer
temperature temperatura
temple templo
ten dez
tennis tênis
tennis court quadra de tênis
tent tenda, barraca
than do que
   she is older than you ela é mais
   velha do que você

to thank agradecer
  thank you obrigado (a)
  thank you, the same to you obrigado (a), igualmente
  thank you very much muito obrigado (a)
that/those aquele (a, es, as)
the o (a, os, as)
theft roubo
their/theirs deles
then então
there ali, lá
thick grosso (a)
thief ladrão
thin fino (a), magro (a)
  the book is thin o livro é fino
  that man is thin aquele homem é magro
to think pensar
third terceiro (a)
thirst sede
thirteen treze
thirty trinta
this/these este (a, es, as), isto
this book este livro
  these boys estes meninos
  these houses estas casas
  this is a pen isto é uma caneta
  this morning esta manhã
thousand mil
three três
throat garganta
through através
to throw up vomitar
Thursday quinta-feira
thus assim
ticket tíquete, passagem
  return ticket passagem de ida e volta
  round-trip ticket, two way ticket, single ticket, one way ticket passagem só de ida
  ticket inspection controle de passagens

tie gravata
tight apertado (a), justo (a)
till caixa
time tempo
timetable horário, quadro de horários
tip gorjeta
tired cansado (a)
to para
tobacco fumo
tobacco shop tabacaria
today hoje
together juntos
toilet banheiro
  where are the toilets, please? por favor, onde fica o banheiro?
token ficha
toll pedágio
tomato tomate
tomorrow amanhã
  the day after tomorrow depois de amanhã
  tomorrow morning amanhã de manhã
  tomorrow night amanhã à noite
tone, dialling tone sinal de discagem
tongue língua
tonsils amígdalas
too much demasiado
tooth dente
toothpaste pasta de dentes
torch lanterna
to touch tocar
tourist turista
to tow rebocar
towel toalha
town centre centro da cidade
town, city cidade
toy brinquedo
traffic lights semáforo
traffic police polícia rodoviária, de trânsito
trailer reboque
trailer trailer
train trem

to **translate** traduzir
translator tradutor
trash can lata de lixo
travel sickness enjôo
travel viagem
tray bandeja
tree árvore
to **trim** aparar
trip viagem
trolley carrinho
   luggage trolley carrinho de bagagens
trousers calças
truck caminhão
trunk *(car)* porta-malas
to **try** tentar
to **try on** experimentar
Tuesday terça-feira
tunnel túnel
to **turn, to come back** voltar
turn signal seta, pisca
twelve doze
twenty vinte
two dois
tyre pneu
tyre repairs borracheiro

U

ulcer úlcera
umbrella guarda-chuva
uncle tio
under sob
underground metrô
to **understand** entender, compreen-
   der
   I don't understand não compreendo
underwater fishing pesca submarina
underwear pants, underpants
   cuecas
until até
upon sobre
to **use** usar
useful útil
usual habitual

V

vacant livre
vacations férias
vaccination vacinação
vacuum cleaner aspirador de pó
van furgão
vegetables verduras, legumes
video camera câmera de vídeo
video recorder aparelho de vídeo
village aldeia
violet violeta
voice voz
volleyball voleibol

W

waistcoast colete
to **wait** esperar
waiter/waitress garçom (nete)
to **walk** andar
wall muro, parede
ward ala
wardrobe armário embutido, guarda-
roupa
warning triangle triângulo (de carro)
was/were era (m), estava (m)
washing machine máquina de lavar
   roupa
to **watch** ver, observar, assistir
watch relógio de pulso
watch out! atenção! cuidado!
watchmaker, clockmaker relojoeiro
water água mineral
   sparkling mineral water água mineral com gás
   drinking water água potável
water-skiing esqui aquático
waterfall catarata, queda-d'água
watermelon melancia
wave onda
way in entrada
way out saída
we nós
weak fraco (a)
weather tempo, clima

wedding casamento
Wednesday quarta-feira
week semana
  last week semana passada
  next week semana que vem
weight peso
  overweight excesso de peso
welcome bem-vindo (a)
well bem
  very well! muito bem!
West oeste
to wet molhar
wet molhado (a)
wet paint pintura fresca
wet suit traje isotérmico
what (o) que, qual
  what time is it? que horas são?
  what's this? o que é isto?
  what's wrong? qual é o problema?
wheel roda
when quando
where onde
  where can I get …? onde eu posso conseguir …?
  where is the …? onde está o (a)…?
which qual (ais)
whisky uísque
white branco (a)
Whitsun Pentecostes
who quem
whooping cough coqueluche
whose de quem, cujo
why por que
width largura
wife esposa
wind vento
window janela
windshield/windscreen wiper limpador de pára-brisa
windshield, windscreen pára-brisa
windsurfing windsurfe
wine vinho
wine list carta de vinhos
wine merchant's adega

144

wing asa
Winter inverno
with com
withdraw (money) retirar, sacar
withdrawal (money) retirada, saque
without sem
woman mulher
wood madeira
wool lã
word palavra
to work trabalhar, funcionar
worse pior
  the worst o pior
wound ferimento, ferida
wrist punho
to write escrever

Y

year ano
  last year ano passado
  next year ano que vem
  I'm … years old tenho … anos
  New Year Ano-Novo
yellow amarelo (a)
Yellow Pages Páginas Amarelas
yes sim
yesterday ontem
  the day before yesterday anteontem
yet ainda
  not yet ainda não
yogurt iogurte
you você (s)
you're welcome de nada
young jovem
your (one person) seu (sua)
your (more than one person) de vocês
youth hostel albergue da juventude

Z

zero zero
zipcode código postal
zipper zíper
zoo zoológico

Janet Evanovich's Stephanie Plum novels are:

"Suspenseful."
—*Los Angeles Times*

"Terrific."
—*San Francisco Chronicle*

"Irresistible."
—*Kirkus Reviews*

"Thrilling."
—*The Midwest Book Review*

"Hilariously funny."
—*USA Today*

"A blast of fresh air."
—*The Washington Post*

"Inventive and fast-paced."
—*San Diego Union-Tribune*

"Superb."
—*Detroit Free Press*

BY JANET EVANOVICH

ONE FOR THE MONEY

TWO FOR THE DOUGH

THREE TO GET DEADLY

FOUR TO SCORE

HIGH FIVE

HOT SIX

SEVEN UP

HARD EIGHT

TO THE NINES

TEN BIG ONES

ELEVEN ON TOP

TWELVE SHARP

LEAN MEAN THIRTEEN

FEARLESS FOURTEEN

FINGER LICKIN' FIFTEEN

SIZZLING SIXTEEN

VISIONS OF SUGAR PLUMS

PLUM LOVIN'

PLUM LUCKY

PLUM SPOOKY

WICKED APPETITE

FULL HOUSE

WITH DORIEN KELLY

LOVE IN A NUTSHELL

THE HUSBAND LIST

WITH CHARLOTTE HUGHES

FULL TILT

FULL SPEED

FULL BLAST

FULL BLOOM

FULL SCOOP

WITH LEANNE BANKS

HOT STUFF

WITH INA YALOF

HOW I WRITE

AVAILABLE FROM HARPERCOLLINS

HERO AT LARGE

MOTOR MOUTH

METRO GIRL

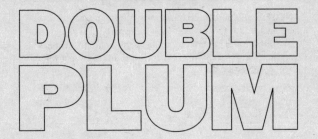

DOUBLE PLUM

TWO BOOKS IN ONE

PLUM LOVIN'
and
PLUM LUCKY

JANET
EVANOVICH

St. Martin's Paperbacks

This is a work of fiction. All of the characters, organizations, and events portrayed in this novel are either products of the author's imagination or are used fictitiously.

DOUBLE PLUM: PLUM LOVIN' copyright © 2007 by Evanovich, Inc. and PLUM LUCKY copyright © 2008 by Evanovich, Inc.

For information address St. Martin's Press, 175 Fifth Avenue, New York, NY 10010.

ISBN: 978-1-250-12272-8

Our books may be purchased in bulk for promotional, educational, or business use. Please contact your local bookseller or the Macmillan Corporate and Premium Sales Department at 1-800-221-7945, ext. 5442, or by e-mail at MacmillanSpecial Markets@macmillan.com.

Printed in the United States of America

St. Martin's Paperbacks edition / January 2017

St. Martin's Paperbacks are published by St. Martin's Press, 175 Fifth Avenue, New York, NY 10010.

10 9 8 7 6 5 4 3 2 1

PLUM
LOVIN'

*I'd like to acknowledge the invaluable
assistance of Alex Evanovich,
Peter Evanovich, and my St. Martin's Press
editor and friend, SuperJen Enderlin.*

Chapter
ONE

Men are like shoes. Some fit better than others. And sometimes you go out shopping and there's nothing you like. And then, as luck would have it, the next week you find two that are perfect, but you don't have the money to buy both. I was currently in just such a position . . . not with shoes, but with men. And this morning it got worse.

A while ago, a guy named Diesel showed up in my kitchen. Poof, he was there. Like magic. And then days later, poof, he was gone. Now, without warning, he was once again standing in front of me.

"Surprise," he said. "I'm back."

He was imposing at just over six feet. Built solid with broad shoulders and deep-set, assessing brown eyes. He looked like he could seriously kick ass and not break a sweat. He had a lot of wavy, sandy blond hair cut short and fierce blond eyebrows. I placed his age at late twenties, early thirties. I knew very little about his background. Clearly he'd been lucky with the gene pool. He was a nice-looking guy, with perfect white teeth and a smile that made a woman get all warm inside.

It was a cold February morning, and he'd dropped into my apartment wearing a multicolored scarf wrapped around his neck, a black wool peacoat, a washed-out three-button thermal knit shirt, faded jeans, beat-up boots, and his usual bad attitude. I knew that a muscular, athletic body was under the coat. I wasn't sure if there was anything good buried under the attitude.

My name is Stephanie Plum. I'm average height and average weight and have an average vocabulary for someone living in Jersey. I have shoulder-length brown hair that is curly or wavy, depending on the humidity. My eyes are blue. My heritage is Hungarian and Italian. My family is dysfunctional in a normal sort of way. There are a bunch of things I'd like to do with my life, but right now I'm happy to put one foot in front of the other and button my jeans without having a roll of fat hang over the waistband.

I work as a bond enforcement agent for my cousin Vinnie, and my success at the job has more to do with luck and tenacity than with skill. I live in a budget apartment on the outskirts of Trenton, and my only roommate is a hamster named Rex. So I felt understandably threatened by having this big guy suddenly appear in my kitchen.

"I hate when you just show up in front of me," I said. "Can't you ring my doorbell like a normal person?"

"First off, I'm not exactly normal. And second, you should be happy I didn't walk into your bathroom when you were wet and naked." He flashed me the killer smile. "Although I wouldn't have minded finding you wet and naked."

"In your dreams."

"Yeah," Diesel said. "It's happened."

He stuck his head in my refrigerator and rooted around. Not a lot in there, but he found one last bottle of beer and some slices of American cheese. He ate the cheese and chugged the beer. "Are you still seeing that cop?"

"Joe Morelli. Yep."

"What about the guy behind door number two?"

"Ranger? Yeah, I'm still working with Ranger." Ranger was my bounty hunter mentor and more. Problem was, the *more* part wasn't clearly defined.

I heard a snort and a questioning *woof* from the vicinity of my bedroom.

"What's that?" Diesel asked.

"Morelli's working double shifts, and I'm taking care of his dog, Bob."

There was the sound of dog feet running, and Bob rounded a corner and slid to a stop on the kitchen linoleum. He was a big-footed, shaggy, orange-haired beast with floppy ears and happy brown eyes. Probably golden retriever, but he'd never win best of breed. He sat his ass down on Diesel's boot and wagged his tail at him.

Diesel absently fondled Bob's head, and Bob drooled a little on Diesel's pant leg, hoping for a scrap of cheese.

"Is this visit social or professional?" I asked Diesel.

"Professional. I'm looking for a guy named Bernie Beaner. I need to shut him down."

If I'm to believe Diesel, there are people on this planet who have abilities that go beyond what would be considered normal human limitations. These people aren't exactly superheroes. It's more that they're ordinary souls with the freakish ability to levitate a cow or slow-pitch a lightning bolt. Some are good and some are bad. Diesel tracks the bad. The alternative explanation for Diesel is that he's a wacko.

"What's Beaner's problem?" I asked.

Diesel dropped a small leftover chunk of cheese into Rex's cage and gave another chunk to Bob. "Gone off the edge. His marriage went into the shitter, and he blamed it on another Unmentionable. Now he's out to get her."

"Unmentionable?"

"That's what we call ourselves. It sounds better than *freak of nature.*"

Only marginally.

Bob was pushing against Diesel, trying to get him to give up more cheese. Bob was about ninety pounds of rangy dog, and Diesel was two hundred of hard muscle. It would take a lot more than Bob to bulldoze Diesel around my kitchen.

"And you're in my apartment, why?" I asked Diesel.

"I need help."

"No. No, no, no, no, no."

"You have no choice, sweetie pie. The woman Beaner's looking for is on your most-wanted list. And she's in my custody. If you want your big-ticket bond, you have to help me."

"That's horrible. That's blackmail or bribery or something."

"Yeah. Deal with it."

"Who's the woman?" I asked Diesel.

"Annie Hart."

"You've gotta be kidding. Vinnie's on a rant over her. I spent all day yesterday looking for her. She's wanted for armed robbery and assault with a deadly weapon."

"It's all bogus . . . not that either of us gives a rat's ass." Diesel was systematically going through my cupboards looking for food, and Bob was sticking close. "Anyway, bottom line is I've got her tucked away until I can sort things out with crazy Bernie."

"Bernie is the . . . um, Unmentionable who's after Annie?"

"Yeah. Problem is, Annie's one of those crusader types. Takes her job real serious. Says it's her *calling*. So, the only way I could get Annie to stay hidden was to promise her I'd take over her caseload. I suck at the kind of stuff she does, so I'm passing it off to you."

"And what do I get out of this?"

"You get Annie. As soon as I take care of Bernie, I'll turn Annie over to you."

"I don't see where this is a big favor to me. If I don't help you, Annie will come out of hiding, I'll snag her, and my job will be done."

Diesel had his thumbs hooked into his jeans pockets; his eyes were locked onto mine, his expression was serious. "What'll it take? I need help with this, and everyone has a price. What's yours? How about twenty bucks when you close a case?"

"A hundred, and nothing illegal or life-threatening."

"Deal," Diesel said.

Here's the sad truth. I had nothing better to do.

And I needed money. The bonds office was beyond slow. I had one FTA to hunt down, and Diesel had her locked away.

"Just exactly what am I supposed to do?" I asked him. "Annie's bond agreement lists her occupation as a relationship expert."

Diesel gave a bark of laughter. "Relationship expert. I guess that could cover it."

"I don't even know what that means! What the heck is a relationship expert?"

Diesel had dropped a battered leather knapsack onto my counter when he popped into my kitchen. He went to the knapsack, removed a large yellow envelope, and handed it over to me. "It's all in this envelope."

I opened the envelope and pulled out a bunch of folders crammed with photographs and handwritten pages.

"She's got a condensed version for you clipped to the top folder," Diesel said. "Got everything prioritized. Says you better hustle because Valentine's Day is coming up fast."

"And?"

"Personally, I don't get turned on by Valentine's Day, with the sappy cards and creepy cupids and the hearts-and-flowers routine. But Annie is to Valentine's Day what Santa Claus is to Christmas. She makes it happen. Of course, Annie operates on a smaller scale. It's not like she's got ten thousand elves working for her."

Diesel was a really sexy-looking guy, but I thought he might be one step away from permanent residence at the funny farm. "I still don't get my role in this."

"I just handed you five open files. It's up to you to make sure those five people have a good Valentine's Day."

Oh boy.

"Listen, I know it's lame," Diesel said, "but I'm stuck with it. And now you're stuck with it. And I'm going to have a power shortage if I don't get breakfast. So find me a diner. Then I'm going to do *my* thing and look for Bernie, and you're going to do *your* thing and work your way down Annie's list."

I clipped a leash onto Bob's collar and the three of us walked down the stairs and out to my car. I was driving a yellow Ford Escape that was good for hauling felons and Bob dogs.

"Does Bob go everywhere?" Diesel wanted to know.

"Pretty much. If I leave him at home, he gets lonely and eats the furniture."

Forty minutes later, Diesel was finishing up a mountain of scrambled eggs, bacon, pancakes, home

fries, and sourdough toast with jam . . . all smothered in maple syrup.

I'd ordered a similar breakfast but had to give up
about a third of the way through. I pushed my plate
away and asked that the food be put in a to-go box. I
drank my coffee and thumbed through the first file.
Charlene Klinger. Age forty-two. Divorced. Four
children, ages seven, eight, ten, and twelve. Worked
for the DMV. There was an unflattering snapshot of
her squinting into the sun. She was wearing sneakers and slacks and a sweater that didn't do a lot to
hide the fact that she was about twenty pounds overweight. Her face was pleasant enough. No makeup.
Not a lot of hairstyle going on. Short brown hair
pushed behind her ears. The smile looked tense,
like she was making an effort, but she had bigger
fish to fry than to pose for the picture.

There were four more pages in Charlene's file.
Harvey Nolen, Brian Seabeam, Lonnie Brownowski,
Steven Klein. REJECT had been written in red
magic marker across each page. A sticky note had
been attached to the back of the file. THERE'S
SOMEONE FOR EVERYONE, the note read. I sup-
posed this was Annie giving herself a pep talk.
And a second sticky note below the first. FIND
CHARLENE'S TRUE LOVE. A mission statement.

I blew out a sigh and closed the file.

"Hey, it could be worse," Diesel said. "You could

be hunting down a skip who thinks it's open season on bounty hunters. Unless you really piss her off, Charlene probably won't shoot at you."

"I don't know where to begin."

Diesel stood and threw some money on the table. "You'll figure it out. I'll check in with you later."

"Wait," I said. "About Annie Hart—"

"Later," Diesel said. And in three strides he was across the room and at the door. By the time I got to the lot, Diesel was nowhere to be seen. Fortunately, he hadn't commandeered my car. It was still in its parking space, Bob looking at me through the back window, somehow understanding that the Styrofoam box in my hand contained food for him.

The bail bonds office is a small storefront affair on Hamilton Avenue, just a ten-minute drive from the diner. I parked at the curb and pushed my way through the front door. Connie Rosolli, the office manager, looked up when I entered. Connie is a couple years older than me, a couple pounds heavier, a couple inches shorter, a lot more Italian, and consistently has a better manicure.

"You must be tuned in to the cosmic loop this morning," Connie said. "I was just about to call you. Vinnie's bananas over Annie Hart."

Vinnie's ferret face appeared in the doorway of his inner office. "Well?" he asked me.

"Well what?"

"Tell me you've got her locked up nice and neat. Tell me you've got a body receipt."

"I've got a lead," I told Vinnie.

"Only a lead?" Vinnie clapped his hands to his head. "You're killing me!"

Lula was on the faux leather couch, reading a magazine. "We should be so lucky," Lula said.

Lula is a 180-pound black woman crammed into a five-foot, five-inch body. At the moment, she was wearing a red skin-tight spandex T-shirt that said KISS MY ASS in iridescent gold lettering, jeans with rhinestones marching down side seams that looked like they might burst apart at any minute, and four-inch high-heeled boots. Lula does the office filing when she's in the mood, and she rides shotgun for me when I need backup.

"What's the lineup look like?" I asked Connie.

"Nothing new. Annie Hart is the only big bond in the wind. It's always slow at this time of the year. All the serious crackheads killed themselves over Christmas, and it's too cold for the hookers and pushers to stand on the street corners. The only good crime we've got going on is gang shooting, and those idiots get held without bond."

"It's so slow Vinnie's going on a cruise," Lula said.

"Yeah, and the cruise isn't cheap," Vinnie said. "So get your ass out there and find Annie Hart. I'm not running a goddamn charity here. I take a hit on Hart's bond, and I'll have to fake a stroke and cash in my cruise insurance. And Lucille wouldn't like that."

Lucille is Vinnie's wife. Her father is Harry the Hammer, and while Harry might understand about the need for the occasional illicit nooner, he definitely wouldn't be happy to see Lucille get stiffed on the cruise.

"It's one of them champagne Valentine's Day cruises," Vinnie said. "Lucille's got her bags packed already. She thinks this is going to rejuvenate our marriage."

"Only way it'll rejuvenate your marriage is if Lucille brings handcuffs and a whip and Mary's little lamb," Lula said.

"So sue me," Vinnie said. "I've got eclectic tastes."

We all did a lot of eye rolling.

"I'm out of here," I told Connie. "I'll be on my cell if you need me."

"I'm going with you," Lula said, grabbing her Prada knockoff shoulder bag. "I'm feeling lucky today. I bet I could find Annie Hart right off."

"Thanks," I said to Lula, "but I can handle it."

"The hell," Lula said. "Suppose you gotta go into some cranky neighborhood, and you need some muscle. That would be me. Or suppose you need to make a doughnut choice at that new place on State Street. That would be me, too."

I cut my eyes to Lula. "So what you're saying is that you want to test-drive the new doughnut shop on State?"

"Yeah," Lula said. "But only if you need a dough-nut real bad."

Fifteen minutes later, I cruised away from Do-nut Delish and headed for the DMV.

"I can't believe you're not eating any of these doughnuts," Lula said, a bag of doughnuts resting on her lap. "These are first class. Look at this one with the pink and yellow sprinkles on it. It's just about the happiest doughnut I ever saw."

"I had a huge late breakfast. I'm stuffed."

"Yeah, but we're talking about primo doughnuts here."

Bob was in the cargo area of the Escape. His head was over the backseat, and he was panting in our direction.

"That dog could use a breath mint," Lula said.

"Try a doughnut."

Lula flipped Bob a doughnut. Bob caught the doughnut midair and settled down to enjoy it.

"Where the heck are we going?" Lula wanted to know. "I thought we were going after Annie Hart. Don't she live in North Trenton?"

"It's complicated. I had to make a deal. Annie Hart is inaccessible until I wrap up her caseload."

"Are you shitting me? And what's that mean anyways? Does that mean you're taking on her customers? Personally, I can't see you doing that. I read her file. She said she was a relationship expert, and I figured that's code for 'ho."

"It's not like that. It's more like matchmaking. First person on my list is Charlene Klinger. She's forty-two and divorced, and we need to find her true love."

"Oh boy, true love. That's a bitch. You sure she wouldn't be satisfied if we just found her some nasty sweaty sex? I got a couple names in my book for that one."

"I'm pretty sure it has to be true love."

Chapter
TWO

Charlene Klinger was behind the counter at the DMV, working the registration-only line. She was prettier in person. Her hair still lacked style, but it was thick and glossy and suited her. Her face was animated, and she smiled a lot. After thirty-five minutes, Lula and I had inched our way up to her. I introduced myself to Charlene and explained I was substituting for Annie Hart.

"That woman is a nut," Charlene said. "I don't know where she came from, but good riddance if she's gone. And I don't need a substitute nutcase. I'm doing fine. I don't want a man in my life. I've got enough problems."

"Didn't you hire Annie?"

"Heck no. She just popped into my kitchen one day. Happens to me all the time. The kids leave the door open and next thing I know, some half-starved cat's wandered into the house and won't leave."

"I was under the impression you wanted to find your true love," I said to Charlene.

Charlene looked at the powdered sugar that had sifted onto Lula's chest. "I'd sooner find a bag of doughnuts. Don't have to shave your legs to enjoy a bag of doughnuts."

"Amen to that," Lula said.

"You're going to have to move along if you don't want to register something," Charlene said. "You hold up the line too long and this crowd will get ugly."

Lula and I left the building and hustled to my car. It was freezing cold, and we walked with our heads tucked down against the wind.

"Now what?" Lula wanted to know.

I slid behind the wheel and pulled another file out of the envelope. "I have more."

Lula picked a doughnut out of the bag. "Me, too."

"Yesterday you told me you were going on a diet."

"Yeah, but it's something new. It's called the afternoon diet. You get to eat all you want until noon. Then the diet starts."

"Next up is Gary Martin. Runs a vet clinic on Route 1. Never been married. Looks like a nice guy." I passed his picture to Lula.

"He looks like a dork," Lula said. "He's wearing a bow tie, and he's got a comb-over. He don't need a matchmaker. He needs a woman with scissors."

I put the car in gear and rolled out of the lot. "According to Annie's file, he needs help getting his girlfriend back."

"And we're gonna help him? Excuse me if I'm a skeptic, but it don't seem to me we're all that good at relationships. I only date losers, and you have commitment issues. Plus, you can't even make up your mind about who you want as your commitment recipient. You're double-dipping with Morelli and Ranger."

"I'm *not* double-dipping."

"You're *mentally* double-dipping."

"That doesn't count. Everyone mentally double-dips. Keep your eyes open for Municipal Animal Hospital."

The Municipal Animal Hospital waiting room was bright and cheery and sparkling clean. And it was empty of patients. A young woman sat behind the big wraparound desk. She was also sparkling clean, but she didn't look all that cheery.

"Yo," Lula said to her. "I'm Lula, and this here's the world-famous Stephanie Plum, and we're looking for Gary Martin."

"He's in surgery," the woman said. "Office hours start at one o'clock."

"Maybe he could squeeze us in between surgeries," Lula said. "It's a personal matter."

"Dr. Martin doesn't like to be disturbed when he's in surgery."

"See, here's the thing," Lula said. "I got a doughnut with my name on it out in the car, and I don't want to sit around until one o'clock. I mean, it's not like ol' Gary's doing open heart. He's cutting the balls off a cat, right?"

I pointed stiff-armed to the door. "Out," I said to Lula.

"Just trying to communicate with Miss Stick-up-her-ass," Lula said.

"Out!"

I waited until Lula left, and then I turned to the receptionist. "Maybe I could leave a note for Dr. Martin."

There was a long awkward pause, and I assumed the receptionist was contemplating hitting the police button on the security system . . . or at the very least unleashing Dobermans from a holding pen. This was a vet office. They had dogs, right?

Finally, the woman exhaled and slid a pad and pen my way. "I guess that would be okay," she said.

I was halfway through the note when Gary Martin emerged from a back room and approached the receptionist.

"Any emergency calls?" he asked her. "Any, um, personal calls?"

She shook her head, no.

"Are you sure? Not a single personal call?"

Gary Martin looked like a big, forty-year-old cherub. He was about five foot six with chubby cheeks and a soft middle. He was wearing a light blue lab coat that was unbuttoned over tan slacks and a yellow button-down shirt. He was entirely adorable in a dorky kind of way. And he was clearly disappointed that no one had called.

I stuck my hand out and introduced myself. "Annie Hart is temporarily indisposed," I said. "I'm her replacement."

I wasn't sure what to expect after Charlene Klinger, but Gary Martin seemed excited to see me. He ushered me into his little office and closed the door.

"I've been waiting," he said. "I was expecting Ms. Hart, but I'm sure you're wonderful, too."

"I understand you need help getting your girlfriend back."

"I don't know what happened. Two weeks ago, she just said it was over. I don't know what went wrong. I must have done something terrible, but I don't know what it was. I was going to ask her to marry me on Valentine's Day. And now I don't know what to do. She won't talk to me on the phone, and she won't let me into her apartment. And last time I tried to talk to her she said I was a pest. A pest!"

"I'm curious," I said. "How did you hear about Annie Hart?"

"It was odd. I found her card in my jacket pocket. Someone must have given it to me. It said Ms. Hart was a relationship expert . . . and I thought, That's just what I need! So I called Ms. Hart, and we had a meeting. That was four days ago." Martin took a photo off his desktop and handed it to me. "Ms. Hart wanted a picture of Loretta."

The sticky note attached to the back told me this was Loretta Flack, and Martin had neatly printed Loretta's address and phone number below her name. The front of the photo showed a smiling blond with a Barbie doll shape. It had been taken at some sort of street fair, and she was holding a teddy bear.

"She's a bartender," Martin said. "She works the lunch shift at Beetle Bumpkin. It's a sports bar just up the road. They have good sandwiches at lunchtime, but Loretta said she didn't want me in there anymore."

"She's pretty," I said.

"Yes, she's way too pretty for me. And probably too young. I don't know why she even went out with me in the first place. I thought maybe you could tell her I joined a gym, and I have a private trainer now. And I think my hair is growing back."

I looked up at the three strands of hair plastered to the top of his dome.

"I thought I might have seen some fuzz this morning," Gary Martin said.

"Anything else you want me to tell her?"

"I'll leave it up to you. You're a relationship expert, right? I mean, you know the right things to say."

Oh boy, we were in trouble. I *never* said the right thing. Lula was right. I was a relationship disaster.

"Sure," I told him. "Leave it to me. I'll get this fixed up."

Lula settled her ass on a Beetle Bumpkin barstool and looked around. "Beetle Bumpkin is one of them new mini chains," she said. "There's one just opened downtown. The sandwiches are good because they fry them. Everything's fried. That's the Beetle Bumpkin secret ingredient."

Loretta Flack was taking an order at the other end of the bar. Her hair was yellow under the Bumpkin bar lights, and her breasts were packed into a red Beetle Bumpkin T-shirt. I figured she was maybe fifteen years younger than Gary Martin.

"Let me do the talking this time," I said to Lula.

"My lips are sealed. I'm only here in case you need backup. Like suppose she tries some karate moves or she pulls a gun on you."

"I don't think that's going to happen."

"You never know. Best to be prepared, I always say. People are unpredictable. I learned that in my human behavior course at the community college. Did I ever tell you I took a human behavior course?"

"Yes."

"It could help in this situation. It's just about qualified me to be a relationship expert. Plus I got a lot of expertise all those years when I was a 'ho. I bet I could relationship the ass off you."

"No doubt. Let me talk anyway."

Loretta made her way down to us. "Ladies?" she said.

"Diet Coke and tuna on rye," I told her.

"I'll have the Beetle special sandwich and cheese fries and a Coke," Lula said.

I looked at my watch. It was twelve-thirty. "What about your afternoon diet?"

"It's more like a suggestion than a rule. And anyway, I thought since we're working on these cases I should keep my strength up. I might get all weak and hypoglycemic if I don't have cheese fries."

"So," Loretta said. "Working ladies."

"Yep. We're relationship experts," Lula said.

"We fix up relationships. You got any that needs fixin'?"

"No. I'm good with relationships. I'm in a dreamy one right now. He's a lawyer."

"You don't look like the lawyer type," Lula said. "You look like . . . some other type."

Loretta drew my drink and slid it down the bar at me. "I'm lots of types. This is a really good job for meeting men. I go out with them and get them to buy me some jewelry and then when it looks like they're gonna say the *L* word, I split. I got this necklace I'm wearing from a veterinarian."

"It's a good necklace," Lula said. "And you look like the veterinarian type more than the lawyer type. Maybe you should go back with him."

"He was a loser," Loretta said. "He kept talking about how he wanted a family." She wrinkled her nose. "Eeeuw, kids. Ick. I hate kids. And he was always rushing off to save some dumb cat or dog. I mean, what's with that? Who wants a boyfriend who makes you rush through dessert just because some cat got run over by a dump truck?"

"What a creep," Lula said. "Imagine rushing you through dessert. I wouldn't stand for that."

"The lawyer's a lot better," Loretta said. "He has a wife and kids, so I don't have to worry about the *L* word. The *L* word is okay if it's insincere."

"Boy, you got it all figured out," Lula said.

Loretta moved off to the other end of the bar.

"What was that?" I asked Lula. "You were supposed to let me do the talking."

"Well excuse me, Ms. Control Freak. It just worked out this way. You weren't taking advantage of the moment."

Turned out it didn't matter a whole lot anyway. I liked Gary Martin, and I hated Loretta Flack. Loretta Flack was bitchzilla. I couldn't in good conscience fix things so that Martin was stuck with Flack.

The sandwiches and fries arrived, and we dug in.

"I'm liking this," Lula said. "We didn't get spit on or shot at all day, and I feel like a big Cupid. Of course, we haven't gotten anybody together like we're supposed to, but it feels like love is in the air. Don't you feel love in the air? How many more cases we got?"

"Three. Next up is Larry Burlew. He's got his eye on someone but can't get to meet her. I've already skimmed the file. Burlew is a butcher. Works at Sal's Meat Market on Broad. The woman of his dreams works in the coffee shop across the street. According to Annie's notes, Burlew is shy."

"That's cute," Lula said. "A shy butcher. I got a good feeling about him. And I wouldn't mind some pork chops for dinner tonight."

Chapter
THREE

Larry Burlew was a big guy. He was over six feet tall, weighed maybe 230 pounds, and had hands like hamhocks. He wasn't bad looking, and he wasn't good looking. Mostly he looked like a butcher . . . possibly because his white butcher's apron was decorated with meat marinade and chicken guts.

The butcher shop was empty of customers when we entered. Burlew was the lone butcher, and he was slicing ribs and arranging them in the display case.

I introduced myself as Annie's assistant, and Burlew blushed red from the collar of his white T-shirt to the roots of his buzz-cut hair.

"Real nice to meet you," he said softly. "I hope this isn't too much trouble. I feel kind of silly asking for help like this, but Ms. Hart came into the shop and left her card, and I just thought . . ."

"Don't worry about it," Lula said. "It's what we

do. We're the fixer-upper bitches. We *live* to fix shit."

"I understand you want to get together with someone?" I asked Burlew.

"There's this girl that I like. I think she's around my age. I see her every day, and she's nice to me, but in a professional way. And sometimes I try to talk to her, but there's always lots of people around, and I never know what to say. I'm a big dummy when it comes to girls."

"Okay," I said, "give me all the necessary information. Who is she?"

"She's right across the street," Burlew said. "She works in the coffee shop. Every morning I go in to get coffee, and she always gets it just right. She always gives me the perfect amount of cream. And it's never too hot. Her name is Jet. That's what it says on her name tag. I don't know more than that. She's the one with the shiny black hair."

I looked at the coffee shop. It had big plate-glass windows in the front, making it possible to check out the action inside. There were three women working behind the counter and a bunch of customers lined up waiting for service. I shifted my attention back to Burlew and saw he was watching Jet, mesmerized by the sight of her.

I excused myself and swung across the street to the coffee shop. Jet was at the register, ringing up a customer. She was a tiny little thing with short, spiky black hair. She was dressed in a black T-shirt, a short black skirt, black tights, and black boots. She wore a wide black leather belt with silver studs, and she had a red rose tattooed on her arm. She looked to be in her early to mid-twenties. No wedding band or engagement ring on her left hand.

I ordered a coffee. "It's for my cousin across the street," I said. "Maybe you know him . . . Larry Burlew."

"Sorry, no."

"He's a butcher. And he said you always give him perfect coffee."

"Omigod, are you talking about the big huge guy with the buzz cut? He comes in here every morning. He talks so soft I can hardly hear him, and then he goes across the street, and he stares in here all day. I'm sorry because he's your cousin and all, but he's kind of creepy."

"He's shy. And he stares in here because . . . he'd like more coffee, but he can't leave the shop."

"Omigod, I had no idea. That's so sweet. That's so sad. The poor guy is over there wishing he had a cup of coffee, and I thought he was one of those pervert stalkers. He should just call over here. Or he could wave, and I'd bring him a cup."

"Really? He'd love that. He's such a nice guy, but he's always worried about imposing."

Jet leaned on the counter and did a little finger wave at Larry Burlew. Even from this distance I could see Burlew's cheeks flush red.

I brought the coffee across the street and gave it to Larry Burlew.

"I've got it all set," I told him. "All you have to do is wave at Jet, and she'll bring you a cup of coffee. Then you'll have a chance to talk to her."

"I can't talk to her! What would I say? She's so pretty, and I'm so . . ." Burlew looked down at himself. He didn't have words.

"You're a nice-looking guy," I told him. "Okay, maybe the chicken guts are a turnoff, but you can fix that by changing your butcher apron before she gets here. And try not to stare at her so much. Only stare when you want a cup of coffee. Staring sometimes can be misconstrued as, um, rude."

Burlew was bobbing his head up and down. "I'll remember all that. Wave for coffee. Don't stare so much. Change my apron before she gets here."

"And talk to her!"

"Talk to her," he repeated.

I didn't actually have a lot of confidence that this would work, so I wrote my cell phone number on a scrap of paper and left it with him.

"Call me if you have a problem," I said.

Burlew did some vigorous head nodding. "Yes, ma'am."

"Before we go I need to buy some pork chops," Lula said. "I have a taste for pork chops."

Diesel was on the couch watching television when Bob and I got home. There was a six-pack of beer and a pizza box on the coffee table in front of him. Some of the beer and pizza were missing.

"I brought dinner," Diesel said. "How'd it go today?"

"What are you doing here?"

"I'm living here."

"No, you're not."

"Sure I am. I have my shoes off and everything."

"Okay, but I'm not sleeping with you."

"No problemo. You're not my type anyway," Diesel said.

"What's your type?"

"Easy."

I rolled my eyes.

"I'm a jerk," Diesel said, "but I'm lovable."

This was true.

I dragged Bob off to the kitchen, gave him fresh water, and filled his dog bowl with dog crunchies. I returned to the living room, helped myself to a piece of pizza, and joined Diesel on the couch.

"Eat up," Diesel said. "We need to work tonight. I've got a line on Beaner."

"No way. I'm the *relationship* person. I'm not the *find-the-crazy-Unmentionable-nutcase* person."

"I need cover. You're all I've got," Diesel said.

"What makes Beaner special? Can he whip up a tornado? Can he levitate a Hummer? Can he catch a bullet in his teeth?"

"No, he can't do any of those things."

"Well, what *can* he do?"

"I'm not telling you. Just try not to get too close to him."

Bob padded in from the kitchen and stood looking at the leftover pizza. I gave him a piece; he ate it in three gulps and put his head on Diesel's leg, leaving a smear of tomato sauce. Diesel scratched Bob behind the ear, the tomato sauce not worthy of registering on Diesel's slob-o-meter.

It was eight o'clock when I parked my yellow Ford Escape in the small lot attached to Ernie's Bar and Grill. I'd been to Ernie's before, and I knew it was more bar than grill. The grill was mostly wasabi peas and pretzels. The bar was mostly middle-aged white guys who drank too much. It was just one block from the government complex, so it was a convenient watering hole for enslaved bureaucrats who were putting in their hours, waiting for death or retirement, whichever came first. At eight o'clock the bar had emptied out the merely desperate and was left to console the truly hopeless.

"Beaner's been here for two nights running," Diesel said. "He's in there now. I can sense it. Problem is, I can't approach him in a public place. I know he's holed up somewhere nearby, but I can't get a fix on it. I want you to try to get him to talk to you. See if you can find out where he lives. Just don't let him touch you. And don't get too close."

"How close is *too* close?"

"If you can feel his breath on your neck, it's too close. He's five feet, eight inches tall, weighs 180 pounds, and looks late forties. He has brown hair, cut short, blue eyes, and he's got a raspberry birthmark on his forehead that extends into his left eyebrow."

"Why don't you follow him when he leaves the bar?"

"Not an option, unless he leaves with you."

I gave Diesel a *Why not?* look, and Diesel mumbled something.

"What?" I asked.

"I can't." More mumbling.

"You want to run that mumbling by me again?"

Diesel slumped in his seat and blew out a sigh. "I keep losing him. He's really sneaky. He turns a corner on me, and he's gone."

"The stealth Beaner."

"Something like that. He scrambles my radar."

"You don't actually think you have radar, do you?"

"No, but I have GPS. And sometimes ESP. And Monday nights I get ESPN."

Okay, he was a little nutty, but at least he had a sense of humor. And hell, who was I to say whether or not he actually had ESP? I mean, I sort of believe in ghosts. And I sort of believe in heaven. And I sort of believe in wishing on birthday candles. I guess Diesel and ESP aren't too far removed. Sort of in the area of radio waves, spontaneous combustion, and electricity. After all, I don't understand any of those things, but they exist.

"Sometimes you just have to go with it," Diesel said.

I left Diesel on that note and sashayed off to the bar. It was easy to spot Beaner in the lineup of losers. He was the only one with a raspberry birthmark on his forehead. The stool next to him was unoccupied, so I climbed onto it and made sure there was some air between us.

Beaner was drinking something amber on ice. Probably scotch. I ordered a beer and smiled at him.

"Hi," I said. "How's it going?"

He didn't return the smile. "How much time do you have?" he asked.

"That bad?"

He threw back the liquid in his glass and signaled the bartender for more.

I took another stab at it. "Do you come here often?" I asked him.

"I live here."

"Must be hard to sleep on that barstool. How do you keep from falling off?"

That almost got a smile. "I don't sleep here," he said. "I just drink here. I'd drink at home but that might indicate alcoholism."

"Where's home?"

He made a vague gesture with his hand. "Out there."

"*Out there* is a big place."

"My wife kicked me out of the house," he said. "Changed the locks on the friggin' doors. Married for two hundred years, and she kicked me out of the house. Packed all my clothes in cardboard boxes and put them out on the front lawn."

"Jeez, I'm sorry."

"What am I supposed to do now? Things were different the last time I dated. It was simple back then. You found someone you liked, you asked their father if you could marry them, then you got married and climbed on board." He took possession of his new drink and tested it out. "Don't get me wrong, it's not like I'm saying that was right.

It's just the way it was. And I knew that way. Now it's all about talking and sensitivity. I've been married for all this time and suddenly she wants to talk. And it turns out we've been having *bad* sex, and now she wants to have *good* sex. Do you have any idea how embarrassing it is to find out you've been doing it wrong for two hundred years? I mean, how friggin' annoying is that? She said I couldn't find my way south of the border with a road map."

"I might know someone who could help you."

"I don't need help. I need my wife to come to her senses. This whole mess is the result of someone trying to help. Things were fine until some meddler stuck her, big fat nose into my marriage. If I get hold of her, I'll fix her good. It'll be the last time she meddles in someone's marriage."

"But if she was trying to help—"

"She didn't help. She made things awful." He chugged his drink, dropped a twenty on the bar, and stood. "I've gotta go."

"So soon?"

"Things to do."

"Where are you going? Are you going home?"

My eyes flicked to the bartender when he took the twenty and the empty glass. A beat later, I turned my attention back to Beaner, but he was gone.

"Where'd he go?" I asked the bartender. "Did you see him leave?"

"I saw him get off the stool, but then he got lost in the crowd."

I left money on the bar and went outside to Diesel.

"He's gone," I said. "We were talking, and he got agitated, and he split."

Diesel was lounging against my car. "I saw him for a second when he walked through the door. A couple people came out with him, and somehow he disappeared behind them before I could get to him." Diesel pushed off from the car, went to the driver's side door, angled himself in behind the wheel, and turned the key in the ignition. "Let's go."

"Wait a minute. This is *my* car. I drive."

"Everybody knows the guy gets to drive."

"Not in Jersey."

"*Especially* in Jersey," Diesel said. "The testosterone level in Jersey is fifteen percent higher than it is in any other state."

Chapter
FOUR

It was still early, so we stopped at a supermarket on the way home.

"What about the shopping cart?" I asked Diesel. "Do you have to drive that, too?"

"I'd get my nuts repossessed if I didn't drive the shopping cart."

A half hour later, we loaded our food onto the checkout belt, and Diesel gave his credit card to the checker.

"Boy, you've got lots of food," the checker said.

"A man's gotta eat," Diesel told her.

I took a peek at the card. "There's no bank name on this card," I whispered to Diesel.

"It's an Unmentionable card," he said. "Good in three solar systems."

I was pretty sure he was kidding.

I crammed the last of the food into my kitchen . . . lunch meat, beer, cheese, peanut butter, pickles, bagels, ice cream, cereal, milk, orange juice, apples, bananas, bread, cream cheese, coffee, half-and-half, crackers, cookies, chips, salsa, carrots, mixed nuts, and God-knows-what-else.

Diesel took a bag of chips and a beer into the living room and remoted the television on. "This is great," he said. "I can catch the end of the hockey game."

I settled next to him and reached into the chip bag. Bob had been sleeping in the bedroom, but the rustle of a chip bag was a Bob alarm, and in a beat Bob was up and expectantly standing in front of me. I fed him a couple chips, and he flopped down on the floor with his head on my foot.

"Beaner isn't such a bad guy," I said. "He's just frustrated. He's been married for a long time, and all of a sudden his wife isn't satisfied with the status quo. I think Beaner would like to fix things, but he just doesn't know how to get up to speed. He doesn't know how to go about talking to his wife. And he says, according to his wife, he sucks in the sack."

"So give him a pill."

"It's not about *that*. Women don't care about *that*. That's a *man* problem."

"Yeah, I get it," Diesel said. "But a pill would have been easy. This is just plain embarrassing. Maybe I don't have to shut him down. Maybe we can reprogram him."

"We?"

"Unmentionables who've crossed the line aren't happy to see me. And bad things happen when Beaner isn't happy. So either you're going to have to convince him to chill and talk to me, or else you're going to have to get him alone somewhere. I can't seem to follow Beaner, but I can follow you."

"What about his listening-and-understanding problem?"

"I suck at that," Diesel said. "That's girl stuff. You're going to have to explain that to him."

"Only if you help me with Annie Hart's cases. I've scored a big zero with two out of three, and I'm not sure the third one will fly."

Diesel's cell phone buzzed.

"Yeah," Diesel said into the phone. "Now what?"

He slouched deeper into the couch and listened with his mouth set tight. "Yeah," he said. "I hear you. I'm working on it. Send everyone a case of whatever the hell it is they need."

"And?" I said when he disconnected.

"Beaner can't find Annie, so he's visiting her friends and relatives, causing havoc."

The next call was from Annie.

"I'm working on it," Diesel said. "I can't approach him in public and have him contaminate a room filled with innocent people." He nodded and listened. "You have to be patient," he said. "I have a partner. She's helping me with your cases, and she's helping me find Bernie Beaner." More talking on the other end. "No, I'm not bringing her to you. You have to trust me."

Diesel disconnected.

"How'd that go?" I asked him. "Does she trust you?"

"Not even a little. She's coming over here."

"What about Bernie? I thought it wasn't safe for Annie to go out because Bernie might get her."

"She'll get help," Diesel said. "She'll be okay."

I took another handful of chips, fed a couple to Bob, and turned my attention back to the game. A few minutes later, my doorbell rang. Diesel got the door and ushered Annie Hart into my living room. She was a little shorter than me, a little plumper, a little older. She had short, curly brown hair and lively brown eyes and a nice mouth. She smiled at Diesel and me, and the smile produced crinkle lines at the corners of her eyes. She was wearing a bright red hooded jacket, jeans, and boots, and she had her purse tucked into the crook of her arm.

Diesel introduced us. "Annie Hart, this is Stephanie Plum. Stephanie, meet Annie Hart."

I stood and extended my hand. "It's a pleasure."

"Have you seen the files?" she asked me.

"Yes."

"It's very important that you help these people

have a good Valentine's Day. And it's so close. Today is Friday and Valentine's Day is Monday. Of
course, the real goal is lifelong love, but truthfully,
that's icing on the cake." She flicked her eyes at
Diesel. "We all love Diesel, but relationships aren't
his strength. Diesel runs on pure testosterone, and
relationships need a little estrogen."

"Pure testosterone . . . that would explain his
wardrobe," I said.

Annie and I took a moment to assess the grungy
thermal shirt, beat-up boots, and two-day beard.

"Exactly," Annie said. "Although, it seems to
work for him."

"You have to go with what you've got," Diesel
said.

"I have a good feeling about you," Annie said
to me. "You have a lovely aura. I hope you don't
mind the intrusion, but I had to see for myself. I
really feel much better now. Call me if you have
problems. Any time of the day or night. I've made
promises to these people, and I hate not to keep a
promise. I've really tried hard with Charlene
Klinger, but I've been terribly off the mark. She
says she doesn't want a man in her life, but I know
that's not true. She's a good person, and she deserves to have a loving helpmate."

"Can I get you something?" I asked. "Coffee? A
drink?"

"I'd love that, but I promised this would be short. Perhaps when everything is settled we can visit. I know you have some romance problems."

I shot a look at Diesel. "Blabbermouth."

"Oh dear, no," Annie said. "Diesel didn't say anything. I just have a sense of these things. What are you doing on Valentine's Day?"

"No plans so far. I guess Diesel and I will be finishing things up for you."

"My word, you're not going to spend Valentine's Day with Diesel, are you?"

"I hadn't actually thought about it."

"Not a good idea," Annie said. "He's a heartbreaker."

"We don't have that sort of relationship," I told her.

"If you spend enough time in his company, the pheromones will wear you down . . . and the dimples."

"Diesel has dimples?"

"Just ignore them," Annie said. "And don't worry about your issue with commitment. As soon as I get out of jail, we'll have a good sit-down, and I'll solve that problem for you. Goodness, the answer is obvious. Clearly you belong with—"

And Annie was gone.

"Did she just disappear?" I asked Diesel.

Diesel was sunk into the couch. "I don't know.

I wasn't watching. I've got hockey on, and the Rangers scored a goal."

"Jeez," I said. "That was weird."

"Yeah, welcome to my world," Diesel said, returning to the bag of chips. "Would you get me another beer?"

I opened my eyes and looked up at Diesel. He was dressed but unshaven, holding a mug of coffee.

"What time is it?" I asked. "And why are you in my bedroom?"

"It's six o'clock. Rise and shine, cutie pie."

"Go away. I'm not ready to rise and shine."

Diesel shoved me over a couple inches, sat on the edge of the bed, and sipped his coffee. "We need to wrap this up before Annie gets restless again."

"What on earth are we going to do at six in the morning?"

"I have plans."

I pushed myself up on my elbow. "You're a real pain in the behind."

"Yeah, people tell me that a lot. You look sexy with your hair all messed, and your eyes kind of sleepy. Maybe I should get under the covers with you."

"What about the early start?"

"This wouldn't take long."

"Easy for you to say. Get out of my bedroom and

put an English muffin in the toaster for me. I'll be out in a minute. And it would help if you'd feed Bob and take him out for a walk."

I took a fast shower, blasted my hair with the hair dryer and pulled it back into a ponytail. I got dressed in a T-shirt and jeans and topped it off with a fleece hoodie.

Diesel was going over Annie Hart's files when I got to the kitchen.

"I fed Bob, and I walked him," Diesel said.

"Did you remember to take a plastic bag for his poop?"

"Sweetheart, I don't do the poop-in-a-bag thing. It's impossible to look like a tough guy when you're carrying a bag of poop. And you might want to think about feeding him less, because apparently whatever goes into a dog comes out of a dog, and it isn't good."

I took my muffin out of the toaster and looked around Diesel's shoulder. He was reading about Charlene Klinger.

"I spoke to her," I told Diesel. "She thinks Annie is a nut, and she doesn't want to get fixed up."

Diesel flipped to Gary Martin.

"He wants our help bad," I said. "Unfortunately, the love of his life is all wrong for him, and I really don't want to stick him with her. He deserves better."

"We're not supposed to change the world," Diesel said. "We're just supposed to set things up for Valentine's Day."

"Valentine's Day isn't going to happen for Gary Martin and Loretta Flack. Flack has maxed out Martin's credit at Tiffany's and moved on to greener pastures."

"That's cold," Diesel said. He turned to Larry Burlew's file. "What about this one?"

"He's got a thing for the girl in the coffee shop across from his butcher shop. I arranged for them to get together, so with any luck he's off the list. I didn't get to the last two cases."

Diesel paged through the rest of the files. "The fourth case is someone named Jeanine Chan. And all it says is she has a problem. Doesn't look like Annie visited her yet. No picture. No case history. And the fifth guy needs help getting married. His name is Albert Kloughn."

I snatched the file out of Diesel's hand. "That's my sister's live-in boyfriend!"

"I remember now," Diesel said. "Last time I was here she found out she was pregnant."

"She had the baby and they had a big wedding planned, and Kloughn had a total panic attack. He broke out in a cold sweat and hyperventilated himself into oblivion. They bailed on the wedding and

ran off to Disney World, but he's never been able
to bring himself to marry Valerie."

"How about we stun-gun him, and when he
wakes up, he's married?"

"You're such a romantic."

"I have my moments," Diesel said.

"Now what?"

"Now you put your boots and mittens on, and we
go out and do our lame-ass cupid thing."

I shoved my feet into my boots, gathered up
my mittens and scarf, and took a moment to call
Morelli. Lots of rings. No answer. His answering
service came on-line. Morelli was underground,
working a sting.

"It's me," I said. "Just wanted to let you know
Bob is fine."

Charlene Klinger lived in a narrow single-family,
two-story house in North Trenton. It had a postage-
stamp yard and a driveway but no garage. A green
soccer-mom van was parked in the driveway. A big
orange cat sat hunkered down and slitty-eyed on
the roof of the van.

Diesel parked my Escape at the curb, and we
made our way to the front door. We rang the bell,
and Charlene's youngest kid let us in and then
instantly disappeared, no questions asked. It was

Saturday morning, and the Klinger household was in full chaos mode. The television was on in the living room, a couple of dogs were barking toward the back of the house, rap was blaring from an upstairs bedroom, and Charlene's voice carried from the kitchen.

"You absolutely cannot have ice cream for breakfast," she said. "And don't you dare put it in your orange juice."

I knocked on the doorjamb and looked in at Charlene. "Hi," I said. "Remember me?"

Charlene looked at me open-mouthed. "What are you doing here? How did you get in?"

"A little boy with red hair and a blue shirt let us in," I told her.

"I swear someday we're all gonna get killed in our sleep. He'll open the door to anyone."

"I was hoping I could have just a few minutes to talk to you."

"I've got nothing to say. I don't want a man in my life. I don't have time to talk to you. And—"

Charlene stopped midsentence, and her eyes widened a little when she saw Diesel.

"This is Diesel," I told Charlene. "He's part of the relationship team. He's our, um, man specialist. Are you sure you don't want a man in your life? They can come in handy sometimes . . . taking out the garbage, scaring away burglars, fixing the plumbing."

"I guess," Charlene said. "Is *he* available?"

"Are you?" I asked Diesel.

"Not even a little," Diesel said.

"You wouldn't want him anyway," I told Charlene. "He's got limitations. I mean, we wouldn't expect Diesel to put a new float in a toilet, right? Plus, I'll bet you'd like a man who could cook sometimes. And Diesel doesn't do that either."

Diesel slid a look at me . . . like maybe he could cook if there was incentive.

"Jeez," Charlene said.

Diesel crossed the kitchen, poured himself a mug of coffee, and slouched against a counter. "There were a bunch of rejected men in your file," he said to Charlene. "Why did you reject them?"

"They rejected *me*. Too many cats. Too many kids. Too old. Too boring."

"So we need to find someone who likes kids," Diesel said. His attention wandered to a cat sleeping on the counter in front of the toaster. "And animals."

"Beyond that, what kind of man do you want?" I asked Charlene.

"Rich?"

"Would you settle for mildly successful?"

"Here's the thing," Charlene said. "I don't want to settle at all. I was serious yesterday when I said I don't have the time or energy for a man right now. I have soup stock cooking on the stove and a week's worth of laundry sitting in the basement next to the washing machine. I have two kids upstairs, listening to rap and figuring out how they can bypass the parental controls on the television. I have a pregnant cat that I know is in the house somewhere but haven't been able to find for two days. My deadbeat ex-husband is learning to surf and living on the beach in Santa Barbara and hasn't sent child support in over a year, so I'm working at the DMV instead of staying home and keeping my kids from turning into juvenile delinquents. I don't need a man. I need a housewife."

"We're counting down to Valentine's Day," I told Charlene. "Let's get the man taken care of first, and then maybe we can work on the housewife."

Charlene turned the flame up under the stockpot. "What would it take to make you go away?"

"A date," Diesel said. "We find you a man, you go out with him, and we leave."

"Is that a promise?" Charlene asked.

"Maybe," Diesel said.

"You have to give us some guidelines," I said to Charlene. "Be honest. What are you really looking in a man?"

Charlene took a moment. "A *good* man," she said. "Someone who fits with me. Someone comfortable."

The cat got up, stretched on the counter, turned, and attempted to settle itself next to the stove. Its tail flicked into the open flame under the soup stock and instantly caught fire. The cat let out a yowl and jumped from the stove to the table. The black Lab that had been sleeping under the table lunged to its feet and went after the flaming cat.

We were all jumping around, trying to catch the cat, trying to avoid the flaming tail. The Lab slid into a table leg and yelped, Diesel grabbed the cat and dumped a quart of orange juice on him, and I slapped out a burning placemat.

"Hard to believe someone would think you were boring," Diesel said to Charlene.

"Something's wrong with Blackie," the red-haired kid said, looking under the table at the Lab. "He's making whiny sounds and holding his leg funny."

We all looked at Blackie. He was for sure holding his leg funny.

"How bad is the cat?" I asked Diesel.

"Could be worse," Diesel said. "He barbecued the tip of his tail, but the rest of him looks okay. Hard to tell, being that he's soaked in orange juice."

Charlene wrapped a towel around the cat. "Poor kitty."

The twelve-year-old and ten-year-old ran into the kitchen.

"What's happening?" the twelve-year-old asked.

"Kitty set hisself on fire, and Blackie broke his leg," the red-haired kid said.

"Bummer," the twelve-year-old said. And he and his brother turned and went back upstairs. As if this happened every day.

"Where am I going to find a vet at this hour on a Saturday?" Charlene said. "I'm going to have to go to the emergency clinic. It's going to cost me a fortune."

"I know someone who'll help us," I told her. "I have his number in my car."

Charlene cradled the cat close to her and grabbed her purse off the counter. "Get your coat and hat," she said to the red-haired kid. "And round up your brothers. Everyone out to the van."

Diesel scooped the Lab off the floor and carried him to the door. "Think Blackie could stand to lay off the chow?" Diesel said. "This dog weighs a ton."

"He could use a bigger yard," Charlene said. "He never gets to run. He appeared on our front porch in the middle of a snowstorm two years ago and just never left."

The four kids trooped out and got into the van,

and I ran to my car for Gary Martin's folder. Diesel locked the house and eased himself into the van with Blackie on his lap, front leg dangling loose. Charlene was in the passenger seat with Kitty still wrapped in the towel. I slid behind the wheel and called Gary Martin on my cell.

"I have an emergency," I told him. "A cat with a barbecued tail and a dog with a broken leg. And I talked to Loretta, but that's a whole other story."

"Is it a sad story?"

"Yeah. The story isn't good."

"My office doesn't open until ten today," Martin said, "but I can come in early. I'll be there in a half hour."

I transferred Bob from the Escape to the rear seat in the soccer-mom van, introduced him to everyone, and took my place behind the wheel.

"Who's the big guy holding Blackie?" the youngest kid asked at the first light.

"His name is Diesel," Charlene said. "Be polite."

"Diesel," the kid repeated. "I never heard of anyone named Diesel."

"Diesel's a train," one of the other kids said.

I adjusted the rearview mirror so I could check Diesel out. Our eyes met and caught for a moment. I couldn't see his mouth, but the little crinkle lines around his eyes told me he was smiling. The Klingers were amusing him.

Lights were on in the clinic when I pulled into the lot. Gary Martin had arrived just in front of us. He still had his coat and hat on when we all swooped in.

"This is Charlene Klinger," I said to Martin. "She's mom to Kitty and Blackie and the four kids."

Charlene introduced the kids. "Junior, Ralph, Ernie, Russell."

Martin looked at Diesel.

"He's with me," I said. "He's the dog-toter."

"I should probably run some film of Blackie's leg, but I don't have an assistant until ten," Martin said.

"I can help," Charlene said. "I've got four kids, three cats, two dogs, a rabbit, and twelve hamsters. I've taped up split lips, delivered kittens, breast-fed four boys, and once we raised chickens from eggs for Ernie's science project."

"The chickens pooped all over the house," Ralph said.

Martin unwrapped the cat enough to look at its tail. "The tail doesn't look too bad," he said. "Mostly he's lost hair, and he's singed the tip. Why is he so sticky?"

"Diesel put the fire out with orange juice," Ralph told him. "It was awesome."

"I need someone to take the cat to the big sink

in the back room and very gently wash the orange juice off him," Martin said. "And I need someone to hold Blackie while I run film."

"I can hold Blackie," Russell said. "This is pretty cool. I might want to be a vet someday. I bet you meet a lot of girls."

"I suppose," Martin said. "I'm not exactly the girl expert. I'm better with animals. Animals think I'm cute. Girls just think I'm bald."

"I think you're cute," Charlene said. "You're cuddly . . . like Fluffy."

"Who's Fluffy?" Martin asked.

"Our rabbit," Ralph said. "He weighs a thousand pounds."

"Everything in our house is overweight," Charlene said. "Except the kids."

Martin exchanged his jacket for a blue lab coat. "Maybe I could take a look at Fluffy someday and suggest a better diet."

"It's not just Fluffy," Ralph said. "We practically have a zoo. Mom takes all the rejects."

Gary Martin and Charlene Klinger were perfect for each other. He wanted kids, and she had a pack of them. They were the same age. They were both animal lovers. And he could doctor up Charlene's menagerie when they set themselves on fire. Plus, Charlene Klinger and Gary Martin looked like they belonged together. They were a matched set. Far better than Gary Martin and Loretta What's-Her-Face.

"Do you make house calls?" I asked Martin. "I was thinking it might be better for you to go to Charlene's house to see her animals since she has so many. And since you'd be doing her a favor she could make dinner for you. I bet you hate to eat alone all the time . . . now that you're alone."

"Are you sure I'm alone?" Martin asked.

"Trust me, you're alone."

"I'd love to have you look at my animals," Charlene said, "but I don't know if you want to eat at my house. It gets real hectic at dinnertime."

"I had three sisters and two brothers," Martin said. "I'm good with hectic."

"Can you fix a toilet?" I asked him. "Can you cook?"

"Sure. You don't grow up in a house with three sisters and two brothers and one bathroom and not know something about toilets." Martin took Blackie from Diesel and headed for x-ray. "And I make a killer pork tenderloin. And I can make brownies."

I took Charlene aside. "Did you hear that? He makes brownies."

"What the hell, I shave my legs anyway," Charlene said. "And he reminds me of Fluffy. I guess I could give it a shot. Do you think he's interested?"

"Of course he's interested," I said. "You're a domestic goddess. Just what he wants."

An hour later, Kitty had the end of his tail wrapped in white gauze, and Blackie had a cast on his front leg.

"It was really nice of you to come in early like this," Charlene said to Martin.

"Happy to be able to help," Martin said. "You have great kids. Russell was a terrific assistant."

"Maybe you could come over and check on Blackie and Kitty and Fluffy sometime," Charlene said.

"Sure," Martin said.

We all stood around, waiting. Gary Martin was slow picking up social cues.

After a long moment, Diesel slung an arm around Martin's shoulders. "Maybe you want to check out Charlene's rabbit *tonight*."

The lightbulb went on in Martin's head. "Tonight would be wonderful! I see my last patient at five o'clock, so I could come over around six."

"We're having pot roast tonight if you'd like to take a chance on dinner with us," Charlene said.

"Boy, that would be fantastic. I'll bring dessert. I won't have time to make my brownies, but I'll stop at the bakery."

We got Charlene and her kids and animals back

to their house, waved good-bye, and angled ourselves into my car.

Diesel gave me a playful punch in the shoulder.
"Are we good, or what?" he said. "Cross two names
off our list."

I answered my cell phone.

"Your sister is coming over for dinner tonight,"
my mother said. "I'm making lasagna, and I've got
an ice-cream cake for dessert. I thought you would
want to come."

"I think I might be working tonight."

"What, you can't take time out to eat? Everybody has to eat."

"Yes, but I have a partner—"

"There's always extra. Bring your partner. Is it
Lula?"

"No."

"Is it Ranger?"

"No."

"Who is it?"

"Diesel."

Silence.

"From that Christmas where our tree burned
up?" my mother finally asked.

"Yeah."

I imagined her making the sign of the cross.

"What are you doing with Diesel?" she asked.
"No, don't tell me. I don't want to know."

Chapter FIVE

It was midmorning and clouds were creeping in above us. We were in front of Jeanine Chan's house, and we were reading her file.

"Not much here," Diesel said. "She's thirty-five. Single. Never been married. No kids. She works at the button factory. File says she has a problem."

Jeanine lived in a single-story, low-rent row house about a quarter mile from my parents' house in the Burg. There were twenty-one units to a block. They were all redbrick. Front doors opened to small stoops that were directly on the sidewalk. Back doors opened to tiny yards that bordered an alley. Two bedrooms, one bath, small eat-in kitchen. No garages. All the units were identical.

I rang the bell twice, the door opened a crack, and Jeanine looked out. "Yes?" she asked.

"We're looking for Jeanine Chan," I said.

"I'm Jeanine."

She was maybe an inch shorter than me. She had

brown almond-shaped eyes and shoulder-length dark brown hair. She was slim and dressed in a gray shapeless sweatshirt and matching sweatpants.

I introduced myself, and then I introduced Diesel.

Jeanine's eyes sort of glazed over when she saw Diesel.

"Annie suggested you might have a problem," I said to Jeanine.

"Who, me?" Jeanine said. "Nope. Not me. Everything's just fine. Hope this wasn't too inconvenient. I have to go now." And she slammed and locked the door.

"That was easy," Diesel said.

"We didn't solve her problem."

"So?"

"So you're paying me to close the deal, and that wasn't closing the deal. Besides, I'm starting to like this matchmaker thing. It's a challenge."

I rang the bell again. And again.

"Now what?" Jeanine said, opening the door, sticking her head out.

"I thought you might want to reconsider. Are you sure you don't have a problem?"

Jeanine's eyes locked onto Diesel.

"Excuse me a minute while I confer with my associate," I said to Jeanine.

I took Diesel by the arm and walked him down the sidewalk to the car.

"It's you," I said to Diesel. "You're making her nervous."

"I have that effect on women," Diesel said, smiling. "It's my animal magnetism."

"No doubt. Wait in the car. I'm going to talk to Jeanine, and I'll be right back."

"Okay, what's the problem?" I said to Jeanine when I closed her front door. "I know there's a problem."

"Annie didn't tell you? Gosh, this is so embarrassing. I don't know how to say this." She sucked in some air and scrunched her eyes closed.

"Hello? Anybody home?" I said after a minute of Jeanine with her eyes closed tight.

"I'm working myself up to it," Jeanine said.

"Boy, this must really be bad."

"It's the worst."

"Murder? Cancer? Chocolate allergy?"

Jeanine blew out a sigh. "I can't get laid."

"That's it?"

"Yes."

"That's not so bad," I said. "I think I can handle that. I just have to find a guy to have sex with you?"

"Pretty much."

"Do you have requirements?" I asked her.

"I used to, but I'm getting desperate. I guess I'd like him to have at least *some* teeth. And it would be good if he wasn't so fat he smothered me. That's about it. I got all panicked when I opened the door because I thought maybe Annie sent that Diesel guy over to get the job done. I mean, I wouldn't mind doing it with him, but I might have to work my way up. He doesn't look like something a beginner would want to tackle. Which brings me to the real problem." Jeanine cracked her knuckles. "I'm a virgin."

"Get out!"

"I don't know how this happened. At first I was being careful. I didn't want to do it with just anyone, right? And then all of a sudden I was in my twenties, and it got embarrassing. I mean, how do you explain being twenty-five years old and never once finding a man who was good enough? And the older I got, the worse it became. It turns out virgins are only popular in high school and harems. No one wants to take responsibility for deflowering a thirty-five-year-old woman."

"Jeez, who would have thought?"

"Yeah, knock me over with a feather. I'm telling you, I've really been trying lately, but I can't get anyone to do it. And now, I've found a man I really like. He's funny and he's kind and he's affectionate. I really think this could turn into something. He might even be the love of my life. Problem is, I have to keep finding excuses not to invite him in . . . like, my cat is sick, or my mother is visiting, or there's a gas leak."

"All because you can't tell him you're a virgin?"

"Exactly. He'll run for the hills. They always do! God, I hate this stupid virginity. What a dumb idea, anyway. I mean, how the heck am I supposed to get rid of it?"

"Maybe a doctor could help you."

"I thought of that, but that's only part of it." She cracked her knuckles. "I don't know how to do it. I mean, I know where it goes and all, but I don't know the process. Like, do I just lay there? Or am I supposed to do something?"

"Usually you do what feels good."

"What if it doesn't feel good? I'm thirty-five. I'm old to be starting out. What if it was *use it or lose it*? I need some instruction. Nothing fancy. I'd be happy with the basics. For instance, am I supposed to moan?"

"Men like it, but I find it distracting."

Jeanine was gnawing on her bottom lip. "I don't think I can moan."

"Are you sure you don't want to just talk this out with the guy you're dating?"

"I'd rather stick a fork in my eye."

"Okay, hang in there, and I'll figure something out."

I left Jeanine and trotted back to Diesel.

"You were in there long enough," Diesel said. "What's her big problem?"

"She's a virgin."

"No kidding?"

"Turns out after a certain age it's not that easy to get rid of your virginity. She said men head for the hills when they find out she's a virgin. Don't want the responsibility of being the first."

"I could see that," Diesel said.

"She thought maybe Annie sent you to do the job."

Diesel grinned. "I could take a crack at it."

I raised an eyebrow.

"What?" Diesel said.

"Men."

Diesel grinned wider and ruffled my hair, and I slapped his hand away.

"Just trying to be helpful," Diesel said.

"Jeanine has a boyfriend. She likes him a lot and doesn't want to lose him, but she's afraid he'll split when she tells him she's a virgin."

"So don't tell him," Diesel said. "Let him figure it out for himself after the deed is done."

"That's sort of sneaky."

"You have a problem with sneaky?"

"There's another issue. She feels like she's sort of dumb about the whole thing. Like at thirty-five she should have some technique behind her."

"I imagine you could help her with that one," Diesel said.

"I guess, but I'm not sure I'm all that expert."

"I could test you out and let you know how you score," Diesel said, the grin back in place. "Rate you on a scale of one to ten."

"Now there's an offer every girl dreams about."

Diesel's phone rang, and he took the call.

"Yeah," he said into the phone. "How bad is it?" He listened for a full minute, disconnected, cranked the car over and put it into gear.

"Where are we going?"

"We're going to look for Beaner. He attacked a woman in a diner two blocks from Ernie's Bar. My source said Beaner went in for breakfast, saw this woman, and went nuts on her because she resembled his wife."

"Jeez. What did he do to her? Is she going to be all right?"

"She'll recover, but it won't be fun." Diesel headed for the center of the city. "I know Beaner is living in the neighborhood around Ernie's. I placed him there a week ago, but I can't get a fix on him. I thought we'd go over and walk around. See if I get a vibe."

I looked back at Bob. "It's freezing. I can't leave Bob sitting in the cold SUV all afternoon."

Diesel hooked a left at the intersection. "We'll drop him off at your apartment. Lock him in your bathroom, so he doesn't eat your couch. Your bathroom is nice and big. He'll be okay."

The neighborhood around Ernie's is a residential and commercial mix. There are office buildings, condo buildings, brownstones, and small businesses like Ernie's Bar all in a jumble. Diesel parked in a lot, and we set out on foot with our collars turned up against the wind and our hands in our pockets to keep warm. We covered a grid of blocks a half-mile square, but Beaner didn't register on Diesel's radar.

We ducked into a deli and got sandwiches and coffee for lunch, happy to be out of the cold.

"This isn't working," I said to Diesel. "I vote we do it my human way and canvass the street, asking questions."

"I'm human," Diesel said. "I just have a few extra skills."

I finished my sandwich and coffee and stood. "You go north and I'll go south, and we'll meet back here at three o'clock."

I started with the girl at the register in the deli, asking if she'd seen a guy with a raspberry birthmark on his face. Her answer was no. I went to the florist next door, the drugstore, the dry cleaner. No one had seen Beaner. I spoke to the doorman at a condo building and the receptionist at a high-rise office building. No Beaner. I went four blocks south, stopping people on the street. I crossed the street and worked my way back to the deli. No luck at all.

By the time I met up with Diesel, wind-driven snow was angling down, stinging my face. Snow is picturesque in Vermont. In New Jersey, it's a pain in the ass. It slows traffic and makes walking treacherous. Dogs turn the snow yellow, and cars churn it into brown sludge.

"Any luck?" Diesel asked.

"None. How about you?"

"Zip."

I felt my cell phone buzz. It was Larry Burlew, and I could barely understand what he was saying. He was talking at warp speed and stuttering.

"It's n-n-not working," he said. "I don't know what to s-s-say to her. She comes over with coffee whenever I wave, but I don't know what to say. What should I say? I just s-s-say *thank you*. I thought I could talk to her, but nothing comes out. I d-d-don't think I can drink much more coffee, but I can't stop myself from waving."

"How many cups have you had?"

"I d-d-don't know. I lost count. Twelve or fifteen, I think."

"We're on our way," I told him. "Try to hang in there, and for God's sake, don't drink any more coffee."

Chapter
SIX

Larry Burlew was pacing when we walked into the shop.

"I don't feel good," he said. "I think I'm having a heart attack. My heart is racing. And my eye is twitching. I hate when my eye twitches like this. Maybe I need a cup of coffee to settle my nerves."

"Put a coat on him and walk him around outside in the cold," I told Diesel. "See if you can get some of the caffeine out of his system."

"Who'll take care of the shop?" Burlew asked. "I can't walk out on the shop."

"I'll take care of the shop," I told him. "No one comes in at this time of the day. Don't worry about it."

Five minutes later, a woman walked in and wanted a pork roast deboned and rolled.

"I'm just the assistant butcher," I told her. "I'm not allowed to debone. The real butcher will be back in an hour, but I'm not sure he'll be fit to use sharp tools. How about a nice roasting chicken?"

"I don't want a chicken," she said. "I need a pork roast."

"Okay, how about this. I'll give it to you for free if you'll take it with the bone in. It's a special promotional deal."

"I guess that would be okay," the woman said.

I took a roast out of the display case, wrapped it in white butcher paper, and gave it to the woman.

"Have a nice day," I told her.

Twenty minutes later, Diesel returned with Burlew.

"How's he doing?" I asked Diesel.

"He's stopped stuttering, and his eye has almost completely stopped twitching. I had to bring him back because I think his nose is frostbitten. This weather sucks. I'm putting in for an assignment in the Bahamas after this."

"Can you do that?"

"No. I go where I'm needed. There aren't a lot of people who can do my job."

"Were there any customers?" Burlew asked.

"No," I told him. "Nobody bought anything."

"The coffee delivery scheme isn't working," Diesel said. "We need to think of something else."

"The coffee delivery scheme is perfectly okay. It's Burlew we need to fix. He needs practice," I said. "I'm going to be the coffee person, and you be Larry. I'll walk in, and you start a conversation with me, so he can see how it's done."

I went outside, and then I came in again.

"Here's your coffee," I said to Diesel, pretending to hand him a cup of coffee.

"Thanks," Diesel said. And he grabbed me and kissed me.

I pushed away from him. "What the heck was that about?"

Diesel was rocked back on his heels, smiling. "I felt like kissing you. It was cold outside, and you're all nice and warm."

"Boy. I wish I could do that," Burlew said. "That was great."

"It wasn't great," I said to Burlew. "That was a bad example. Diesel's a nut. I'm going to go out and come in again, and this time I'm going to hand *you* the coffee."

I went outside and stood on the sidewalk for a moment, sucking in cold air. The kiss had actually been pretty damn terrific. Not that it was going to lead to anything, but it was terrific all the same. I pulled myself together and came back in and pretended to hand Burlew a cup of coffee.

Burlew took the coffee and looked at me blank-faced.

"What do you say?" I asked him.

"Thank you."

"What else?"

Burlew was stumped.

"Tell her your name," I said.

"Larry Burlew."

"My name is Jet," I told him.

Silence.

I jumped back in. "Tell her you think her name is unusual. Ask her if it means something."

"That's stupid," Diesel said. "He'll sound like a dork."

"What would you suggest?"

"I'd get right to it. I'd tell her I was going to catch the Knicks game at the sports bar down the street, and I'd ask her if she wanted to join me."

"You can't just say 'Thanks for the coffee' and then ask her out to a bar. It's too abrupt. And how do you know she's a Knicks fan?"

"It doesn't matter. It's a guy thing. It makes him look like a guy. If he says something dorky about her name, she'll think he's a pussy. Anyway, if she wants to go out with him, she'll say *yes*. If she doesn't say *yes*, you know it's a lost cause and you move on."

"I don't like basketball," Burlew said.

"What do you like?"

"I like opera."

Diesel was hands on hips. "You're shitting me."

Burlew fixed his attention on the display case. "There's a pork roast missing. Are you sure you didn't sell anything?"

"I gave it away. It was a charity thing. Girl Scouts."

Diesel's attention wandered to the street. "Hey, get this," he said. "Coffee Girl must be off work for the day. She's got her coat on, and her purse over her shoulder, and it looks like she's coming over here. She's out of the coffee shop and crossing the street."

"Oh no," Burlew said. "She doesn't have more coffee, does she?"

"No," Diesel said. "No coffee."

The bell chimed on the front door, and Jet walked in. "Hi," she said to me. "Your cousin is going to make me employee of the month for selling so much coffee." Her attention turned to Diesel. "*Hello*," she said.

"He's gay," I told her. "Flaming."

Jet sighed. "I knew he was too good to be true." She looked over at Larry Burlew.

"Straight as an arrow," I said.

Jet nodded. "It's important to know stuff like that about your . . . butcher. Like, is he married?"

"Nope. Totally available."

"So I would be smart to buy meat here?"

"You wouldn't regret it," I said.

"Good. I feel like steak tonight."

Diesel slid a look at me. "Carnivore," he whispered.

Jet directed her attention to Burlew. "What looks tasty?"

"Do you want to grill it, or broil it, or pan-fry it?" Burlew asked.

"I don't know. Something healthy."

"I have a great recipe that I do with sirloin," Burlew said. "I marinate it and then I broil it with vegetables."

"That sounds terrific," Jet said. "Maybe you could show me how to do it."

"Sure," Burlew said. "It's real easy. I could do it tonight if you want. And I'll bring the steak and stuff with me."

Jet wrote her address on a scrap of butcher paper. "Come over whenever you're done with work. I'll get some wine." And she left.

Diesel and I looked at Burlew.

"What the hell was that?" Diesel asked.

"I'm good when it comes to meat," Burlew said.

It was twilight when we left the butcher shop. Streetlights were glowing behind swirling snow, and Trenton was looking cold but cozy.

"We're hot at this relationship shit," Diesel said. "We do things all wrong, and it all turns out right."

We drove back to Beaner's neighborhood and cruised several blocks. Diesel stopped in front of Ernie's, and I ran in to take a fast look. No Beaner in sight, so I returned to the car.

"It's too early," Diesel said. "We should come back around eight."

"We need to get to my parents' house anyway," I told him. "I said we'd be there for dinner."

"We?"

"I didn't want you to feel left out."

"I remember your parents. They run a loony bin."

"Okay. Fine. Drop me off at the door."

"No way," Diesel said. "I wouldn't miss this for anything."

"We just have to make a fast stop at my apartment to get Bob."

A half hour later, we opened my bathroom door, and Bob looked out at us, all droopy-eyed and drooling and panting. He did some pathetic whimpering noises, opened his mouth, and said *Gak!* And barfed up a roll of toilet paper.

"Better than a couch," Diesel said.

I cleaned up the toilet paper and put a new roll in the holder. By the time I was done, Bob was completely perked up, affectionately rubbing against Diesel, spreading dog slime the length of his leg.

"Probably I should change clothes before we go to your parents' house," Diesel said.

For sure.

Diesel pulled a pair of jeans and a shirt out of his backpack. They were exact duplicates of what he was wearing, minus the slime and pizza sauce. No better, no worse. He peeled his shirt off, unlaced his boots, and stepped out of his boots and jeans.

"Good God," I said and whirled around, so I wasn't facing him. Not that it mattered. The image of Diesel in briefs was burned into my brain. Ranger and Morelli, the two men in my life, were physically perfect in very different ways.

Ranger was Cuban American with dark skin and dark eyes and sometimes dark intentions. He had a kickboxer's body and Special Forces skills. Morelli was hard and angular, his temperament Italian, his muscle and skill acquired on the street. Diesel was put together on a larger scale. And while I couldn't see details, I suspected he was larger *everywhere.*

My grandmother was setting the table when we arrived. The extension was in, and the kitchen chairs and a kid's high chair had been brought out to seat ten. Valerie and Albert were already there. Albert was watching television with my dad. I could hear Valerie in the kitchen talking to my mom. Her oldest girl, Angie, was on the floor in the living room coloring in a coloring book. The middle kid, Mary Alice, was galloping around the dining room table, pretending she was a horse. The baby was on Albert's lap.

All action stopped when Diesel walked in.

"Oh jeez," my father said.

"Nice to see you again, sir," Diesel said.

"I remember you," Mary Alice said. "You used to have a ponytail."

"I did," Diesel said, "but I thought it was time for a change."

"Sometimes I'm a reindeer," Mary Alice said.

"Is it different from being a horse?" Diesel asked her.

"Yeah, 'cause when I'm a reindeer I got antlers, and I can fly like Rudolph."

"Can not," Angie said.

"Can, too."

"Can not."

"I can fly a little," Mary Alice said.

I cut my eyes to Diesel.

Diesel smiled and shrugged.

I let Bob off his leash, left Diesel in the living room to charm my father, and went to the kitchen to check in with my mother. "Is there anything I can do?" I asked.

"You can spoon the red sauce into the gravy boat, and you can try to talk some sense into your grandmother. She won't listen to me."

"Now what?"

"Have you seen her?"

"She was setting the table."

"Did you take a good look?"

Grandma Mazur shuffled into the kitchen. She was in her seventies, and gravity hadn't been kind. She was all slack skin and dimpled flesh draped on a wiry frame. Her hair was steel gray and permed. Her teeth were bought. Her eyes didn't miss much. Her lips were horribly swollen.

"We're oud a nakins," she said. "There's no ore in da china canet."

"Omigod," I said. "What happened to your mouth?"

"Sexy, hunh?" Grandma said.

"She had her lips plumped up," my mother said. "She went to some idiot doctor and had herself injected."

"An nex eek I'n gettin' ass inlans," Grandma said. "No ore saggy ass for ee."

"Ass implants are serious," I told her. "You might not want to do that."

"Ere's a sale on inlans nex eek," Grandma said. "I hade ta niss a sale."

"Yes, but implants have to be incredibly painful. You won't be able to sit. Why don't we just find a sale on shoes? We can go to Macy's and then have lunch in the food court."

"Okay," Grandma said. "At sounds like un."

My mother took the lasagna and I took the red sauce and Grandma took a basket of bread to the table. Everyone seated themselves and dug in.

Grandma Mazur took some lasagna and poured herself a glass of red wine. She forked some lasagna into her mouth and took a sip of wine, and everything fell out of her mouth, onto her lap.

Bob rushed over and ate the food off Grandma's lap, and then settled himself back under the table, ever alert.

"Ny lith are oo ig," she said. "Dey don ork."

My mother jumped up and returned with a straw for Grandma and a tumbler of booze for herself.

My father had his head bent over his lasagna. "Just shoot me," he said.

"I like lasagna," Albert Kloughn said. "It stays on your plate. And if you don't use too much red sauce, hardly any gets on your shirt."

Kloughn was a struggling lawyer who got his degree from the Acme School of Law in Barbados.

He was a nice guy, but he was as soft as a fresh-nuked dinner roll, and his upper lip broke out into a sweat when he got nervous . . . which was a lot.

"How's the law business?" I asked him.

"It's good. I even have a couple clients. Okay, one eventually died, but that happens sometimes, right?"

"And how's the new house?"

"It's working out real good. It's a lot better than living with my mother."

"And what about getting married?"

Kloughn turned white, farted, and fell off his chair in a faint.

Diesel got up and dragged Kloughn to his feet and sat him back in his chair. "Take a deep breath," Diesel said to Kloughn.

"How embarrassing," Kloughn said.

"Dude," Diesel said, "everyone feels like that about marriage. Get over it."

"Poor snuggle uggums," Valerie said, spoon-feeding Kloughn some noodles. "Did him hurt himself?"

Diesel draped an arm across my shoulders and put his mouth to my ear. "We definitely want to go with the stun gun. In fact, I think we should stun-gun *both* of them."

"Maybe you can get Albert to take a walk with you after dinner, and you can talk to him. He got in touch with Annie and asked for help, so he's obviously motivated."

"That would be high on the list of things I don't want to do. Second only to getting zapped by Beaner."

"About Beaner . . . just exactly what is it that happens when he zaps someone?"

"You don't want to know. And I don't want to tell you. Let's just leave it alone for now."

"I've been thinking about Beaner. Maybe we should talk to *Mrs.* Beaner. Does she live in the Trenton area?"

"She lives in Hamilton Township."

"Is she Unmentionable? Does she have scary, evil skills?"

"She's mildly Unmentionable. Doesn't do much with it. Mostly parlor tricks. Bending spoons and winning at rummy. I interviewed her when I got the Beaner assignment."

"And?"

"You know everything I know. She said she was tired of marriage. Wanted to try something else. She told me Beaner blamed it all on Annie Hart, but Annie didn't have anything to do with it. Annie was just a friend. She didn't know where Beaner was staying, but clearly it was in the Trenton area because he was determined to get even with Annie."

"That's it? Why didn't you ask her to lure Beaner over to discuss things, and then you could jump out of the closet and do your bounty hunter thing and capture Beaner?"

"She knows better than to be around when Beaner goes down. There'll be fallout, and she wants no part of it."

"What about you? Aren't you afraid of Beaner?"

"It takes a lot to damage me, and Beaner doesn't have that kind of power. The best he could do is make me mildly uncomfortable."

"Okay, how about this? We get Mrs. Beaner to lie to her husband. Set up a bogus meeting."

"Tried that. She wouldn't do it."

I mushed a piece of bread around in my leftover sauce. "You know what *that* means."

Diesel did a palms-up. He didn't know what it meant.

"She still cares about him," I said. "She doesn't want to betray him. She doesn't want him captured and neutralized or whatever it is that you do."

Diesel helped himself to a second chunk of lasagna. "Maybe. Or maybe she just doesn't want to get involved."

"I could talk to her."

"Probably not a bad idea," Diesel said. He looked at his watch. "Here's the plan. I get Albert out into the air and walk him around the block and try to figure out what the heck he wants to do about getting married. You talk to your sister and see if she's on board. And at eight, we try our luck at Ernie's Bar. If thing's don't work out, tomorrow you visit Mrs. Beaner."

Chapter
SEVEN

We were in my car, on our way to Ernie's. It had stopped snowing, but the sky was moonless black, and the air had a bite to it.

"How'd it go with Albert?" I asked Diesel.

"He didn't faint, but he wasn't real coherent. From what I can tell, he wants to get married, but the thought of the ceremony freaks him out. Apparently the poor guy's even tried getting hypnotized, but he still can't get down the aisle."

"How about tranquilizers?"

"He said he tried them and had an allergic reaction and went gonzo."

"I talked to Valerie, and she pretty much told me the same thing. Not that I didn't know it already. He's really a sweet guy. He loves the kids, and he loves Valerie, and I know he would love *being* married. It's *getting* married that's the problem."

Diesel cruised down the street and pulled to the curb across from Ernie's.

"Is he in there?" I asked Diesel.

"I don't think so," Diesel said after a couple beats, "but it wouldn't hurt for you to take a look anyway."

I crossed the street, pushed through the big oak door into the warm pub, and hiked myself up onto a barstool. No trouble claiming a seat. Ernie's was an after-work place, not a Saturday night date destination, and it was eerily empty. A few regulars nursed drinks at the bar and numbly watched the overhead television. The tables were empty. The lone bartender ambled over to me.

"What'll it be?" he asked.

"I'm looking for a friend. He was here last night. Has a birthmark on his face. His name's Bernie."

"Yeah, I know the guy. Didn't know his name was Bernie. Not real talky. Pays in cash. He hasn't been in today. We get a different crowd during the week. Saturday and Sunday it's real slow. Were you supposed to meet him?"

"No. Just thought I might run into him."

I left the bar and returned to the car. "He's not there," I told Diesel. "The bartender said he hasn't seen him. Maybe we spooked him off this afternoon. Maybe he saw us walking around looking for him."

Diesel was behind the wheel with his phone in his hand. "I have a problem," he said. "Annie isn't answering. I check on her four times a day. This is the first time she hasn't answered."

"Maybe she's in the shower."

"She knows I call at this time. She's supposed to be there. I'm having a guy I know drop in on her. He lives in her building."

"Why aren't you staying with him?"

"He has a girl living with him. And he'd drive me nuts. You drive me nuts, too, but in a more interesting way."

Oh boy. "Do you think Beaner found Annie?"

Diesel did a palms-up. "Don't know."

Diesel's phone rang, and he looked at the readout. "It's Flash," he said to me.

"The guy in Annie's building?"

"Yeah."

A minute later, Diesel disconnected, put the car in gear, and pulled into the stream of traffic. "She isn't in the apartment. The door was locked. Nothing seemed to be disturbed."

"Did she take her purse?" I asked him.

Diesel looked at me blank-faced. "Don't know."

"Boots? Coat?"

"Don't know."

"Were the lights left on?"

"Don't know." He hung a U-turn and headed for the center of the city. "Let's go take a look."

Twenty minutes later, we were on a side street

in downtown Trenton. Diesel used a passkey to get into an underground garage, parked the car, and we took the elevator to the seventh floor, leaving Bob in the car. There were four apartments on the floor. Diesel knocked on 704 and unlocked the door. We stepped inside and looked around. Lights were on. There was a purse on the kitchen counter. Wallet and assorted junk inside the purse. No keys. I checked closets. No winter coat or jacket. No boots.

"Here's what I think," I said to Diesel. "She took her keys and winter coat, but she left her purse behind. So I think she stepped out for a moment and didn't intend to go far. Maybe she just needed air or wanted to walk a little. And then maybe something unexpected happened to her."

It was a nice apartment. Not fancy, but tastefully decorated and comfortable. Small kitchen, living room, dining alcove, single bedroom, and bath.

"It's a pleasant apartment," I said to Diesel, "but I can see where Annie would get squirrelly after being cooped up here for a few days. Her phone wasn't in her purse. Why don't you try calling her phone again?"

Diesel dialed Annie on his cell. After a couple beats, we heard the phone ringing. We followed the sound to the bedroom and found her cell phone on the floor by the bed.

"I don't know what to think," I said to Diesel. "I

take my phone everywhere with me. I don't know why she'd leave her phone here, except that it's on the floor so maybe it fell out of her pocket."

Diesel wrote a note on a sticky pad in the kitchen and pasted the note to the refrigerator. The message was simple. CALL ME IMMEDIATELY.

We locked up behind ourselves and took the elevator to the garage. We drove out to the street, and I had a genius idea. We were only two blocks away from the Pleasure Treasure. It was open until ten on Saturdays, and it probably had a book Jeanine-the-Virgin would find helpful.

"Turn right at the next corner," I told Diesel. "There's a sex-toys store two blocks from here, and we might be able to find a book for Jeanine."

I could see Diesel smile in the dark car. "Just when I think my day's in the toilet you suggest a sex-toys store. Honey, you're a ray of sunshine."

"I hate to rain on your parade, but I know about this place because I made a bust here in the fall."

"Then let's hope this trip is more fun, because I could really use some fun."

Diesel parked in the small lot next to the store. I promised Bob a bedtime snack if he'd be a good dog just a little longer, and Diesel and I went inside. We were the only shoppers. A solitary clerk was behind the counter reading a movie star magazine. She looked up when we entered and sucked in some air when she saw Diesel. She was in her twenties and completely punked-out with black-rimmed eyes and multiple piercings.

"Just browsing," I told her.

"Sure," she said. "Let me know if I can help."

Diesel followed me to the book section, selected a book, and thumbed through.

"Is it good?" I asked.

"Yeah, look at this," Diesel said. "Have you ever tried this?"

I looked at the picture. "That's got to be uncomfortable, if not impossible."

"Hey, pictures don't lie. They're doing it." He draped an arm around me and put his mouth to my ear. "I bet I could do it."

"You're a sick man. Maybe we should ask Raccoon Woman if she has a starter book. If we show this to Jeanine, she's liable to check herself into a nunnery."

Diesel pulled another book off the shelf. "This looks more basic. It starts off with anatomy. And there are photographs . . . of everything. We should buy two of these."

It was sort of embarrassing to be looking at crotch shots with Diesel. "Sure," I said, "buy two." I glanced at my watch. "Jeez, look at the time. If we hurry, we can catch the end of the game."

"What game is that?" Diesel wanted to know.

"I don't know. Any game."

Diesel moved to the video section. "We should get Jeanine a movie. They've got some good ones."

"No. No movies for Jeanine. Jeanine isn't into moaning, and they always do a lot of moaning in the movies."

"Moaning is fun," Diesel said.

I cut my eyes to him. "Do you moan?"

"Not usually."

"Why not?"

"I'd feel stupid."

"Exactly. Just pay for the books with your phony credit card and let's go home."

"Bet I could make *you* moan," Diesel said, smiling.

"I feel like moaning now," I told him. "And it has nothing to do with sex."

I unwrapped my scarf and hung it on a hook on the wall next to my front door. I draped my heavy winter jacket over the scarf and exchanged my snow boots for shearling slippers.

"I can't believe you bought all that stuff," I said to Diesel.

"It's for Jeanine . . . unless you want to take something for a test drive."

"No."

"Are you sure? We've got a bag full of fun here. I bet we've got samples of every condom ever invented."

"No!"

Diesel set the bag on the kitchen counter and went to the refrigerator. He backed out with a couple beers. "You know what your problem is? You're too uptight."

"I'm not uptight. I've got a boyfriend, and I don't mess around."

"Admirable, but this living arrangement would work better if you had fewer scruples," Diesel said. "I don't fit on the couch."

"Do you fit on the floor?"

"That's cruel," Diesel said.

I took a beer from him and unwrapped a loaf of bread that had been sitting on the counter. We made a stack of peanut butter sandwiches, gave one to Bob, and took the beer and the rest of the sandwiches into the living room and turned the television on.

"I want to know about Beaner," I said to Diesel. "What are his powers? What kind of chaos does he cause?"

"I'd like to tell you, but then I'd have to kill you . . . ."

"Tell me anyway."

"I'd really rather not."

"Great. Don't tell me. I'll get the story from Mrs. Beaner tomorrow."

"Okay, I'll tell you," Diesel said, "but if you laugh, I swear I'll turn you into a toad."

"You can't actually do that, can you?"

"The better question is, *Would I?* And the answer is, *No.*"

"About Beaner."

Diesel washed a sandwich down with half a beer. "He can give you a rash."

"A rash?"

"Yep."

"That's it?"

"Sweetie pie, this isn't any ordinary rash. It's the mother of all rashes. It makes you itch *everywhere*. It's nonstop torture for anywhere from three days to three weeks. It's related to poison sumac and looks like hives. Doesn't necessarily leave scars unless you start carving yourself up with a knife because you can't stand the itching."

"Wow."

Diesel sunk low into the couch and closed his eyes. "Who am I trying to kid? It's a rash, for crying out loud. How bad can a rash be?" He pressed the heels of his hands into his eyes. "Used to be I tracked dangerous sexual deviants and insane despots. Last time I was here I disabled a guy who shut down the northeast power grid at Christmas. That's the kind of stuff you can get your teeth into." He sunk lower and groaned. "And now I'm hunting Mr. Itchy. Do you have any idea what this does for my image?"

"It's not good?"

"It's a nightmare. There's no way to even put a decent spin on it. Big bad Diesel is out to shut down a poor slob whose only claim to fame is his ability to give people hives."

I burst out laughing. "I like it."

I went to the kitchen and brought a bag of cookies back to Diesel. I opened the bag, and we each took a cookie and Bob got two.

"How does he do it?" I asked Diesel. "Is this some kind of contact skin disease?"

"I don't know how he does it. I've never actually seen it happen firsthand, but I know he can spread the rash without contact."

"Maybe Beaner would give Annie a rash, and be done with it. Maybe he just needs to get it out of his system," I said to Diesel.

Diesel shook his head. "He's nutso. He was stalking her, reinfecting her every chance he got. It was ugly. Annie had hives on top of hives."

"Tell me more about Beaner."

"He has some minor skills. He's good with mechanical things. Used to own a garage. Sold it last year and is sort of retired. Probably was driving his wife nuts hanging around the house. He's pretty much a normal guy with the exception of this rash thing. And until a week ago, it was completely undercover. People would break out in unexplained hives, and that was the end of it. When his wife left, and he decided Annie was responsible, he went public. For the first couple days it was just directed at Annie, but then he lost control and started lashing out at random people whenever he got angry."

"Bummer."

"Yeah, big whoopitydo. Anyway, I was told to shut him down."

"You don't mean *shut him down* as in . . . permanently?"

"*Shut him down* as in pull the plug on his power."

"You can do that?"

"I have ways."

I was curious about those ways, but I didn't think he'd tell me. And probably it was better not to know, so I ate two more cookies and shoved off the couch. "I'm going to bed. See you in the morning."

I woke up to the sun shining through the vertical crack in my bedroom curtain and a heavy arm draped across my chest. Diesel was sprawled next to me, looking more disreputable than ever with a four-day-old beard. Like I don't have enough problems with the men in my life, now I have a third guy crawling into my bed. Too much of a good thing. At least I was still wearing my pajamas. That was comforting.

I eased away from Diesel, slithered from under the arm, and rolled out of bed. I grabbed some clean clothes, locked myself in the bathroom, and hopped into the shower. I had a full day ahead of me. Talk to Mrs. Beaner and check on Gary Martin, Charlene Klinger, and Larry Burlew. I had the Pleasure Treasure bag to take to Jeanine. And then there was Annie Hart. I was hoping Annie was back in her apartment, but I thought it was unlikely.

By the time I emerged from the bathroom, Diesel was out of bed, standing at my kitchen counter, eating a bowl of cereal.

"I fed and walked the dog," Diesel said. "I didn't know what to do about the rat."

"Hamster."

"Whatever."

I gave Rex fresh water, filled his bowl with hamster crunchies, and poured out some cereal for myself. "Have you heard from Annie?" I asked Diesel.

"No. She didn't answer when I called this morning, so I had Flash check on her apartment again. Still empty." He put his cereal bowl in the dishwasher. "I need to go solo this morning and try to get a fix on Annie. I'm going to jump in the shower and take off. I wrote Beaner's wife's address on the pad on the counter. Her name is Betty. She's expecting you. I don't know how helpful she'll be, but you can give it a shot. I'll be on my cell. The number's also on the pad."

"Do you have a car?"

"I can get one."

Okay, I wasn't going to ask questions about that either.

I was standing at the counter, enjoying a second cup of coffee, when Diesel walked into the kitchen. His hair was still damp, and he smelled like my shower gel. He had his jacket on, and his scarf wound around his neck. "Catch up with you later," he said.

I blinked, and he was gone. Not magically. Out the door, down the hall, to the elevator.

I rinsed my cup and went to the bathroom to brush my teeth. I turned to leave the bathroom and bumped into Ranger. I shrieked and jumped away.

"Didn't mean to startle you," he said.

Usually I sense Ranger behind me by the change in air pressure and the hint of desire. I wasn't paying attention today, and I was caught by surprise.

"Men keep sneaking up on me," I told him.

"I saw Diesel leave."

"Do you know Diesel?"

"From a distance," Ranger said. "Is Diesel a problem?"

"No more than usual. We're sort of working together."

"I have to go out of town for a couple days. Tank will be here. And I'll be on my cell. I need to talk to you when I get back." He brushed a light kiss across my lips and left.

"The man of mystery," I said to the closed door.

"I heard that," Ranger said from the other side.

Chapter
EIGHT

I dropped Bob at my parents' house and asked them to dog-sit. I had coffee with my mother and Grandma, and by the time I rolled down Betty Beaner's street, it was a little past nine. I parked in her driveway and checked out her house. Average suburbia in every way. Two-story colonial. Landscaped front yard. Fenced back yard. Two-car garage. Freshly painted.

I rang the bell, and Betty answered on the second ring. She was shorter than me and pleasantly round. She had a round face with a nice mouth that looked like it smiled a lot, round wide-open eyes, rounded hips, and big round breasts. She was a Rubenesque woman. She looked to be around fifty.

I extended my hand. "Stephanie Plum."

"I've been expecting you," she said. "Diesel called."

"We thought you might be able to help us with Bernie."

"I can't believe he's running around giving out hives like a senile old fool. I swear, the man is an embarrassment."

I followed her through the living room and dining room and into the kitchen. She'd been at the small kitchen table, reading the paper, drinking coffee. It was a charming room decorated in warm tones. Rusts and yellows mostly. Small-print wallpaper and matching curtains on the windows.

Betty poured a cup of coffee out for me, and we sat at the table. I looked down at the paper and realized she'd been looking at the want ads.

"Getting a job?" I asked her.

Betty had a red pen on the table by the paper, but none of the ads were circled. "I've been thinking about it. Problem is, I can't do anything. I've been a housewife all these years."

"Two hundred?"

She smiled. "Yes. At least, it seems like that. Actually, Bernie and I have been married for thirty-five years. He was working in a garage, and I took my car in there to get fixed, and next thing we were married."

I sipped my coffee, and I looked at Betty Beaner. She didn't seem angry when she spoke of Bernie. If anything, there was affection. And tolerance. In fact, she reminded me of my mom. My parents didn't have the perfect marriage, but over the years they'd developed a plan to make things work. My mother made my dad feel like he was king of the castle, and my dad abdicated the kingdom over to my mom.

"I know I'm going to sound nosey," I said, "but I haven't got a lot of time, and I'm trying to help Diesel fix things. What went wrong?"

"Snoring."

"That's it? That's the whole thing?"

"Have you ever tried to sleep with a man who snores?"

"No. The men in my life don't snore."

"Bernie didn't used to snore and then one day there it was . . . he was a snorer."

"Aren't there things you can do about snoring?"

"He refuses to believe he snores. He says I'm making a big thing of it, but he wakes me up all night long. I'm always tired. And if I go sleep in the guest room, he gets mad. He says married people should sleep together. So, the hell with him, I'm filing for divorce."

"He thinks this is about talking and sex."

"Of course it's about talking. Talking about snoring! It's not like I wanted to have big touchy-feely discussions with Bernie. It's not like I asked him to join a book group or something. I just wanted him to listen to me. When I say I can't sleep, I mean *I can't sleep!*"

"And what about the sex?"

"I threw that in as a bonus. I figured, what the heck, if I was going to complain, I might as well do it right."

Betty circled an ad in the paper with the red pen. "Here's one I bet I could do. They're looking for tollbooth money collectors on the Turnpike."

"Have you thought about counseling?"

"Are you kidding? Do you think a man who won't admit to snoring is going to sign up for counseling? I even tried recording him. He said it was a trick. He said it for sure wasn't him."

"If I could get Bernie to admit to snoring, would you take him back?"

"I don't know. I'm getting used to being alone. The house is nice and quiet. And I get to watch whatever I want on television. Of course, it was a real pain to have to shovel the walk when it snowed."

"This looks like a three-bedroom house. Suppose I could get you your own room with your own television for those nights when Bernie snores? And suppose I could throw in better sex? I don't know firsthand, but I suspect Diesel knows what he's doing. I could get him to talk to Bernie."

This got both of us smiling. Diesel and Bernie discussing sex. Worth the price of a ticket right there.

* * *

I decided to take the Pleasure Treasure bag to Jeanine while I was in sex-help mode, so I called and told her I was on my way over.

"Thank goodness," Jeanine said. "I have a date tonight. I was afraid I was going to have to fake an appendicitis attack."

Twenty minutes later, I was at her door.

"Here it is," I said, shoving the bag at her. "Everything you need to know about sex . . . I think."

Jeanine looked inside. "What is all this?"

"You've got a beginner's-guide-to-sex book. And a video that I've never actually seen but Diesel thought looked hot. And then there are some oils. Directions are included. Assorted condoms. And the salesclerk threw in a vibrating penis as a bonus."

Jeanine pulled the penis out of the bag. "Eeeuuw."

I agreed. It wasn't the most attractive penis I'd ever seen. But then, maybe it wasn't a fair comparison because lately I'd seen some top-of-the-line equipment.

"It was free," I said by way of apology.

Jeanine paged through the book. "This looks helpful. I always wanted to buy a book like this but could never get up the nerve."

"I thought you could read the book, and then if you have questions, you can call me, and I'll try to answer them."

"Maybe I should start with the movie," she said. "Do you want to watch it with me?"

"Think I'll pass. My experience with these movies is that they're made for men and mostly show a lot of boob."

"That would be disappointing," Jeanine said. "I can see that in the locker room at the gym." She peeled a sticky strip off the front cover and gasped. "Holy cow."

I looked over her shoulder. "Double holy cow."

"It's a man," Jeanine said. "And he's naked. I haven't seen a lot of men, so I'm no expert, but I didn't think they came this big."

I took a closer look. "They must have used Photoshop. This is a horse wanger."

"It says on the cover that it's all real and nothing's been retouched."

I took my jacket off. "I guess I could spare a few minutes to make sure everything's authentic. Wouldn't want you getting wrong information. Go ahead and pop that bad boy into the DVD player."

"It's eleven o'clock," Jeanine said. "Almost lunchtime. Maybe we need a glass of wine to get through this."

I agreed. This had all the earmarks of a movie that required booze.

Twenty minutes later, we were sipping wine and leaning forward, eyes glued to the screen.

"This is a car crash," I said. "One of the worst movies ever made. And I can't tear myself away from it."

"Yeah," Jeanine said. "I might have to watch it again just to make sure I've got it all straight."

The doorbell rang, and we both jumped.

Jeanine squeezed her eyes shut. "Please God, don't let it be my mother."

"Does your mother live in the Burg?"

Jeanine hit the pause button. "She lives in Milwaukee."

"So chances are good it's not your mother."

"It was a gut reaction."

Jeanine opened the door, and Grandma leaned to the side to see around Jeanine. She spotted me on the couch and gave a little finger wave.

"I knew that was your car out front," Grandma said. "I'm on my way to the funeral home now that my lips have deflated enough so I can talk. Elaine Gracey is being laid out for a special noon viewing. Your father's off to the lodge with the car, so I had to walk and I'm about froze." She gaped at the television screen where Big Chief and Vanessa Dickbender were frozen in full rut. "I bet you're watching cable," Grandma said. "These reality shows just keep getting better and better. I wouldn't mind sitting down to watch some. Just until I get warmed up. Are you drinking wine? A glass of wine would be real nice."

I heard a car door slam outside, and moments later Jeanine's bell rang again. Jeanine opened the door, and Lula looked in at us.

"I was driving by on my way back from church, and I saw the car and I thought I saw Grandma come in here," Lula said. "Are you guys having a party? Dang, whose hairy ass is that on your television screen?"

"Big Chief," Jeanine said.

"He's the best," Lula said, taking her coat off, pushing in next to Grandma on the couch. "Are we having wine?"

Jeanine brought two more glasses and the bottle, and I hit the PLAY button.

"Now see this here," Lula said, watching Dickbender work over Big Chief. "I've done this lots of times, and she's doing it all wrong."

"Lula was a professional," Grandma told Jeanine. "She was the best on her corner."

"Darn right," Lula said. "I knew what I was doing."

Jeanine filled Lula's glass with wine. "Maybe you could give me some pointers."

"Sure," Lula said. "I'm retired now, so I can share my secrets to being a successful 'ho. The thing is, you gotta get a good rhythm going. My signature move was to do it to 'Jingle Bells.' Everybody loves 'Jingle Bells.' " Lula beat out the rhythm on the coffee table. "Jingle bells. Jingle bells. Jingle *all* the *way* . . . unh!"

"Boy," Jeanine said, "this is just what I need to know."

"Yep," Lula said, "you just keep singing 'Jingle Bells,' and before you know it you can collect your fifteen dollars and leave."

"I could do that," Grandma said. "I can sing 'Jingle Bells,' and I could use an extra fifteen dollars."

Vanessa Dickbender let out a shriek, and we all sucked in some air.

"What was that?" Jeanine wanted to know. "What happened?"

"That might have been a orgasm," Lula said.

"Yikes," Jeanine said. "It sounded painful."

Lula sat back. "Yeah, it was probably fake, but I guess it was supposed to be a big one."

Jeanine poured herself another glass of wine.

"I think he's getting to the end," Lula said. "I can tell on account of all the veins have popped out in Big Chief's face, and he looks like he's gonna have a heart attack. How long's he been doing this anyway?"

"It's been going on for about forty minutes now," I told her.

"Nobody got staying power like Big Chief," Lula said. "He did it in the back of a car one time for ninety minutes. The film is a classic. And I hear they had to hook him up to one of them IV fluid bags when he was done."

"This is kind of scary," Jeanine said. "Maybe I should learn CPR."

"It won't be scary," I said to Jeanine. "You'll be fine. Just keep singing 'Jingle Bells.' "

It was early afternoon when I dropped Grandma off at my parents' house.

"Sorry you missed the viewing," I told her.

"That's okay," she said. "It's not every day I get to see a real good educational film. And I'll get another crack at Elaine tonight."

I watched to make sure Grandma got inside, and then I took off. I drove two blocks, and my cell phone rang.

"I'm right behind you," Diesel said. "Pull over and park. I want to talk to you."

I parked at the curb and got out of my car. Diesel did the same. He was driving a shiny black Corvette that was in direct contrast to all the other salt-and-grime-encrusted cars on the road.

"Nice car," I said. "Clean."

"How'd it go with Betty Beaner?"

"Turns out Bernie snores."

"And?"

"Betty can't sleep. She wants her own room, so she can sleep."

"That's it?"

"She wants a television in the room. And she wants better sex."

"Honey, we *all* want better sex."

I raised an eyebrow.

"What?" Diesel said.

"Someone needs to talk to Bernie."

"Not me."

"I thought you were the big sex hotshot."

"I do okay, but I'm not giving Bernie a birds and bees talk. Guys don't do that. It's . . . weird."

"Yes, but you're an Unmentionable guy."

Diesel had his thumbs hooked into his jeans pockets, and his face set on *Don't mess with me.*

"Fine," I said to him. "Have it your way. Don't talk to poor Bernie. Go shut him down."

"I don't believe this," Diesel said. "It just gets worse and worse. Bad enough I have to play Cupid to a butcher, button maker, and veterinarian . . . now I have to be sex therapist for a guy who gives people a rash."

"It could be fun. Male bonding and all that. And while we're on the subject of sex instruction, I delivered the bag to Jeanine and watched the movie with her."

This got a grin out of Diesel. "Did you like it?"

"It was horrible, but we watched it twice."

Diesel laughed out loud.

"It's the ultimate chick flick. When Dickbender screamed at the end, Jeanine turned white and had a third glass of wine. How's the Bernie hunt going?"

"It's not. I can't find him," Diesel said. "I'm getting no vibes at all. Does his wife know how to get in touch with him?"

"No. I left her my card, and she said she'd call if he made contact. How about Annie? Anything on her?"

"Can't find her either," Diesel said. "It's like the two of them have gone to the moon."

"They can't actually do that, can they?"

"Honey, we're a little freaky . . . we're not NASA."

I was hit by a gust of wind, and I hunkered down into my jacket, my breath making frost clouds in front of me. Diesel pulled me close and snuggled me into him, and I instantly felt warm. The heat burned in my chest, curled through my stomach, and headed south.

My voice rose an octave. "What are you doing?"

"I'm warming you," Diesel said.

"I don't need to be *that* warm."

"Hey, I'm just sharing body heat. I can't help it if it gets you all bothered."

"I'm not all bothered."

Diesel smiled down at me.

"Oh crap!" I said, looking up at him. "You've got dimples."

"That isn't all I've got."

I jumped away. "I'm leaving. I'm going to check on Charlene Klinger."

Chapter
NINE

Charlene was in her little front yard, walking Blackie around in circles, trying to get him to tinkle.

"Maybe he needs a fire hydrant or a tree," I said.

"That's the problem," Charlene said. "He can't put any weight on his front leg, so he falls over if he lifts his back leg."

"How did dinner go last night?"

"Hard to tell. Junior spilled his milk as soon as we sat down to the table, and it made a flood, and we all got dripped on. And when we were trying to mop up the milk, Blackie got the pot roast and ran away with it. So we had peanut butter and jelly for dinner. And while we were eating our sandwiches, Fluffy got loose and ate Gary's shoelaces and left jelly beans under the table.

"I had gotten a movie for when the kids went to bed, but Gary was sort of soaked with milk, so he left early. He looked like he was thinking about kissing me good night at the door, but the kids were all standing there watching, so he shook my hand and left."

"Wow."

"Yeah, it was a night to remember. Maybe we should go to plan B and find me a housewife."

"But he must like you if he was thinking about kissing you when he left."

"I guess."

"Do you like him?"

"Sure. What's not to like? He's nice to the kids and the animals. And he's even nice to me. And he's cute and cuddly. And he seems very stable. I just can't imagine anyone wanting to take on the chaos."

I was used to having dinner with a kid who thought she was a horse, a grandmother who set the tablecloth on fire on a regular basis, and a future brother-in-law who fainted and farted at the mention of marriage. I didn't see where Charlene had more than the normal amount of chaos.

Ralph had been standing in the doorway, taking it all in. "Maybe we should set the cat on fire again," he said. "Just a little."

I told Charlene to hold off on the cat, and I got back into my car and searched through Gary Martin's file for his phone number. I called his home phone and got his machine. I tried his cell and got his message service. The message service said he was in emergency surgery, so I headed for his clinic. Twenty minutes later, I pulled into his lot, looked in my rearview mirror, and saw Diesel pull in behind me.

I got out of the Escape and went back to Diesel. "How do you always know where to find me?"

Diesel shrugged. "I can tune in to you."

"You have my car bugged, don't you?"

Again, the smile with the dimples. Most guys look cute with dimples. Diesel got dimples, and the temperature went up ten degrees.

"Don't you dare dimple me," I said to him.

"Can't help it. It just happens. Do you have Annie's file with you? I need to see it."

I got the file from my car and slid onto the passenger seat, next to Diesel. "Not a lot in this. Just the usual bond agreement and personal information."

Diesel scanned the paperwork. "Annie's lawyer secured her bond from Vinnie. Standard procedure. The lawyer is one of us. She went back to her house in Hamilton Township, and two days later Bernie started harassing her. I was called in, and we moved her out to the safe house. I find it hard to believe someone discovered the safe house. I think Annie must have left voluntarily."

"Have you been back to her house? Maybe she just wanted to go home."

"I sent Flash. He said the house was locked and dark, but I think we should see for ourselves."

I shelved Gary Martin, rammed myself back into the Escape, and followed Diesel across town to Annie's house. It was exactly what I would have expected. A tidy cape with two front dormers. White siding and black shutters. Very traditional. White picket fence around the small yard. A red heart on the mailbox. We parked in the driveway and walked to the front door.

"There's bad energy here," Diesel said.

I took a step back. I didn't want to walk in and find Annie dead on her living room floor. "How bad are we talking about? Do I want to wait out here?"

"Not that bad. *Disrupted* would be a better word."

Diesel opened the door, and we walked into the dark, silent foyer. He flipped a light on, we worked our way through the house, and it was clear that the house had been tossed. Couch cushions were scattered, drawers were left open, beds were torn apart, toilet-tank tops were on the floor. No stone unturned. We checked all the closets, the basement, and the crawl spaces. No bodies found.

We left Annie's house exactly as we found it, Diesel locked the door behind us, and we angled ourselves into his 'vette to talk.

"Someone was looking for something," I said to Diesel.

"Yeah, and there might have been a struggle in the foyer. The vase was knocked off the sideboard onto the floor."

"The obvious person is Bernie, but I don't know why he'd have reason to search the house. Do you suppose the police did this, searching for the supposedly stolen property?"

"No," Diesel said. "This doesn't feel like a police search. And I doubt the police would go to this trouble for a charge I can almost guarantee will be dismissed. Annie's wanted for armed robbery and assault with a deadly weapon. A guy named Stanley Cramp claims Annie walked into his pawnshop, robbed him, and shot him in the foot. No weapon was found, but two witnesses can place Annie at the scene. Neither of them saw the robbery or assault happen."

Diesel was turned toward me in the small car. His arm was resting on my seat back, and he was absentmindedly stroking my neck with his fingertip while he was talking. It was soothing and disturbingly erotic, all at the same time, and I was working hard to pay attention to the conversation and not to the warm fingertip.

"Why was Annie in a pawnshop?" I asked Diesel.

"Annie said she went into the pawnshop on a

whim. She said she saw a necklace in the window that intrigued her. The two witnesses were in the shop when she went in. The witnesses left. Annie left shortly after that without the necklace. And minutes later the call went in to 911."

"How was she identified?"

"She'd parked in front of the shop, and Stanley Cramp took her plate down."

"What is she accused of taking?" I asked Diesel.

"The necklace. Nothing else."

"Have you talked to Stanley Cramp?"

"Not yet, but I think it's time. I'd like you to do it. See if you can charm something out of him. If that doesn't work, feel free to shoot him in the other foot."

"That would be tough," I told him, "since I haven't got a gun."

Diesel reached under his seat and pulled out a Glock.

"I'm not going to take that!" I said.

"Why not?"

"I hate guns."

"You can't hate guns. You're a bounty hunter."

"Yes, but I almost never shoot people. Bounty hunters only shoot people on television."

Diesel raised an eyebrow.

"Okay, so maybe I shot a couple guys, but it wasn't my fault."

"Just take the friggin' gun," Diesel said. "Stanley Cramp isn't a nice person."

"Where am I going to find this guy?"

"He lives in an apartment over the pawnshop, but at this time of day he'll be working. The pawnshop is a one-man operation, open seven days a week."

I got out of Diesel's 'vette and into my Escape. I drove into the center of the city and took the side street that led to the pawnshop. I parked two doors down on the opposite side of the street. I left my car, crossed the street, and glanced at Diesel parked one store down. I rang the bell next to the front door and got buzzed in. High security.

Stanley Cramp looked like life had pretty much been sucked out of him. He was about five foot nine and scrawny. Mid-fifties with thinning oily black hair that was badly in need of a cut. His clothes were a size too large. His teeth were tobacco-stained. He had bloodhound bags under his eyes and skin the color and texture of wet cement. He looked like he'd be better placed in a body bag than standing behind the counter in a pawnshop.

I approached the counter and sent Cramp a flirty smile, and Cramp turned to see if someone was standing behind him.

"I hope you don't mind," I said to him. "I was freezing out there, and your shop looked cozy and warm. And I saw you in here all by yourself."

"You aren't looking to . . . you know, make money, are you? Because I think you're real cute, but I don't have any money. I bet on the wrong horse yesterday, and I got cleaned out."

Oh great, he thought I was a hooker. Not exactly a flattering appraisal, but I could get some mileage out of it. "Do you bet on the wrong horse a lot?"

"Yeah, unfortunately. I used to always win, and then my luck turned, and now I keep getting deeper and deeper in the crapper."

"Jeez, that's too bad. Still, you're lucky you have this pawnshop. Is it yours?"

"Yeah, sort of. I owe some people money, but I'll take care of that as soon as my luck changes."

I wandered around, looking in the cases. "You used to have a real pretty necklace in the window, but I haven't seen it lately."

"The one with the red stone? It got stolen. Some lady came in and robbed me and shot me in the foot."

"Get out!"

"Honest to God. I still can't get a shoe on that foot."

"That's horrible. Did she get arrested?"

"Yeah, but the cops didn't recover the necklace."

"Wow."

"I got a bottle of real good hooch behind the

counter," Cramp said. "You want some to help get you warmed up?"

"Sure."

Cramp pulled out a bottle of Jack Daniel's and set it on the display case. "Help yourself."

"Do you have a glass?"

"I have glasses upstairs. That's where I live."

"Maybe we could go upstairs."

"Yeah, that'd be real good, but like I told you, I don't have any money."

"Well, what the heck, it's cold, and I don't have anything better to do. Let's go upstairs anyway."

Cramp looked like he was going to keel over.

"But what about the shop?" I asked.

"I'll close it," Cramp said, hurrying to the front door, throwing the bolt, changing the sign around to say CLOSED. "There's never much business on Sunday anyway." He took the bottle of Jack and motioned me to the rear of the pawnshop. "I have stairs that go up to my apartment," he said. "We don't even have to go out."

The stairs were narrow and dark and creaky, leading to a small apartment that was also narrow and dark and creaky. The front room had a television on a card table, and opposite the television was a daybed covered with a floral quilt. A scarred end table had been placed to one side of the daybed.

Cramp got a couple glasses from the kitchen. He set the glasses on the end table and filled them with the Jack. "Down the hatch," he said, and he emptied his glass.

I sipped demurely at mine. "It's nice up here," I said.

Cramp looked around. "Used to be nicer before my luck changed. I had some real good pieces, but you know how it is when you're in retail. You have to turn a profit when you get a buyer."

"I bet you were sorry to get robbed of the necklace. It looked expensive."

"I wish I never saw that necklace. Look what it got me . . . a shot-up foot."

"I think it's an interesting story. It could probably even be a movie."

"You think?" Cramp poured himself more Jack. "Yeah, I guess it could make a movie."

Okay, I had him. He wasn't a smart guy, and he was a little drunk, and it was going to be easy to get him rolling on an ego trip.

"Who hocked the necklace?" I asked Cramp. "Was it someone glamorous?"

"Well, not movie-star glamorous, but she was okay. In her twenties. Big bazoos. Sort of rat's-nest hair, but when you got bazoos like that it don't matter, right? That's why I remember her. I'm not good with names, but I remember a good rack."

Charming.

"Anyway, it was the same story I hear every day," Cramp said. "She got the necklace from her boyfriend. Her boyfriend turned out to be a jerk. She wants some money for the necklace."

Cramp tossed his Jack down his throat. Glug, glug, glug. This could explain his embalmed appearance.

"Keep going," I said. "I want to hear the rest of the story."

"Sure," he said. "I never thought much about it, but it's a pretty good story. And it gets even better. I hock the piece for Ms. Big Boobs, and a couple weeks down the road this guy comes in and wants the necklace. He's got the claim ticket. I ask him what happened to the girl with the hooters, and he says I should shut my pie hole and give him the necklace.

"Now here's where it gets good. This is the part that would be good for the movie. Almost all the jewelry in the shop is fake. I got a guy who fences the stuff when it comes in and makes me paste. It's a win-win deal for me, right? I get the money from the fence, and then I either sell the paste to a customer, or the idiot who hocked it in the first place buys it back. Most of the time people can't even tell it's fake. And if they suspect it's fake, they're too embarrassed to do anything about it. Pretty smart, hunh? I thought of it all by my-self."

"Wow," I said. "Cool."

"Yeah. So anyway, this guy is standing in front of me with the claim ticket for the necklace, and all of a sudden I recognize him. It's Lou Delvina. He's the jerk boyfriend! I mean, Lou Delvina. Jesus. Do you know who Lou Delvina is?"

"I've heard of him," I said to Cramp.

Everyone in Trenton knew Lou Delvina. For twenty years, he was a shooter for the north Jersey mob, and then he got his own real estate and moved into the Trenton area. He wasn't big-time, but he made the most of what he had. I'd heard stories about Delvina, and none of the stories was good. Delvina was a very scary guy.

"If you know who Delvina is, you know the prob-lem I've got," Cramp said. "I sort of stole a necklace from someone who would kill me if he found out. And chances are sort of good he'd find out, since I'm guessing he knows paste when he sees it."

"Jeez," I said. "You must have been messing your pants."

"Big time. But that was when it happened. My luck swung around. Delvina's standing there with his claim ticket, and he gets a phone call. And it's not a good call because his face gets all red and his eyes get beady and squinty. Little rat eyes. And he tells me he has to go, but he'll be back for the necklace, and I should take real good care of it."

"I would have left town," I said to Cramp.

"See, that's what most people would think, but I'm smarter than that. A couple women came into the shop to browse. Locals. And then another woman came in all by herself. And I knew she wasn't local because I saw her park. Right in front. So as soon as they all left I faked a robbery. Good, right?"

"Definitely movie stuff. I bet Brad Pitt could play your part."

"Brad Pitt would be good," Cramp said. "I could see Brad Pitt doing it."

"What did you do with the necklace? Did you plant it on the woman?"

"No. I trashed the necklace. There's a crawl space under the back room, and I threw it down there. I threw the gun down there after I shot myself, too."

"You shot yourself?"

"Yeah, I got carried away. I wanted to make it look real, but it hurt like a bitch. I didn't think it would hurt so much. Anyway, I guess it was worth it because everyone bought the story. I told everybody the lady walked out with the necklace. The cops went after her, and Delvina went looking for her, too. Delvina really wants that necklace."

"Does the real necklace still exist?"

"Hell, no. The stones got reset right away. I don't know what my guy does with the setting. Melt it down, maybe." Cramp looked at the bottle of Jack. Almost empty. "You think we can get to it now?"

"To it?"

"Yeah, you know, the thing we came up here for."

I felt my cell phone buzz in my bag. I retrieved the phone and answered the call.

"Are you okay?" Diesel asked.

"Yeah."

"Do you need help?"

"There's no emergency, but assistance might be good at this point. Where are you?"

"I'm just outside the pawnshop."

"It's locked."

"Not anymore." And he disconnected.

"Who was that?" Cramp asked.

"My pimp."

"Jesus, I told you and told you I don't have any money. What do you want? Take anything in the shop. How about some jewelry? It's all fake but it's still good shit."

Diesel strolled into the front room and looked at Cramp, and I could see Cramp start to sweat through his shirt.

"Is there a problem?" Diesel asked.

"No problem," Cramp said. "I told her to take anything she wanted from the shop. Hell, she didn't even do anything."

Diesel slid a look my way. "Is that right?"

I shrugged.

Cramp looked at Diesel. "Are you going to hit me?"

"Maybe," Diesel said.

Cramp's nose was running and his eyes were red-rimmed and tearing up. I was starting to feel sorry for him. He was such a pathetic little worm.

"You aren't a cop, are you?" Cramp asked me.

"No. I'm not a cop."

Cramp looked over at Diesel.

"He's not a cop either," I said. "Actually, I'm not sure *what* he is."

Diesel didn't crack a smile. "Do we have any more business here?"

"No. He hasn't got any money."

"Then it looks to me like we're done here," Diesel said. "Let's roll."

"Here's a parting message," I said to Cramp. "If it looks too good to be true, it probably is."

Diesel wrapped his arm around my neck when we got outside. "What was with the profound message?"

"He thought I was a hooker and he was going to get a freebie."

Diesel hugged me to him. "The guy's a moron. Anyone can see you're not the sort of girl who gives freebies."

"Gee, thanks. I told him you were my pimp."

"Lucky me."

"He has the supposedly stolen necklace and the assault gun in a crawl space under the back room. Do you think we should get it?"

"No, but I think you should call it in to Morelli. Let him send someone over to retrieve it."

I filled Diesel in on Delvina.

"Good work," Diesel said. "You learned a lot."

"And what about Annie? Do you think it's possible that Delvina has Annie?"

"I think it's possible that Delvina tossed Annie's house and wants the necklace. I don't see how Delvina could get to Annie."

"Coincidence? Maybe she stepped out for air, and he happened to be driving down the street."

"That's a *big* coincidence."

"I haven't got anything else."

"Me either," Diesel said. "Let's talk to Mr. Delvina."

"Oh no. *You* can talk to Delvina. You're Iron Man. And you don't live here. I'm just wimpy Stephanie from the Burg. If Delvina shoots holes in me, all my vital fluids will leak out, and I'll end up looking like Stanley Cramp."

"Wouldn't want any fluids to leak out of you that weren't supposed to," Diesel said. "I'll track Delvina, and you check on Annie's couples. We're coming up on Valentine's Day. Don't want any snafus."

Chapter
TEN

My phone rang while I sat in my car watching Diesel drive away.

"Hey, cupcake," Morelli said. "Just checking in. Anything I need to know?"

"Speak of the devil. I was just going to call you. I have some information to share. Vinnie bonded out a woman named Annie Hart. She supposedly robbed a pawnshop and shot the owner in the foot."

"I remember that," Morelli said. "The pawnshop owner is a little weasel named Stanley Cramp."

"Yeah. Turns out Cramp faked the robbery and shot himself in the foot. The gun and the necklace are in a crawl space under the back room. I can give you more details later, but you should get someone over there before Cramp decides to get rid of the evidence."

"I'll call it in. How's everything else?"

"It's really slow at the bonds office. Only one big

outstanding . . . and that was Annie Hart. Bob is good. He's visiting with my parents today. Diesel's in town."

"Diesel?"

"Yeah, you remember Diesel, right?"

"Ranger's half-brother."

"He's not Ranger's half-brother."

"He might as well be. They both run in the fast lane with their lights off."

"You used to do that."

"No. I was an asshole. I never actually thought I was Batman."

"I see your point."

"I'm locked away in a sleazoid motel, doing my cop thing. Do I need to come home?"

"Nope. I've got it all under control."

"Good to know," Morelli said. "I should have this wrapped up Tuesday or Wednesday. See you then." And he disconnected.

I cut down to Klockner Boulevard and then to Hamilton and left-turned into the Burg. I eased to a stop in front of my parents' house and killed the engine. Grandma was at the storm door, looking out at me, driven there by some mysterious inner radar that tells her when a granddaughter is approaching. Not that different from Diesel, when you think about it.

"Just in time," Grandma said to me, holding the door open. "Your sister is here, and we got a nice coffee cake from the bakery."

Bob heard my voice and came thundering down the hall, ears flopping, tongue out, google-eyed. He slid on the polished wood floor and plowed into me, knocking me into the wall.

I scratched his head and gave him a hug, and he galloped back to the kitchen and the coffee cake.

"He's been such a good boy," Grandma said. "It makes a house feel like a home when you got a dog in it. And he didn't hardly eat anything this time. The *TV Guide* and a loaf of bread, but the good thing was he horked up the plastic wrap."

Valerie was at the little kitchen table. She had the baby on her lap and coffee in front of her.

"Where are the girls?" I asked.

"Playgroup," Valerie said. "They go every day now."

I sliced off a chunk of coffee cake and out of habit I stood at the sink to eat.

My mother put a plate and fork and napkin on the table. "Sit," she said. "It's not good for your digestion to eat at the sink. You eat too fast. You don't even chew. Did you chew that piece of cake?"

I didn't know if I'd chewed it. I couldn't even remember eating it, but my hand was empty, and I had crumbs on my shirt, so I guess that said it all.

I pulled a chair out across from Valerie and sat down. It was too late to eat my cake in a civilized manner . . . unless I had a second piece. I checked out the waistband on my jeans. Snug. Shit.

"Sorry I made Albert faint at the table," I said to Valerie. "I thought he was sort of over the marriage phobia."

"It's hideous," Valerie said. "The man is never going to marry me. I didn't mind at first. I thought he just needed time. Now I don't know what he needs."

"He needs his head examined," Grandma said.

"He had it examined," Valerie said. "They didn't find anything."

We all pondered that for a moment.

"Anyway, it's important that we get married," Valerie said. "I'm pregnant again."

We were all dumbfounded.

"Is that good news?" Grandma asked.

"Yes. I want to have another baby with Albert," Valerie said. "I just wish I was married."

Okay, that was the deal-breaker. Albert Kloughn was going down. He was going to marry my sister. I was going to make it happen.

I scraped my chair back. "Gotta go. Things to do. People to see. Is it okay if I leave Bob here just a little longer?"

"He's not here forever, is he?" my mother asked.

"No! I'll be back for him. I promise."

I hurried out of the kitchen and drove the short distance to Jeanine's house. Her date was due to arrive any minute, and I thought it wouldn't hurt to do a last-minute courage check. I parked in front of her house, ran to the door, and rang the bell.

The door was thrown open, and Jeanine stood there buck naked. "Ta daaaah!" she sang out.

We locked eyes, and we both let out a shriek. I clapped my hands over my eyes, and Jeanine slammed the door shut. A minute later, the door reopened and Jeanine appeared, wrapped in a blanket.

"I thought you were Edward," she said.

"How much have you had to drink?"

"Enough. And you'll be happy to learn I watched the movie three more times and practiced moaning." Her eyes rolled back in her head. "Ohhhh," she moaned. "Oh yeah. Oh yeah." She opened her eyes and looked at me. "How was that?"

A door opened two doors down, and an elderly man looked out at us. He shook his head and muttered something about lesbians and retreated back into his house.

"That was pretty good," I said, "but you might want to adjust the volume."

"Do you think the naked greeting is too much? I figured I'd get it over and done, so we could make our six o'clock dinner reservation. I was afraid if

I waited until after dinner I'd get nervous and throw up."

"Glad to see you've got it all figured out."

Jeanine took a deep breath and cracked her knuckles. "Maybe I need another drinky poo."

"Probably you've had enough drinky poos," I told her. "You don't want to get horizontal until your date shows up."

I jogged back to the Escape, slipped behind the wheel, and punched in Charlene Klinger's number.

"He called," she yelled into the phone. "He wants to take me to dinner. What do I do?"

"You go to dinner with him."

"It's not that simple. I don't know what to wear. And I need a babysitter. Where am I going to get a babysitter at this late notice?"

"I'm on my way," I told her, putting the car in gear. "I'll be there in a half hour."

Junior opened the front door and let me in.

"Where's your mom?" I asked.

"Upstairs. She's going nuts because she can't find anything to wear, and she got her hair stuck in a torture device."

I trooped upstairs and found Charlene in the bathroom with a curling iron in her hand.

"Stephanie Plum, full-service matchmaker,

available for wardrobe consultation and babysitting," I told Charlene.

"Are you sure you can handle the kids?" she
asked me.

"Piece of cake."

Truth is, I'd rather get run over by a truck than
spend an hour with Charlene's kids, but I didn't
know what else to do.

"I thought I'd wear this pants suit," she said.
"What do you think?"

"The pants suit is good, but the shirt isn't sexy."

"Oh God, am I supposed to be sexy?"

I ran to her bedroom and sifted through the pile
of clothes on her bed. I found a V-necked sweater
that I thought had potential and brought it into the
bathroom.

"Try this," I told her.

"I can't wear that. It's too low. I bought it by mistake."

I unbuttoned her out of the shirt and dropped the
sweater over her head. I took a step back, and we
both looked in the mirror.

Charlene had *a lot* of cleavage. "Perfect," I said.
"Now you're a domestic goddess *and* a sex goddess."

Charlene looked down at her boobs. "I don't
want to give him the wrong idea."

"And that would be, what?"

"I don't know. I'm not good at this. I never have a second date. Everyone always disappears halfway through the *first* date. What am I supposed to do on a second date? Should I . . . you know?"

"No! You don't *you know* until the third date. And then, only if you really like the guy. I've had years where I didn't *you know* at all."

Junior was watching. "Boy, you have a lot of skin," he said to his mother. "And your hair looks funny."

Charlene's attention moved from her boobs to her hair. "I got the curling iron caught in it, and some of it got singed off."

I finger-combed some conditioner into Charlene's singed hair and fluffed her out with a round brush and hair dryer.

"You must not be a Jersey native," I said to Charlene.

"I moved here five years ago from New Hampshire."

That would explain the hair.

I pulled some lip gloss and blush out of my bag and swiped some on Charlene. The doorbell rang, and Charlene gripped the bathroom counter for support.

"Remember," I said to her, "you're a goddess."

"Goddess," she repeated.

"And you don't put out until the third date."

"Third date."

"Unless he gets carried away with your cleavage and asks you to marry him . . . then you could accelerate the process."

I walked Charlene down the stairs and helped her get into a coat. I told Gary Martin to behave himself and get Charlene home before her ten o'clock curfew. And I closed the door after them and turned to face her kids.

"I'm hungry," Ralph said.

The other three stared at me in sullen silence.

"What?" I said to them.

"We don't need a babysitter," Russell said.

"Fine. Pretend I'm something else. Pretend I'm a friend."

Russell looked me up and down.

"How old are you?" I asked him.

"Sixteen."

"I don't think so."

"He's twelve," Ralph said. "And he got a bone in school last week and got sent home."

"It's *boner,* dipshit," Ernie said.

Ralph stood on tiptoes and got into Ernie's face. "Don't call me dipshit."

"Dipshit, dipshit, dipshit."

I looked at my watch. I'd been on duty for three minutes and I'd lost control. This was going to be a long night.

"Everyone into the kitchen," I said. "I'm going to make dinner."

"What are you going to make?" Ralph wanted to know.

"Peanut butter sandwiches."

"I don't like peanut butter," Ralph said.

"Yeah, and that's not dinner. That's lunch," Ernie said. "We need to have meat and vegetables for dinner."

I took my phone out and dialed Pino's Pizza. "I need three large pies with peppers, olives, onions, and pepperoni," I told them. "And I need it fast." I gave them the address and turned back to the kids. "Vegetables and meat, coming up."

"I'm going upstairs," Russell said.

Ernie followed. "Me, too."

Junior ran off to the back of the house and disappeared.

"You have to feed Kitty and Blackie and Fluffy and Tom and Fritz and Melvin. And you can't give Blackie any pizza because he's lactose internet."

"Do you mean lactose intolerant?"

"Yeah. He gets the squirts. He squirts all over everything."

I went to the kitchen, and I put some cat crunchies in a bowl for Kitty and some dog crunchies in a bowl for Blackie and some rabbit pellets in a bowl for Fluffy.

"Tom and Fritz and Melvin are the outside cats," Ralph said. "Mom can't catch them, so she just feeds 'em."

I fed the outside cats and realized I hadn't seen Junior in a while.

"Where's Junior?" I asked Ralph.

Ralph shrugged. "Junior runs away a lot," he said.

I yelled for Junior, but Junior didn't show. Ralph and I went upstairs to look for Junior and found Russell and Ernie surfing porn sites.

"They do this all day long," Ralph said. "It's why Russell gets bones."

"It's *boner*," Ernie said. "Bone-*errrr*!"

"Doesn't your mom have parental controls on this computer?" I asked Russell.

"They're broken," Russell said.

"Russell's a geek," Ralph said. "He can break anything. He broke the television so we can watch naked people."

"Anyway, my mother doesn't care what I do," Russell said. "It's not like I'm a kid."

"Of course you're a kid," I said to him. "Shut that off."

"I don't have to," Russell said. "You're not my mother. You can't tell me what to do."

I punched Diesel's number into my phone.

"Help," I said when he answered.

"What's up?"

"I'm babysitting for Charlene, and I've lost a kid, and two more are surfing porn sites, and it's going to look real bad if I have to shoot them."

"I'm not actually a kid person," Diesel said.

"I ordered pizza."

"Honey, you need to come up with something better than pizza as a bribe."

"Okay, you can sleep in the bed . . . but you have to stay on your side."

"Deal."

Diesel and the pizza arrived at the same time. Diesel paid the delivery kid and brought the pizza inside. He dropped the three boxes on the table, opened one, and took a piece.

"You have one kid sitting at the table," Diesel said. "Where are the others?"

"Two are upstairs and refuse to come down. I can't find Junior."

Diesel stood silent for a moment. He turned slightly and looked around the room. He ate some of his pizza and popped the top on a can of soda. "He's under the sink," Diesel said.

I opened the under-the-sink cabinet door and peeked in at Junior. "Do you want pizza?"

"Can I eat it in here?"

I gave him a piece of pizza on a paper towel and closed the door on him.

"Can I have a piece?" Ralph asked.

"Knock yourself out," Diesel said. "I'm going to get your brothers."

Ralph and I helped ourselves to pizza, and Diesel disappeared up the stairs. There was a lot of kid yelling followed by silence. Moments later, Diesel ambled into the kitchen with Russell and Ernie. He had both of them by the backs of their shirts, and their feet weren't touching the floor.

Diesel plunked Russell and Ernie down and selected a second piece of pizza. "Looks like I'm going to be here for a while," he said to Russell and Ernie. "Might as well make it worthwhile. Do you guys play poker? Have you got any money?"

Diesel, Russell, Ernie, and Ralph were still at the kitchen table when Charlene got home. I was watching television. Junior was asleep on the couch next to me.

"How'd it go?" I asked Charlene.

"I think this was the first time in five years no one spilled milk at dinner. It felt weird. And he kissed me good night at the door. That felt weird, too, but I liked it. He's a really nice man."

"Is he your true love?"

"Too early to tell, but he has potential. He's in-

vited me and the kids to his house for dinner tomorrow night."

Diesel meandered in from the kitchen. "Just in
time," he said to Charlene. "We were playing pepperoni poker, and we ran out of pepperoni."

Ralph was trailing behind Diesel. "He won all
the pepperonis, and then he ate them," Ralph said.

I raised an eyebrow at Diesel.

"I'm good at cards," Diesel said.

"You were playing with kids!"

"Yeah, but they cheat."

"He said if he caught us cheating again, he'd
turn us into toads," Ralph said. "He can't do that,
can he?"

"What's with this toad thing?" I said to Diesel.

"Idle threat," Diesel said. "Sort of."

I stuffed myself into my jacket and hung my bag
on my shoulder. "Have fun tomorrow night," I told
Charlene. "Keep in touch."

Diesel followed me out and walked me to my car.

"What's happening with Annie?" I asked him.

"Can't find her. Can't find Bernie. And now I
can't find Lou Delvina. He has a house in Cran-
berry, but the only one in the house is his wife.
There's a two-car garage with just one car in it. I
have someone checking on other properties. He's
not at his social club. He's not at his place of
business."

"It's only nine o'clock. He could be lots of places."

"True. I have Flash watching his house."

My phone buzzed.

"Thank the Lord I got you," Lula said. "You're not gonna believe this one, and don't hang up because this is my one phone call."

Chapter

ELEVEN

"Where are you?" I asked Lula.

"I'm in jail. Where the heck do you think I am with one phone call? Anyways, I need someone to bond me out of here."

"I'll have to get Connie. Vinnie left for his Valentine's cruise with Lucille." I looked at my watch. "It's nine o'clock Sunday night. Connie's going to have to get a judge out of his jammies to set bond. What are the charges?"

"Destruction of personal property and tying a idiot's dick in a knot. And Tank's here, too."

Tank was second in command at Ranger's security company. He was Ranger's best friend, and he watched Ranger's back. He was a big guy who didn't talk much but carried a real big stick. From time to time Lula managed to snag him and have her way, and the next morning Tank would look like the living dead. To my knowledge this was the first time she'd gotten him arrested.

"Tank and me were at this bar," Lula said. "And some drunk-ass moron started on Tank. How Tank had no neck. And how Tank looked like Shrek, except Tank wasn't green. And I was getting real annoyed because okay, all that's true, but I didn't like this guy's attitude, you see what I'm saying? And then he started calling me Shrek's fat 'ho . . . and that's when I hit him. And things sort of went in the toilet after that."

Diesel was smiling when I disconnected. "Ranger's gonna be pissed. He works hard to keep a clean, low profile."

"You know Ranger?"

"From a distance."

I called Connie and told her about Lula and Tank.

"Can you get them out?" I asked Connie.

"Probably. I'll have to make some phone calls. I'll get back to you."

Diesel and I got into my Escape. I turned the heat on high, and Diesel cracked his window.

"How do you know Ranger?" I asked him.

Diesel shrugged. "I hear things. I assume Connie is buying a judge?"

"This is a small community. We try to be civilized to each other. Connie will call in a favor."

Diesel was looking relaxed next to me, but I knew his priority was to find Annie, and it had to be on his mind.

"I know you're worried about Annie," I said. "Am I keeping you from whatever it is that you do?"

"I have wheels turning. I'll need to move when I get a call. Until then, I'm all yours."

Connie called back. "I've got the paperwork in motion. I'm going to pick it up now, and I'll meet you at the booking desk in a half hour. I'm assuming Lula and Tank are being held at the station."

"Yep. Ten-four." I turned to Diesel. "This is going to take some time. Would you mind picking Bob up at my parents' house and bringing him home for me?"

"No problem. Call me if you run into trouble."

The Trenton police are housed in a redbrick bunker in a part of town that knows a lot about crime firsthand, mandating that police cars be locked in a lot surrounded by razor wire. Unfortunately, Connie and I didn't qualify for the razor-wire lot and were forced to park on the street, which was more or less a supermarket for chop-shop scouts. Connie drove over in a crapola Beetle she kept for just such an occasion. I got two fake antennae and a big fake diamond-encrusted cross out of my console. I hung the cross on my mirror, and I stuck the antennae to the roof rack. If you didn't look too close, you'd think I was a dealer and would most likely kill you if I caught you messing with my car.

It was after normal business hours, so we had to get ourselves buzzed in. Connie was already processing the release when I arrived. There wasn't a lot going on. Too late for rush-hour road rage and too early for drunken domestic violence. A lone sad-sack gangbanger sat chained to a chair that was bolted to the floor. The amount of snot on his shirt suggested he'd been pepper-sprayed.

My buddy Eddie Gazarra was on duty behind the desk. "Sorry about Lula and Tank," he said. "I wasn't here when they came in, or I would have called you right away. Some numbskull rookie dragged their asses in here, and there wasn't anything we could do once they were booked."

"It's okay," I said. "We'll get them bonded out."

Gazarra went back to the holding cell and got Lula and Tank.

"There's no justice to this world," Lula said. "I get taken to jail, and the meany that called me a fat 'ho isn't even here."

"He's at the hospital getting his nuts extracted from his nose," Gazarra said. "He'll get charged as soon as he can walk without spitting up blood."

"How about me?" Lula said. "I got a scratch on my arm, and I'm gonna get a bruise, too. And this here's a new sweater that someone grabbed hold of and tore a hole in."

Tank wasn't saying anything. He took his belt

and shoelaces and pocketed the plastic bag with his incidentals . . . wallet, keys, loose change.

"More bad news," Gazarra said. "They towed and impounded a red Firebird that was parked illegally in a handicap space in front of the bar."

"That's my baby!" Lula said. "And it wasn't parked illegal. It had two inches sticking over the line. There was only two inches in the dumbass handicap spot."

Gazarra passed me a piece of paper. "Here's the address for the impound lot and the citation for the car. My advice is to pick it up tomorrow, because your girlfriend here is probably blowing over the alcohol limit, and with the kind of luck she's having, she'll be brought back here for DUI."

We all trudged out of the station, happy to find both cars still at the curb, unmolested. Connie zipped away, hoping to catch her television show, and I loaded Tank and Lula into my Escape.

"How about you?" I said to Tank. "Did you drive to the bar?"

Tank just looked at me.

I couldn't hold the smile back. "You drove there in a Rangeman vehicle, didn't you?"

Tank nodded. "Ranger's gonna kill me."

"Ranger doesn't have to know."

"Ranger knows everything," Tank said. His eyes held mine. *"Everything."*

Oh boy.

"What bar did you two trash?"

"Sly Dog," Tank said. "The car's in the lot alongside the bar."

Sly Dog was a watering hole for people coming to and going from events at the Sovereign Bank Arena. The complexion of the bar changed according to the event, and I wasn't sure what was going on tonight. Could have been a rock concert or a hockey game or monster trucks. It sat just outside the Burg and was maybe a half mile from Lula's apartment.

I took Perry Street to Broad Street and sailed through the center of the city, coming up behind the arena and the bar. I pulled into the lot and parked behind the black Rangeman SUV.

Lula was in the seat beside me, and Tank was in the back. I slid a look at Lula. "Is there a plan?"

"Hey, Shrek," Lula yelled back to Tank. "You got a plan?"

"Guess I should take you home," Tank said.

"Yeah," Lula said. "That would be the polite thing to do. Might have to stop at the drugstore on the way. Wouldn't want to run out of . . . you know, *anything*."

I checked Tank out in the rearview mirror, and our eyes met, and he smiled.

* * *

It was eleven o'clock by the time I got home. Lights were off in my apartment with the exception of a nightlight burning in the bathroom, throwing light into the bedroom. Diesel and Bob were asleep in bed, side by side. Diesel was bare skin for as far as I could see with an arm thrown over Bob.

I slipped into the bathroom and changed into a T-shirt and boxers. I tiptoed to the other side of the bed and crept in next to Bob.

"Did everything work out okay?" Diesel asked, his voice soft in the dark room.

"Yeah. We bonded them out, and then they went home together. This is probably a strange thing to say, but it was . . . nice. I think they really like each other."

"They're lucky."

"Is there someone like that for you? Someone you really like?"

"Right now I really like you. And I'd like you even better if you'd swap places with Bob."

"No way."

"Had to try," Diesel said.

At one o'clock, Diesel's cell phone rang. By the time I was awake and oriented, Diesel was in the middle of a conversation with the caller.

"Don't lose him," Diesel said. "Double-team if you have to and call me if he moves."

I was half sitting, propped on one elbow. "What was that?" I asked when Diesel put his phone back on the night table.

"Lou Delvina just rolled in. Parked in the driveway and scratched himself all the way from the car to his house. Flash said he got a good look at him through the kitchen window, and Delvina is covered with hives."

"Bernie!"

"Yeah, looks like it. Don't know how they're connected, but it can't be friendly if Delvina is scratching."

Bob had moved off the bed sometime during the night, and there was a big empty space between Diesel and me.

Diesel patted the space. "You could move over here," he said.

"I don't think so."

"It's warm and comfy."

"I'm warm enough."

"I could make you warmer."

"Jeez," I said. "You never give up."

"It's one of my better qualities."

It was bright sunshine when I opened an eye to Diesel. He was standing at bedside, showered and shaved and wearing a clean shirt.

"Where'd the clean shirt come from?" I asked.

"Flash brought me some clothes this morning."

"Where'd Flash get the clothes?"

"I don't know. Didn't ask."

"And you shaved. What's the occasion?"

"It's Valentine's Day. I wanted to be ready in case you got all romantic on me."

Valentine's Day. How could I forget! I dragged myself out of bed and looked at the clock. Nine. I did a sigh.

"Have a tough night?" Diesel asked.

"I don't want to talk about it."

"I could have made it a good night."

I narrowed my eyes at him. "I said I *don't* want to talk about it. I'm feeling cranky. Give me some room. And stop smiling at me with those damn dimples."

He handed me a mug of hot coffee. "I'm just trying to get your blood circulating. We have a man in motion. Lou Delvina left his house ten minutes ago. Flash is a beat behind him. I'm heading out. Do you want to be in on this?"

"No. Yes."

Diesel was hands on hips, looking down at me.

"Yes," I said. "Give me a minute."

"Forty seconds would be better."

I picked some clothes off the floor and ran into the bathroom with them. I was dressed and out in record time with a hairbrush in my hand. I grabbed a ball cap off the dresser and rammed my feet into boots. Diesel stuffed me into my jacket and handed me a new mug of coffee, and we were out of the apartment, down the hall to the elevator.

"Bob!" I said. "What about Bob?"

"I walked him and fed him. He'll be fine. He's sleeping in a patch of sun in the dining room."

We took the 'vette with Diesel driving. He peeled out of the lot and headed west on Hamilton Avenue to Route 1. He took the Route 1 bridge into Pennsylvania, and I looked across to the Warren Street bridge. TRENTON MAKES—THE WORLD TAKES was the message on the bridge. I hadn't a clue what it meant.

"How do you know where you're going?" I asked him.

"I can feel Flash in front of me. There are a couple people I connect to, and Flash is one of them. I can't always connect, but it's strong today. Probably because he's excited to be on the chase."

"Can you connect to me?"

"Sometimes."

"So you didn't bug my car?"

"No, I didn't bug your car. I dropped the bug into your purse. GPS is more reliable than this hocus-pocus crap. Unless it's raining. I have real problems in the rain. Nothing works in the rain."

We were off Route 1 and heading north toward

Yardley. Traffic was moderate. Diesel drove into Yardley and pulled to the side of the road.

"What's up?" I asked him.

"Lost Flash. It feels like he's behind me."

Diesel punched a number into his cell phone. "Lost you," he said. He turned in his seat and looked out the back window. "Yeah," he said, "I see the sign. Get me a couple of those glazed sticks and coffee." Diesel looked over at me. "Everyone stopped to get doughnuts. Do you want anything?"

"Double your order."

"Make that four glazed sticks and two coffees," Diesel told Flash.

Five minutes later, Diesel pulled back into traffic. "We have a visual," he said. "That's Flash in the blue Honda Civic in front of us. Two cars ahead of him is a black Lincoln with Jersey plates. I imagine that's our man, Delvina."

We followed Flash and Delvina for an additional ten minutes, taking a road that hugged the Delaware River. There were houses on either side of the road. Large older houses on partially wooded lots mixed with small summer cottages. We saw the black Lincoln turn into a riverside driveway and disappear behind a six-foot-high privacy hedge. Flash slowed and parked on the shoulder one house down. We parked behind him and got out of the 'vette. Flash met us halfway with the coffee and doughnuts.

"I don't think you've met," Diesel said. "Flash, Stephanie. Stephanie, Flash."

Flash was maybe five foot ten with spiked red hair and a bunch of diamond studs in his ears. He was slim, and you might place him in high school until you looked closely and saw the fine lines around his eyes. He was wearing jeans and sneakers and a ski jacket with a bunch of lift tickets hooked onto the zipper tag. I suspected he was a boarder.

I took a doughnut and coffee and thought this would be really nice if it was a social occasion. We stood there for a while, drinking coffee and eating doughnuts, waiting to see if the Lincoln was just dropping off or picking up. Fifteen minutes went by.

Diesel finished his coffee and put his cup into the empty doughnut bag. "Time to go to work," he said.

Flash crumpled his cup and added it to the bag. I tossed my remaining coffee and trashed my cup.

"There were two guys in the Lincoln," Flash said. "Delvina and a driver. Delvina came home under his own power last night and parked in the garage. This morning, the Lincoln picked him up. The driver looks like old muscle."

"It would be better if we could do this in the

dark," Diesel said, "but I don't want to wait that long."

We were standing in front of Delvina's next-door neighbor's house. It was a large colonial with a shake roof and cedar siding, no gated drive, and no privacy hedge. No lights on inside the house. There was still a dusting of snow left on the driveway. No tire tracks in the snow. The walk hadn't been salted or shoveled. Clearly, no one was living there at this time of the year. There was a patch of woods, maybe thirty feet wide, between the two houses.

"No one's in this cedar house," I said. "We can sneak along the tree line and scope things out."

Diesel beeped the 'vette locked, and we walked the cedar house property until Delvina's house could be seen peeking through the vegetation. We moved into the patch of woods to get a better look, trying to stay hidden behind scrubby evergreens.

The Delvina house was large and rambling. Two stories. The house had a four-car garage, but the Lincoln was parked in a circular drive, by the front door. There weren't a lot of windows on this side of the house. A small window up and a small window down. Most likely bathrooms. Interior plantation shutters, closed tight. Another upstairs window with drapes. Bedroom, no doubt. A large swath of frozen lawn lay between us and the house.

"We need to see inside the house," Diesel said. "We need a head count."

"Hang tight," Flash said. "This is a job for the Flashman."

Flash ran across the lawn, plastered himself against the building, and stood listening.

"Is speed his Unmentionable thing?" I asked Diesel.

"So far as I know he's not Unmentionable. He just runs fast."

Flash was creeping around the house, periodically stopping and listening, looking in windows. He turned a corner and disappeared, and Diesel and I waited patiently. Five minutes passed and my patience started to evaporate.

"Chill," Diesel said to me. "He's okay."

A couple minutes later, Flash popped into view and sprinted across the lawn, back to us.

"Delvina and his driver are in there. They're both covered with hives. They've got some kind of white cream on, but it's obviously not helping. Annie is there. She looks okay, except she has hives, too. She's wearing an ankle bracelet with a long length of chain that's attached to something in another room. I think it's a powder room. I couldn't really be sure from my angle. Everyone is in the back of the house, in the family room that's part of the kitchen. And there's another guy in chains. I think it must be Bernie. I've never seen Bernie in person, but I've seen his picture, and I think this is Bernie. I can't see the birthmark because he's also covered in hives, and his face is dotted with the white cream."

"That's weird," Diesel said. "Why would Bernie give himself hives?"

"I don't know," Flash said, "but these aren't happy people. They're all talking at the same time and waving their hands around and scratching."

"Anyone else in the house?" Diesel asked.

"Not that I could see."

"I need to get in the house, and bring Annie and Bernie out," Diesel said. "I don't want to go in like gangbusters and take a chance on someone getting hurt. I need a diversion."

Now I knew why I'd been invited along. "I guess that would be me," I said.

Diesel handed me the keys to the 'vette. "Do a damsel-in-distress routine. If you can draw them to the front of the house, we can go in the back."

I ran to the 'vette and took the wheel. I waited until there were no cars in sight, pulled around the Civic, and right-turned hard into Delvina's drive. The property wasn't gated, but the hedge had been carved into a topiary column on either side of the driveway entrance. I deliberately put the 'vette into a skid that took out Delvina's topiary column and positioned the car well into the yard. I fought the airbag and lurched out of the slightly bashed-in 'vette.

I pasted what I hoped was a dazed expression on my face and started up the driveway toward the house. I was halfway there when the door opened, and Delvina's driver looked out at me.

"What the hell was that?" he asked.

I did my best lower-lip tremble, and thought about sad things like roadkill and orphaned birthday cakes left at the bakery, and managed to sort of get a tear going down my cheek. Truth is, the tear was a challenge, but the trembling was easy. It was starting from my knees and working its way up all by itself. For the better part of my life I'd heard stories about Lou Delvina, and they all involved a lot of blood.

"I don't know what happened," I said. "All of a sudden the car went into a skid, and I h-h-hit the hedge."

Delvina appeared behind his driver, and my heart jumped into my throat.

"What the fuck happened to my hedge?" Delvina yelled.

"She skidded into it," his driver said. "Sonovabitch. You know how hard it is to grow a hedge that size?"

"I'm really sorry," I said. "I must have hit some ice on the road."

Delvina was power-walking down his driveway, swinging his arms, head stuck forward. He was a sixty-year-old bandy-legged fireplug with a lot of black hair and black caterpillar eyebrows. Hard to tell the normal color of his complexion as it was all red hives and white salve and looked to be purple under the salve.

"I don't fucking believe this," Delvina said. "Is there anything else that could friggin' go wrong? This whole week is caca."

Delvina marched past me and went straight to his hedge. "Oh jeez, just *look* at this," he said. "One of the plants is all broken. There's gonna be a big hole here until this grows."

I'd sort of gotten over the weak-knee thing, since I'd had a chance to check both guys out and knew they weren't packing. Maybe an ankle holster, but that didn't worry me so much. I'd seen cops try to get their gun out of an ankle holster and knew it involved a lot of swearing and hopping around on one foot. I figured by the time Delvina could get his gun off his ankle I'd be long gone, running down the road. In fact, I was having a hard time not going narrow-eyed and pissy because I'd gone to all the trouble to manufacture a tear and no one was noticing. I mean, it's not every day I can pull that off.

The driver had joined Delvina. "Maybe you could do a transplant or something," the driver said. "You know, one of them grafts."

"Christ, my wife's gonna go apeshit on this. This is gonna ruin her whole garden club standing if we can't get this fixed." Delvina had his hand under his shirt and down the front of his pants. "Oh man, I got hives inside and out. I swear to God, you should just shoot me."

"It's them people," the driver said, scratching his ass. "They're putting the juju on us. I say we dump them in the Delaware."

Delvina looked back at the house. "You could be right. I'm getting tired of them anyway. And I'm starting to think the heartsy-fartsy lady doesn't have what we want."

Delvina and the driver started to walk back to the house, and so far, I hadn't gotten any kind of a sign from Diesel, mystical or otherwise, that the coast was clear.

"Hey," I yelled to Delvina. "What about my car?"

"What about it?" Delvina asked. "Don't it drive? It don't look so bad to me."

"You got a cell phone, right?" the driver said.

"Call your club. You got a new 'vette. You probably belong to a club. Like AAA or something."

The right side of the 'vette was scraped, and the front right light was smushed in. Pieces of hedge were stuck in the headlight and slightly crumpled hood. I got behind the wheel and raced the motor.

Delvina and his driver were hands on hips, looking at me like I was another hive on their backside. It was cold, and they were standing there in shirtsleeves. They weren't excited about doing the backyard mechanic thing. Fortunately, they were full-on chauvinists who couldn't see me for anything more than a dumb bimbo. If Flash had run into the hedge, neither of them would have left the house without a nine rammed into the small of his back. Still, I was trying their patience, and it was only a matter of time before they figured it out and they went for the ankle holster.

I had one eye on Delvina and one eye looking beyond him to the patch of woods. Finally Diesel emerged and gave me a thumbs-up. I did a small head nod to Diesel and blew out a sigh of relief.

"You're right," I said to Delvina. "I guess the car's okay. Sorry about your hedge." And I carefully backed up, changed gears, and rolled down the driveway and out onto the road. I had my teeth clamped into my lower lip, and I was holding my breath. Sprigs of hedge were flying off the grille, and the right front tire was making a grinding sound, but I kept going until I was around a bend in the road.

Chapter
TWELVE

I pulled to the shoulder and sat and waited, and after a couple minutes, the blue Honda Civic came into view. Diesel got out and jogged over to me.

"Are you okay?" he asked.

"Yes. Do you have Annie and Bernie in the Civic?"

Diesel picked some hedge off the windshield wiper. "Yes. Is this car driveable?"

"The right-side tire is making grinding noises."

Diesel checked out the right-side tire and pulled a large piece of hedge from the wheel well.

"That should help," he said. "Hop over the console. I'm driving."

I scrambled into the passenger seat, and Diesel took the wheel. He eased onto the road, drove a short distance, and made a U-turn. Flash did the same. Diesel waved Flash on, and Flash took the lead. We flew past Delvina's house and retraced our route until we were over the bridge and back in Jersey.

"So far as I can tell, Delvina doesn't know about Annie's apartment," Diesel said. "I'm going to bring Annie and Bernie there to regroup."

"Did Bernie give himself hives?"

"Apparently he went out of control and infected everyone around him, including himself. I didn't get a chance to find out much more than that."

We motored through town, parked in the underground garage, and took the elevator to Annie's floor. Diesel opened the door, and I turned and looked at Flash and grimaced. His face was breaking out in hives.

"Oh shit," Bernie said to Flash. "I'm really sorry. I'm not doing it on purpose, I swear. The rash is just leaking out of me."

Flash scratched his stomach. "They're coming out all over. What do I do?"

"Get away from Bernie and try a cortisone cream," Diesel said.

Flash ran down the hall and punched the elevator button.

Bernie limped into Annie's apartment. "I've got hives on the bottom of my feet," he said to Diesel. "I've got them everywhere. You have to help me. I don't ever want to see another hive."

I was keeping as far away from Bernie as possible. I was in the hallway leading to the bedroom, looking at everyone else in the living room.

"What about Annie?" Diesel said. "Are you going to leave her alone?"

"I've been chained to Annie for two days. I don't ever want to see her again either."

"I thought we bonded," Annie said.

Bernie scratched his arm. "Yeah, maybe. I guess you're okay. I don't know. I can't think straight. I just want to soak in some cold water or something."

"I talked to Betty," I said to Bernie. "She'd like to stay married, but she has some requests."

"Anything! Cripes, look at this. I've got a hive under my fingernail!"

"I'm going to take you home and get you some salve," Diesel said, "but first I need to know about Delvina. How'd he manage to get you and Annie?"

"I was nuts," Bernie said. "I was trying to get to Annie, but you moved her out of her house, and I couldn't find her. So I got this idea that maybe she left something behind that would give me a clue. You know, like an address written on a pad. It happens all the time on television. Problem was, I broke into her house and ran into two goons who were tearing the place apart. I'm so dumb. I just walked right in on them."

"Delvina was the original owner of the necklace," Annie said. "We overheard him and his driver talking and pieced the story together. The necklace had a bank account number engraved on the back of it. It sounded like Delvina was being investigated for tax fraud, and he didn't want the necklace on his property, so he gave it to his girlfriend. When he found out she hocked it, he almost had a seizure." Annie started to scratch her arm and stopped in mid-scratch and rammed her hands into her pockets. "He came really close to getting the necklace back, but for some reason the pawnshop owner decided to fake the robbery. So of course, Delvina came looking for me."

"It was bad timing that I happened along," Bernie said. "They didn't find the necklace in Annie's house, but since I broke in they figured I had to have some connection to Annie. And then they were fooling around and found her number in my cell phone. So one of Delvina's men called her and said he was me."

"He sort of sounded like you," Annie said. "He said he had something important to say to me. I was hoping you'd calmed down and wanted to talk. I didn't want to miss the opportunity."

"Annie didn't want to go far, so they set a meeting for a coffee house half a block away. When she got there, they snatched her," Bernie said.

"Why didn't you take your purse?" I asked Annie.

"I was just walking down the street for a couple minutes," Annie said. "I had some money and my key in my pocket, and I thought I had my phone, but it must have fallen out of my pocket somewhere. I didn't think I needed anything more than that."

"They brought us to Delvina's summer house on the river," Bernie said. "That was Saturday night. They chained us up, and I went sort of gonzo, and everyone broke out in hives, including me. Then Delvina and his two goons packed up and left. I guess they didn't know what to make of the hives. And then the next morning, Delvina and some other guy showed up and started asking about the necklace, but every time they'd come near us the hives would get worse and pretty soon they couldn't stand it anymore and went away. Good thing we were chained to the bathroom, and the chain was long enough to reach to the refrigerator in the kitchen. They came back this morning and next thing, you rescued us."

"How are my last five cases?" Annie asked. "Are they all going to have a good Valentine's Day? Are they on their way to love everlasting?"

"I don't know about the love everlasting," I said. "But I'm pretty sure they'll all have a good Valentine's Day. Except for Albert Kloughn. Kloughn is last up."

"Oh dear," Annie said, "it's getting late."

"Not to worry. I have a plan." I looked over at Bernie. "You've stopped scratching," I said to him.

"I'm too tired to scratch."

Too bad Bernie was so tired. I wouldn't mind driving him to a couple people I knew and spreading some hives around. For starters, there'd be my ex-husband, Dickie Orr, and my arch-nemesis, Joyce Barnhardt.

"I'm going to take you home to your wife," Diesel said to Bernie. "I'm going to drop you off at the curb, and you're on your own."

"You'll do no such thing," Annie said. "You'll drive us to a drugstore so Bernie can get a Valentine's card and a box of candy. And then we'll all go in and make sure things run smoothly between Bernie and Betty."

Annie had good intentions, but I was starting to think she came from the Planet Ick!

"I heard that," Diesel said to me.

"Did not."

"Did so."

"It was a thought!"

"And?"

"It's almost noon," I said to Annie and Diesel. "You can drop me off at my apartment on your way to Bernie's house in Hamilton Township. I need to check on Bob and get my car. Then I have to see if Lula needs a ride to get her Firebird out of impound. And I want to see how Jeanine and Charlene and Larry Burlew are doing. And last but not least, here's my plan for Kloughn and my sister. I thought I'd tell them I was getting married, and I needed them to be witnesses. I'll tell my parents and my grandmother the same thing. Then everyone will congregate at my parents' house. We'll get a justice of the peace to show up, and at the last minute we'll swap me out for Valerie and Albert Kloughn. I'm afraid if I don't fib to them someone will leak to Kloughn, and he'll be on a plane to Buenos Aires."

"Brilliant," Annie said. "I can facilitate the justice of the peace and the paperwork. I have very good connections for that sort of thing."

Diesel looked down at me. "Who's going to be the bogus groom?"

"It's going to have to be you. You're all I've got today."

"Do I get a conjugal night?"

"Afraid not," I told him.

"We'll see," Diesel said.

"We have a lot to accomplish," Annie said. "We should get moving. We can take my car. We won't all fit in Diesel's Corvette."

I called Valerie as soon as I got back to my apartment. "I'm getting married this afternoon," I said to her. "I want you and Albert to be my witnesses."

"Holy cow," Valerie said. "This is so sudden. Who are you going to marry?"

"Diesel."

Silence.

"Hello?" I said to Valerie.

"Are you sure you want to marry him?"

"Yep. Can you come to the wedding?"

"Sure," Valerie said. "What time?"

"Four o'clock. And I'm going to get married at home."

"Does Mom know?"

"Not yet."

"Oh boy."

"Maybe we shouldn't tell her," I said. "Maybe we should just all show up."

"That sounds like a better way to go," Valerie said. "If you give her four hours, she'll hire caterers and a band and have the house filled with flowers and two hundred people."

"Yeah, but I can count on you and Albert to be there, right?"

"Absolutely. Are you pregnant?"

"Uh, maybe."

"This will be so amazing. We can have our babies together."

"I didn't say for sure."

"I know, and I won't tell anyone. My mouth is zippered shut."

"Thanks, Val."

Bob was in the kitchen, smiling at me.

"Wipe that goofy expression off your face," I said to Bob. "You're not fooling anyone. You ate my couch. There are big holes in all the cushions, and all the insides are coming out."

There was a piece of fiberfill stuck to Bob's lip. I picked it off and dropped it on the floor with all the other big fluffy blobs of fiberfill.

"I hope this works," I said to Bob. "The alternative is stun gun, and I don't think that would look great in Val's wedding album."

I took Bob out for a walk around the block. When he was empty, we drove to the bonds office.

Lula and Connie were huddled together when I walked in.

"Look at this big-ass box of chocolates I got," Lula said, working her way around a lump of caramel. "I got it from my sweetie for Valentine's Day. This here's gonna be the best Valentine's Day ever."

Connie and Lula had the huge red heart sitting on Connie's desk. The top was off and the box was half empty.

"You better get some before they're all gone," Connie said to me. "We decided this was lunch."

"Which sweetie sent this?" I asked Lula.

"The *big* sweetie," Lula said. "And anyways, I only got one sweetie now. He's my great huge gigantic hunk of burning love. You don't think Ranger will actually kill him, do you?"

"Ranger and Tank are like brothers."

"Yeah, but remember in *The Godfather* where they offed poor Fredo?"

"Ranger's not going to *off* Tank."

I suspected Ranger would privately think the whole jail thing was pretty funny.

"What's up today?" Lula wanted to know.

"I'm going to check on Jeanine and Charlene and Larry Burlew. Want to ride along?"

"Hell yeah. I could use some air after eating all this candy. I'm feeling seasick. And what's with that nasty red thing in the middle of your forehead? You keep scratching at it. And you got another one in the middle of your cheek."

I ran to the bathroom and looked in the mirror. I had hives! Shit. Double shit.

First stop was the drugstore for salve. Second stop was the DMV. Charlene was behind the counter, looking all smiley-faced. She waved when she saw us, and we cut to the front of the line.

"Excuse us," Lula said to a bunch of grumblers. "We're here doing Cupid patrol. And you need a attitude adjustment or Cupid's gonna pass you by this year."

"I want to thank you again for babysitting," Charlene said.

"No problem. Just wanted to make sure everything was okay."

"Better than okay," Charlene said. "What's on
your face?"

"See, now isn't that nice," Lula said on the way
out of the building. "Don't that make you feel all
warm inside? I told you love was in the air."

Next stop was Larry Burlew's butcher shop.

Burlew was waiting on a customer, so Lula and
I stepped to the side. I looked across the street at
the coffee shop and saw Jet waving to me. She
smiled and gave me a thumbs-up. I thumbs-upped
her back.

The customer left, and I stepped forward. "How
did the dinner work out?" I asked Burlew.

"It was wonderful. The meat was perfect. And
we served it with baby carrots and new potatoes.
And then last night we made rack of lamb, and it
was sensational."

"Yeah, but did you get any?" Lula wanted to
know.

"Sure," Burlew said. "There was plenty to go
around. We even had leftovers."

Lula cut her eyes to me. "Gonna have to get Diesel to talk to him in private."

"I made restaurant reservations tonight for Jet
and me," Burlew said. "It's Valentine's Day." He
looked more closely at me. "Do you have hives?

You know, they're usually an allergic reaction to something. Have you had any shellfish lately?"

"Have a wonderful night," I said to him, trying really hard not to scratch the hive on my forehead. "Call me if you need any more help."

"Is he a apple dumpling, or what?" Lula said, sliding into the Escape. "That Jet is a lucky woman. Not every girl gets a man who has a way with meat like that."

I looked in my rearview mirror and dabbed on more salve.

It was a workday, and Jeanine would be at the button factory and inaccessible, so I tried calling her on her cell.

"'Lo," Jeanine said.

"It's Stephanie Plum," I told her. "I'm just checking in to see if everything's okay. Why don't I hear any machine noises in the background?"

"I'm home with the worst hangover in the history of the world."

"How'd it go last night?"

"I think it went okay. Can't remember a lot of it, but he was still here when I woke up this morning, so that's a real good sign, right?"

"Right!"

"Turned out he wasn't a virgin, but he wasn't all that experienced either, so we watched the movie together and tried a bunch of stuff, and then I think we passed out. Anyway, he sent me flowers this morning, and we're going out again tonight."

"Wow, that's great, Jeanine. I'm really happy for you."

"Yeah, I'm happy, too, but I'm going to get off the phone and throw up now."

"I think Bob needs to celebrate all this romance shit with a large fries," Lula said. "He's been a real good dog just sitting back there, but he looks hungry."

"Bob ate a couch this morning."

"Well okay, then I need the large fries. I need some carbs and grease to balance out all the chocolate."

I hit the drive-through window at Cluck-in-a-Bucket and got a monster bucket of fries and a couple sodas and a cheeseburger for Bob. I parked in the Bucket lot and tossed Bob his burger.

Diesel pulled up beside me, got out of his 'vette, and leaned in the window. "Oh man, is that a hive on your forehead? Honey, it's *huge.*"

"Do you have any?"

"No," Diesel said. "My immune system is exceptionally strong."

"He's good," Lula said. "He found you without a phone call. He's like a white Ranger."

"I'm carrying a bug," I said to Lula.

"You mean like James Bond shit? Like when he

gets stuff from one of the alphabet men. Who is it?
M? Q? Z?"

"Is there a special Unmentionable guy who
makes bugs for you?" I asked Diesel.

"No. I bought the little devil on the Internet.
EBay. Got a real good price. Only used once by
some guy who thought his wife was cheating.
Wanted to let you know Annie has everything arranged. The justice of the peace will be at your
parents' house promptly at four."

Lula paused with her fries. "Say what?"

"It's a long story," I said. "The short version is
Diesel and I are pretending to get married, so we
can get Kloughn to marry Valerie."

"Does Morelli know about this?"

"It's *pretend*."

"I'm not even gonna ask if Ranger knows. Poor
ol' Diesel here be dead if Ranger knew."

I looked at Diesel.

"Maybe," Diesel said, "but not likely. It's hard
to kill me. I don't have to get dressed up for this,
do I?"

"I better be invited to this," Lula said. "I'd be really pissed off if you got married without inviting
me. And if you want to keep your job, you better
invite Connie, too."

"It's not a real wedding," I told her.

"Hell, I don't care. Pretend. Real. It's a wedding. Is there gonna be cake?"

"No cake."

"What kind of cheap-ass wedding hasn't got cake?"

"She's right," I said to Diesel. "We should have a cake."

"I can see I need to take charge of this," Lula said. "Here's what we gonna do. Drop me off at the office, and I'll round up Connie, and we'll go get a cake. Then you and Diesel and Bob can go welcome the guests, 'cause it's almost four."

"There aren't any guests," I said. "This is a family wedding."

"Whatever," Lula said. "Let's get going."

"How'd it go with Bernie?" I asked Diesel on the way to my parents' house.

"He's back with Betty. At least for a while. And he's lost his ability to give people hives. When we get Kloughn married off, all the loose ends will be tied, and you can have Annie."

"Probably the charges will be dropped by the time I bring Annie in. If not, I'll make sure she's immediately bonded out again, so she doesn't sit in jail."

"Appreciate it," Diesel said. "She's from the Planet Ick, but she's a good person."

Chapter
THIRTEEN

"This is a surprise," my mother said when Diesel and Bob and I walked through the door. "Are you staying for dinner?" Her eyes got wide. "What's that on your forehead?"

"It's a hive, and we just came to visit."

"You don't get hives," my mother said. "I've never known you to get hives."

Grandma bustled in from the kitchen. "Look at this, it's the big guy! Isn't this a treat."

"Thanks," Diesel said.

I gave him an elbow. "She's talking about Bob."

A car door slammed behind us, and Mary Alice galloped into the house. She was followed by Angie and Albert and Valerie with the baby. They were all dressed up.

"Goodness," my mother said. "What's going on?"

"Did you tell her?" Valerie asked.

"No. I just got here."

"Well, tell her!" Valerie said. "This is so exciting!"

The doorbell rang. It was Annie and the justice of the peace.

"Oh dear," Annie said when she saw my forehead.

Annie was hives from head to toe, but they were fading, and she was uniformly covered in white salve and makeup.

My father was in the living room, watching television. He turned the sound up and hunkered down in his chair.

I looked at Diesel. He was rocked back on his heels, smiling. "Go ahead, honey," he said to me. "Tell them the happy news."

"I'm getting to it," I said.

"What?" Grandma wanted to know. "What?"

"Diesel and I have decided to get married . . . today."

My mother went white and made the sign of the cross. "Holy Mary, mother of God . . ."

"What about Joseph?" Grandma asked.

I could feel panic rising in my throat. I looked to Diesel for help.

"He's out of town," Diesel said.

I inadvertently made a sort of strangling sound. "Ulk."

"It was all I could think of," Diesel whispered. "I'm not good at this crap."

My mother sucked in some air. "You're pregnant," she said.

"No!"

"Isn't this fab?" Valerie gurgled. "Two new babies!"

Now my father was on his feet. "Babies? Who's having babies?"

"Stephanie," Valerie said. "She's going to have a baby, and she's getting married."

My father was confused. He looked around the room. No Joe. No Ranger. His eyes locked on Diesel. "Not the psycho," he said.

Diesel blew out a sigh.

My father turned to my mother. "Get me the carving knife. Make sure it's sharp."

The doorbell rang again, and Lula and Connie rushed in with the cake. It was a huge wedding cake. Three tiers with a bride and groom on top.

"We got it," Lula said. "Mary Beth Krienski got cold feet and called off her wedding over the weekend, and we got this kick-ass bargain cake. Tasty Pastry was getting ready to heave it into the Dumpster. We got there just in time."

"It's yellow cake with lemon between the layers," Connie said.

"Put the cake on the dining room table," Grandma

said. "Do I look okay for the pictures? Is my hair okay?"

Pictures! Val would want wedding pictures. "I didn't think to bring a camera," I said.

"That's okay," Valerie said. "I brought my camera."

"Yeah, and Connie and me stopped at the store and got one of them happy-snappy things," Lula said.

"You gotta have pictures of the bride," Grandma said.

All eyes turned to me. I'd gotten rushed out of the house this morning. I was still wearing the clothes I grabbed off the floor, and I had a ball cap on my head. And two big red hives on my face.

"That's okay, pumpkin," Diesel said to me. "I think you look . . . cute."

I introduced Annie and the justice of the peace, and Albert Kloughn broke out in a sweat.

"I thought I recognized you," he said to Annie. "We met just once, and it was a while ago."

Annie smiled at him. "It's so nice to see you again, Albert."

Albert was wearing a suit and tie, and he tugged at his shirt collar. "Can't breathe," he said.

"I'm in a hurry to get married," I yelled.

"We need to get some papers signed," Annie said. "Albert, you sign here as a witness. And Valerie. And here for Stephanie."

I watched Diesel sign. "Just Diesel?" I said to him. "No last name?"

"That's all I've got," Diesel said. "My name's Diesel."

"I need a bathroom," Albert said.

"No!" I told him. "You're gonna have to hold it. Everyone get in their places. Valerie, you stand next to me. And Albert, you stand next to Diesel."

The justice of the peace jumped into action and whipped out his little book with the ceremony in it.

Lula snapped a picture and my mother started crying.

Albert stood rooted to the spot, his face white but his cheeks stained red. Diesel grabbed Albert by the back of his suit jacket and dragged him to his side, so we were all four in a row.

"Are we ready to begin?" the justice asked.

"Yes," I said, "but we need to change places. This is actually going to be Valerie's and Albert's wedding."

Albert went down to his knees, and Diesel yanked him up to his feet, still holding tight to Albert's jacket.

The justice started reading from his script. "Dearly beloved—"

"Skip ahead to the *I do* part," I said to the justice.

The justice thumbed over a couple pages in his book.

"I'm going to be sick," Albert said.

"Dude," Diesel said. "Suck it up."

Albert went down to his knees again. "I got this thing about weddings."

"You were okay when you thought it was mine," Diesel said. "Just pretend it's mine."

"I can't pretend," Albert said. "I'm no good at pretending."

"We could have a double wedding," Valerie said. "Simultaneous. Then Albert could concentrate on being the best man."

I felt another hive break out on my chin. "I need my salve," I said. "Somebody get me some salve."

"It's not a bad idea," Annie said. "The universe would rest easier if Diesel was married."

"I'm *not* marrying Diesel!" I told Annie.

"Hey," Diesel said, "a lot of women would give anything to snag me."

"I'm not a lot of women."

"No shit," Diesel said. He shifted Albert from one hand to the other. "Can we get on with it? This guy's getting heavy."

"Would you really marry me?" I asked Diesel.

"Not forever, but a night might be fun."

Good grief.

"I'm confused," my father said. "Who's getting married?"

"Albert and Valerie are getting married," I said.

I turned to Albert. "Here's the choice. You can go through this with your eyes open, or I can go get my stun gun, and you can get married with your eyes closed and your body twitching on the floor. My sister is pregnant again, and I'm going to make sure she's married."

Albert's mouth was open and his eyes were glazed.

"I'm going to take this as a choice to keep eyes open," I said to the justice of the peace. "Start reading. And hurry up."

"Do you—" the justice said to Albert.

"He does," we all said in unison.

"Me, too," Valerie said.

And Valerie and Albert were married.

"Let's cut the cake," Lula said.

My grandmother trotted in with a cake knife, and we clustered around the cake. It was a great cake, except Bob had eaten all the icing off one side.

"It's better this way," Grandma said. "You got a choice like white meat or dark meat, only this time it's icing or no icing."

I ran upstairs to the bathroom to look for more salve.

Diesel came up a minute later with a piece of cake for me. "That was a nice thing you did for your sister," Diesel said.

"How's Albert?"

"Deliriously happy."

"I think they've found true love."

Diesel nodded and fed me a piece of cake. "I have to go. I'm being reassigned."

"So soon?"

"Yeah, but I'll be back. You owe me a night."

"I do *not* owe you a night."

"I was willing to go the distance," Diesel said. "That has to be worth something."

"How about beer and pizza?"

"It's a start," Diesel said. "And don't worry about Delvina. I changed him into a toad."

The doorbell rang, and I heard Grandma hustle to get the door.

"Stephanie," she yelled up the stairs. "There's a flower delivery guy here, and he's got a bunch of flowers for you. The flower guy said two of these were supposed to go to your apartment, but I said you'd take them all here."

I went downstairs with Diesel following, and I took three boxes from Grandma.

The first box held a single perfect long-stemmed red rose. No card.

The second box held a dozen yellow roses. The message on the card was . . . LOVE, JOE.

The third box held a bouquet of daisies. The hand-scrawled note said . . . VALENTINE'S DAY SUCKS, USUALLY.

Valentine's Day didn't suck this year, I thought.

I felt someone brush a kiss across the nape of my neck, and I turned to Diesel, but the only thing behind me was the cake plate sitting on the bottom step.

PLUM LUCKY

*I'd like to acknowledge the invaluable assistance
of Alex Evanovich, Peter Evanovich, and
my St. Martin's Press editor and friend,
SuperJen Enderlin.*

ONE

My mother and grandmother raised me to be a good girl, and I have no problem with the *girl* part. I like men, malls, and carbs. Not necessarily in that order. The *good* part has been spotty. I don't steal cars or sniff glue, but I've had a lot of impure thoughts. And I've acted on a bunch of them. Not limited to, but including, snooping through a guy's closet in search of his underwear. On the surface, this doesn't sound like a majorly hot experience, but this was no ordinary guy, and I couldn't find any underwear.

My mother and my Grandma Mazur are *really* good. They pray every day and go to church regularly. I have good intentions, but religion, for me, is like tennis. I play an excellent mental game, and in my mind's eye I look terrific in the little white skirt, but the reality is I never actually get onto the court.

It's usually when I'm in the shower that I think of things spiritual and mystical and wonder about the unknown. Like, is there life after death? And just what, exactly, is collagen? And suppose Wonder Woman actually exists. If she was discreet, you might not know, right?

Today is St. Patrick's Day, and when I was in the shower this morning, my thoughts were about luck. How does it work? Why are some people flat-out lucky and others not so lucky? Virgil said fortune favors the bold. Okay, so I read that on the stall door in the ladies' room of the multiplex last week, and I don't personally know Virgil, but I like his thinking. Still, there has to be something else going on besides being bold. Things we can't comprehend.

My name is Stephanie Plum, and I try to leave the incomprehensible in the shower. Life is tough enough without walking around all day wondering why God invented cellulite. I'm a skip tracer for my cousin Vinnie's bail bonds agency in Trenton, New Jersey, and I spend my day hunting felons who are hiding in attics. It was a little after nine A.M. and I was on the sidewalk in front of the bonds office with my sidekick, Lula.

"You're a holiday shirker," Lula said. "Every time a holiday comes up, you don't do your part. Here it is St. Patrick's Day and you don't have no green on you. You're lucky there's no holiday police because they'd haul your boney behind off to the shirker's dungeon."

"I don't own anything green." Okay, an olive drab T-shirt, but it was dirty.

"I own lots of green. I look good in it," Lula said. "But then, I look good in all colors. Maybe not brown on account of it blends with my skin tone. Brown's too much of a good thing on me."

Lula's borderline too much of a good thing in lots of ways. It isn't exactly that Lula is fat; it's more that she's too short for her weight and her clothes are too small for the volume of flesh she carries. Her attitude is Jersey times ten, and today her hair was candy-apple red. She was packed into shamrock-green animal-print stretch pants, a matching green sequin-encrusted stretchy top, and spike-heeled dark green suede ankle boots. Lula was a hooker before she took the job at the bonds office, and I was guessing this outfit was left over from the St. Patrick's Day fantasy collection.

Truth is, I sometimes feel a little boring and incredibly pale when I'm with Lula. I'm of Hungarian and Italian descent, and my complexion is more Eastern European than Mediterranean. I have shoulder-length, unexceptional, curly brown hair, blue eyes, and a nice nose that I inherited from the Mazur side of the family. I was in my usual jeans and sneakers and long-sleeved T-shirt that carried the Rangers hockey team logo. The temperature was in the fifties, and Lula and I were bundled into

hooded sweatshirts. Lula's sweatshirt said KISS ME
I'M PRETENDING I'M IRISH, and mine was gray with
a small chocolate ice cream stain on the cuff.

Lula and I were on our way to get a Lucky
Clucky Shake at Cluck-in-a-Bucket, and Lula was
rooting through her purse, trying to find her car
keys.

"I know I got those keys in here somewhere,"
Lula said, pulling stuff out of her purse, piling
everything onto the hood of her car. Gum, lip balm,
stun gun, cell phone, a forty-caliber nickel-plated
Glock, Tic Tacs, a can of Mace, a personal-mood
candle, a flashlight, handcuffs, a screwdriver, nail
polish, the pearl-handled Derringer she got as
a Valentine's Day present from her honey, Tank,
a musical bottle opener, a roll of toilet paper,
Rolaids . . .

"A screwdriver?" I asked her.

"You never know when you'll need one. You'd
be surprised what you could do with a screwdriver.
I got extra-strength cherry-scented condoms in
here, too. 'Cause you never know when Tank might
be needing some emergency quality time."

Lula found her key, we piled into her red Firebird, and she motored away from the curb. She
turned off Hamilton Avenue onto Columbus Avenue, and we both gaped at the gray-haired, wiry
little old lady half a block away. The woman was

dressed in white tennis shoes, bright green stretch pants, and a gray wool jacket. She had a white bakery bag in one hand and the strap to a large canvas duffel bag in the other. And she was struggling to drag the duffel bag down the sidewalk.

Lula squinted through the windshield. "That's either Kermit the Frog or your granny."

Grandma Mazur's lived with my parents ever since my Grandpa Harry went to the big trans-fat farm in the sky. Grandma was a closet free spirit for the first seventy years of her life. She kicked the door open when my grandpa died, and now nobody can get her back in. Personally, I think she's great . . . but then, I don't have to live with her.

A car wheeled around the corner and rocked to a stop alongside Grandma.

"Don't look like there's anybody driving that car," Lula said. "I don't see no head."

The driver's side door opened, and a little man jumped out. He was slim, with curly, short-cropped gray hair, and he was wearing green slacks.

"Look at that," Lula said. "Granny's wearing green and the little tiny man's wearing green. Everybody's wearing green except you. Don't you feel like a party pooper?"

The little man was talking to Grandma, and Grandma wasn't looking happy with him. Grandma started inching away, and the little man snatched the strap of the duffel bag and yanked it out of Grandma's hand. Grandma roundhoused the man on the side of his head with her big black purse, and he dropped to his knees.

"She handles herself real good, considering she's so old and rickety," Lula said.

Grandma hit the little man again. He grabbed her, and the two of them went down to the ground, locked together, rolling around kicking and slapping.

I wrenched the door open, swung out of the Firebird, and waded into the mix. I pulled the little man off Grandma and held him at arm's length.

He squirmed and grunted and flailed his arms. "Let me go!" he yelled, his voice pinched from the exertion. "Do you have any idea who I am?"

"Are you okay?" I asked Grandma.

"Of course I'm okay," Grandma said. "I was winning, too. Didn't it look like I was winning?"

Lula clattered over in her high-heeled boots, got Grandma under the armpits, and hoisted her to her feet.

"When I grow up, I wanna be just like you," Lula said to Grandma.

I swung my attention back to the little man, but he was gone. His car door slammed shut, the engine caught, and the car sped down the street.

"Sneaky little bugger," Lula said. "One minute

you had a hold of him, and then next thing he's driving away."

"He wanted my bag," Grandma said. "Can you imagine? He said it was his, so I asked him to prove it. And that's when he tried to run off with it."

I looked down at the bag. "What's in it?"

"None of your beeswax."

"What's in the bakery bag?"

"Jelly doughnuts."

"I wouldn't mind a jelly doughnut," Lula said. "A jelly doughnut would go real good with the Lucky Clucky Shake."

"I love them shakes," Grandma said. "I'll share my doughnuts if you take me for a shake, but you gotta leave my duffel bag alone. No one's allowed to snoop in my duffel bag."

"You don't got a body in there, do you?" Lula wanted to know. "I don't like carrying dead guys around in my Firebird. Messes with the feng shui."

"I couldn't fit a body in here," Grandma said. "It's too little for a body."

"It could be a leprechaun body," Lula said. "It's St. Patrick's Day. If you bagged a leprechaun, you could make him take you to his pot of gold."

"I don't know. I hear you gotta be careful of them leprechauns. I hear they're tricky," Grandma said. "Anyways, I haven't got a leprechaun."

* * *

The day after St. Patrick's Day, I woke up next to Joe Morelli, my almost always boyfriend. Morelli's a Trenton cop, and he makes me look like an amateur when it comes to the impure thoughts. Not that he's kinky or weird. More that he's frighteningly healthy. He has wavy black hair, expressive brown eyes, a perpetual five o'clock shadow, an eagle tattoo from his navy days, and a tightly muscled, entirely edible body. He's recently become moderately domesticated, having inherited a small house from his Aunt Rose.

Commitment issues and a strong sense of self-preservation keep us from permanently cohabitating. Genuine affection and the impure thoughts bring Morelli to my bed when our schedules allow intersection. I knew from the amount of sunlight streaming into my bedroom that Morelli had overslept. I turned to look at the clock, and Morelli came awake.

"I'm late," he said.

"Gee, that's too bad," I told him. "I had big plans for this morning."

"Such as?"

"I was going to do things to you that don't even have names. Really hot things."

Morelli smiled at me. "I might be able to find a few minutes. . . ."

"You would need more than a few minutes for what I have in mind. It could go on for hours."

Morelli blew out a sigh and rolled out of bed. "I don't have hours. And I've been with you long enough to know when you're yanking my chain."

"You doubt my intentions?"

"Cupcake, my best shot at morning sex is to tackle you while you're still sleeping. Once you're awake, all you can think about is coffee."

"Not true." Sometimes I thought about pancakes and doughnuts.

Morelli's big, orange, shaggy-haired dog climbed onto the bed and settled into the spot Morelli had vacated.

"I was supposed to be at a briefing ten minutes ago," Morelli said. "If you take Bob out to do his thing, I can jump in the shower, meet you in the parking lot, and only miss the first half of the meeting."

Five minutes later, I handed Bob over to Morelli and watched his SUV chug away. I returned to the building, took the elevator back to my second-floor apartment, let myself in, and scuffed into the kitchen. I started coffee brewing, and my phone rang.

"Your grandmother is missing," my mother said. "She was gone when I got up this morning. She left a note that said she was hitting the open road. I don't know what that means."

"Maybe she went to a diner with one of her friends. Or maybe she walked up to the bakery."

"It's been hours, and she's not back. And I called all her friends. No one's seen her."

Okay, so I had to admit it was a little worrisome. Especially since she'd had the mysterious duffel bag yesterday and had been attacked by the little man in the green pants. Seemed far-fetched that there would be a connection, but the possibility made my stomach feel squishy.

"This is your grandmother we're talking about," my mother said. "She could be on the side of the road hitchhiking a ride to Vegas. You find people, right? That's what you do for a living. Find your grandmother."

"I'm a bounty hunter. I'm not a magician. I can't just conjure up Grandma."

"You're all I've got," my mother said. "Come over and look for clues. I've got maple link sausages. I've got coffee cake and scrambled eggs."

"Deal," I said. "Give me ten minutes."

I hung up, turned around, and bumped into a big guy. I shrieked and jumped back.

"Chill," he said, reaching out for me, drawing me close for a friendly kiss on the top of the head. "You just about broke my eardrum. You need to learn to relax."

"Diesel!"

"Yeah. Did you miss me?"

"No."

"That's a fib," he said. "Do I smell coffee?"

Diesel drops into my life every now and then. Actually, this visit makes it only three times, but it seems like more. He's solid muscle, gorgeous, and scruffy, and he smells like everything a woman wants . . . sex and fresh-baked cookies and a hint of Christmas. Okay, I know that's an odd combination, but it works for Diesel. Maybe because he's not entirely normal . . . but then, who is? He has unruly sandy blond hair and assessing brown eyes. He smiles a lot, and he's pushy and rude and inexplicably charming. And he can do things ordinary men can't do. At least, that's the story he tells.

"What are you doing here?" I asked him.

"I'm looking for someone. You don't mind if I hang out here for a couple days, do you?"

"Yes!"

He glanced at my coat. "Are you going somewhere?"

"I'm going to my mother's for breakfast."

"I'm in."

I blew out a sigh, grabbed my purse and car keys, and we trooped out of my apartment and down the hall. Mrs. Finley from 3D was already in the elevator when we entered. She sucked in some air and pressed herself against the wall.

"It's okay," I said to her. "He's harmless."

"Hah," Diesel said.

Diesel was wearing an outfit that looked like it belonged in the street-person edition of *GQ*. Jeans with a rip in the knee, dusty shit-kicker boots, a T-shirt advertising Corona beer, a ratty gray unzipped sweatshirt over the shirt. Two days of beard. Hair that looked like he'd styled it with an eggbeater. Not that I should judge. I wasn't exactly looking like a suburban sex goddess. My hair was uncombed, I had my feet shoved into Ugg knock-offs, and I had a winter coat buttoned over a pair of Morelli's sweatpants and a flannel pajama top imprinted with duckies.

We all scooted out of the elevator, and Diesel followed me to my car. I was driving a Chevy Monte Carlo clunker that I'd gotten on the cheap because it didn't go in reverse.

"So, Mr. Magic," I said to Diesel, "what can you do with cars?"

"I can drive 'em."

"Can you fix them?"

"I can change a tire."

I filed that away in case I needed a tire changed, wrenched the door open, and rammed myself be-hind the wheel.

* * *

My parents live in the Burg, short for the Chambersburg section of Trenton. Houses and aspirations are modest, but meals are large. My mother dumped a mess of scrambled eggs and over a pound of breakfast sausages onto Diesel's plate. "I got up this morning, and she was gone," my mother said. *"Poof."*

Diesel didn't look too concerned. I was guessing in his world, *poof, and you're gone* wasn't all that unusual.

"Where did you find the note?" I asked my mother.

"On the kitchen table."

I ate my last piece of sausage. "Last time she disappeared, we found her camped out in line, waiting to buy tickets to the Stones concert."

"I have your father driving around looking, but so far he hasn't seen her."

My father was retired from the Post Office and now drove a cab part-time. Mostly, he drove the cab to his lodge to play cards with his friends, but sometimes he picked up early-morning fares to the train station.

I drained my coffee cup, pushed back from the table, and went upstairs and looked around Grandma's room. From what I could tell, she'd taken her purse, her gray jacket, her teeth, and the clothes on her back. There was no sign of struggle. No bloodstains. No duffel bag. There was a brochure for Daffy's Hotel and Casino in Atlantic City on her nightstand.

I traipsed back downstairs to the kitchen. "Where's the big bag?"

"What big bag?" my mother wanted to know.

"Grandma had a big bag with her yesterday. It's not in her room."

"I don't know anything about a bag," my mother said.

"Did Grandma just get her Social Security check?"

"A couple days ago."

So maybe she bought herself some new clothes, stuffed them into the duffel bag, and got herself on an early bus to Daffy's.

Diesel finished his breakfast and stood. "Need help?"

"Are you any good at finding lost grand-mothers?"

"Nope. Not my area of expertise."

"What *is* your area of expertise?" I asked him.

Diesel grinned at me.

"Besides that," I said.

"Maybe she just took off for a nooner with the butcher."

My mother gasped. Horrified that Diesel would

say such a thing, and doubly horrified because she knew it was a possibility.

"She wouldn't leave in the middle of the night for a nooner."

"If it's any consolation, I don't feel a disturbance in the force," Diesel said. "She wasn't in harm's way when she left the house. Or maybe I'm just feeling mellow after all those sausages and eggs."

Diesel and I have similar jobs. We look for people who have done bad things. Diesel tracks down people with special talents. He refers to them as Unmentionables. I track down people who pretty much have no talent at all. I call them Fugitives. Whatever name you use for the hunted, the hunter has a job that relies heavily on instinct, and after a while you become tuned in to the force. Okay, so that's kind of Obi-Wan Kenobi, but sometimes you walk into a building and get the creeps and know something ugly is waiting around the corner. My creep-o-meter is good, but Diesel's is better. I suspect Diesel's sensory perception is in the zone ordinarily reserved for werewolves. Good thing he isn't excessively hairy or I'd have to wonder.

"I'm going back to my apartment to shower and change. And then I'm going to the office," I told Diesel. "Can I drop you somewhere?"

"Yeah. My sources tell me the guy I'm looking

for was on Mulberry Street yesterday. I want to look around. Maybe talk to a couple people."

"Is this guy dangerous?"

"Not especially, but the idiots following him are."

"I found a brochure for Daffy's in Grandma's room," I told my mother. "She probably took a seniors' bus to Atlantic City and will be back tonight."

"Omigod," my mother said, making the sign of the cross. "Your grandmother alone in Atlantic City! Anything could happen. You have to go get her."

Ordinarily, I'd think this was a dumb idea, but it was a nice day, and I hadn't been to Atlantic City in ages. It sounded like a perfectly good excuse to take a day off. I had five open cases, but nothing that couldn't wait. And I wouldn't mind putting distance between Diesel and me. Diesel was a complication I didn't need in my life.

An hour later, I was dressed in jeans, a long-sleeved, V-neck sweater, and a sweatshirt. I drove to the bail bonds office, parked at the curb, and walked into the office.

"What's up?" Lula wanted to know. "We gonna go out and catch bad guys today? I'm ready to kick ass. I got ass-kickin' boots on today. I'm wearing a thong two sizes too small, and I'm feeling mean as hell."

Connie Rosolli grimaced. Connie is the office manager, and she's pure Burg Italian American. Her Uncle Lou was wheelman for Two Toes Garibaldi. And it's rumored her Uncle Nunzo helped turn Jimmy Hoffa into a dump truck bumper. Connie's a couple years older than me, a couple inches shorter, and a lot more voluptuous. If Connie's last name was a fruit, it would be Cantaloupe.

"Too much information," Connie said to Lula. "I don't *ever* want to know about your thong." Connie took a file off her desk and handed it to me. "Just came in. Kenny Brown. Wanted for grand theft auto. Twenty years old."

That meant unless he weighed three hundred pounds, he could run faster than me and was going to be a pain in the ass to catch.

I stuffed the Brown file into my shoulder bag. "Grandma Mazur's hit the road. I think she might be at Daffy's, and I told my mother I'd check on her. Anyone want to tag along?"

"I wouldn't mind going to Atlantic City," Lula said.

"Me, too," Connie said. "I can forward the office calls to my cell phone."

Lula had her bag on her shoulder and her keys in her hand. "I'm driving. I'm not riding to Atlantic City in a car with no reverse."

"I almost never need reverse," I told her.

Connie locked the office, and we all piled into Lula's Firebird.

"What's Granny doing in Atlantic City?" Lula asked.

I buckled myself in. "I'm not certain she *is* in Atlantic City. It's just my best guess. But if she is there, I imagine she's playing the slots."

"I'm telling you, she had a leprechaun in that duffel bag yesterday," Lula said. "And she took him to Atlantic City. It's just the place to take a lucky leprechaun."

"You don't really believe in leprechauns, do you?" Connie asked Lula.

"Who, me? Hell, no," Lula said. "I don't know why I said that. It just come out of my mouth. Everybody knows leprechauns aren't real, right?" Lula turned onto Broad. "Still, there's a lot of talk about them, and that talk has to come from somewhere. Remember that Christmas when Trenton was overrun with elves? If there's elves, there might be leprechauns."

"They weren't elves," I told her. "They were vertically challenged people wearing pointy rubber ears, and they were trucked in from Newark as a marketing strategy for a toy factory."

"I knew that," Lula said. "But some people thought they were elves."

* * *

It takes about an hour and a half to get from Trenton to Atlantic City. Forty minutes, if Lula's behind the wheel. It's flat-out highway driving until you get to Pleasantville. After that, it's not all that pleasant since the Jersey poor back up to the Jersey Shore in Atlantic City. We drove past several blocks of hookers and pushers and empty-eyed street kids, and then suddenly the landscape brightened and we were at Daffy's. Lula parked in the garage, and we fixed our makeup, sprayed our hair, and hoofed it through the maze that leads to the casino floor.

"It's going to be hard to spot Grandma Mazur," Connie said. "This place is filled with old people. They bring them in by bus, give them a carton of cigarettes, a ticket to the lunch buffet, and show them how to stick their credit cards in the slot machines."

"Yeah, people in Jersey know how to enjoy old age," Lula said.

It was true. All over the country, we were warehousing old people in nursing homes, feeding them Jell-O. And in Jersey, we were busing them into casinos. Dementia and heart disease didn't slow you down in Jersey.

"You could probably order dialysis off the room service menu here," Lula said. "I tell you,

I'm glad I'm gonna spend my golden years in Jersey."

"We'll all go in a different direction and look for Grandma," I said. "We'll keep in touch by cell phone."

I was halfway through a tour of the blackjack tables and my phone rang.

"I found her," Connie said. "She's at the slots, playing poker. Go to the big dog in the middle of the room and turn left."

Daffy's was one of the larger, newer casinos on the Boardwalk. In a misguided effort to out-theme Caesars, the conglomerate owners had chosen to design the casino after the chairman's ten-year-old beagle . . . Daffy. There was a Daffy Doodle bar and a Daffy Delicious restaurant, and Daffy paw prints on the purple-and-gold carpet. The crowning glory was a twenty-foot, two-ton, bronze Daffy that shot laser beams out of its eyes. The dog barked on the hour and was located dead center in the main casino.

I turned left at the big bronze Daffy and found Grandma hunched on her stool in front of a Double Bonus Video Poker machine, concentrating on the combinations. Bells were dinging, lights were flashing, and Grandma kept hitting the PLAY button.

Randy Briggs was standing behind Grandma.

He was clutching the duffel bag to his chest, alternately looking around the room and watching Grandma play. Briggs is a forty-something computer geek with thinning sandy blond hair, cynical brown eyes, and all the charm of Attila the Hun. Holding the bag was awkward for Briggs because Briggs is only three feet tall and his arms barely wrapped around the bag. I've known him for a couple years now and wouldn't go so far as to say we're friends. I suppose we have a professional relationship, more or less.

"Hey," I said to him. "What's up?"

"The usual," Briggs said. "What's up with you?"

"Just hanging out." I looked at the duffel bag. "What's in the bag?"

"Money." Briggs cut his eyes to Connie and Lula. "I've been hired to guard it, so don't anybody get ideas."

"I got ideas," Lula said. "They have to do with sitting on you until you're nothing but a grease spot on the carpet."

Grandma stopped punching the PLAY button and looked around at us. "I'm on a hot streak. Don't get too close or you'll put the whammy on me."

"How much have you won?" I asked her.

"Twelve dollars."

"And how much have you poured into the machine?"

"Don't know," Grandma said. "I'm not keeping track."

"I smell buffet," Lula said. "There's a buffet around here somewhere. What time is it? Is it time for the lunch buffet?"

All around us, seniors were checking out of their machines, getting on their Rascals, and powering up their motorized wheelchairs.

"Look at this," Lula said. "These old people are all gonna beat us to the buffet, and we're gonna have to take leftovers."

"I hate buffets," Briggs said. "I can never reach the good stuff."

"I can reach everything," Lula said. "Every man for himself. Watch out. Coming through. Excuse me."

"I guess it wouldn't hurt to get something to eat," Grandma said. "I've been playing this machine for four hours and my keister is asleep. We gotta get a move on, though, so we don't get behind the feebs with walkers and them portable oxygen tanks. They take forever to get through the line."

The buffet was held in the Bowser Room. We bought our tickets, loaded our plates, and sat down.

"No offense," I said to Briggs, "but you seem like an odd choice to guard the money."

Briggs dug into a pile of shrimp. "What's that

supposed to mean? You think I'm not honest? You think I can't be trusted with the money?"

"I think you're not tall."

"Yeah, but I'm mean and ferocious. I'm like a wolverine."

"I want to know more about the money," I said to Grandma. "Where did you get the money?"

"I found it fair and square."

"How much money are we talking about?"

"I don't know exactly. I kept losing my place when I was counting, but I figure it's close to a million."

Everyone stopped eating and looked at Grandma.

"Did you report it to the police?" I asked her.

"I thought about it, but I decided it wasn't police business. I came out of the bakery, and I saw a rainbow. And I was walking home, looking at the rainbow, and I fell over the bag with the money in it."

"And?"

"And it was St. Patrick's Day. Everybody knows if you find a pot of gold at the end of a rainbow on St. Patrick's Day, it's yours."

"That's true," Lula said. "She's got a point."

"I always wanted to see the country, so I took some of the money, and I bought myself an RV," Grandma said. "And this here's my first stop."

"You can't drive," I said to Grandma. "Your license was revoked."

"That's why I hired Randy," Grandma said. "I got a real good deal on the RV because it used to be owned by a little person. The driver's seat is all set up. Soon as I saw it, I thought of Randy. I remembered when you two were on that case with the elves."

"They weren't elves," I told Grandma. "They were little people trucked in from Newark. And you can't keep this much money."

"I'm not keeping it," Grandma said. "I'm spending it."

"There are rules. You have to report it, and then wait a certain amount of time before it becomes yours. And you probably have to pay taxes."

I couldn't believe I was saying all this. I sounded like my mother.

"That doesn't apply here," Grandma said. "This is lucky money."

"Guess that's why you won the twelve dollars," Lula said.

"You should take some money," Grandma said. "I got plenty." She looked over at Briggs. "Give everyone one of them bundles."

"I don't think that's a good idea," I said to Grandma. "Suppose someone puts in a claim and you have to give the money back?"

"That's the beauty of it," Grandma said. "This here's not ordinary money. It's lucky money. You use it to win more money. So there'll always be money if we need it."

"You've been gambling for four hours and you've only won twelve dollars!"

"It took me a while to get my rhythm, but I'm hot now," Grandma said.

"Are you sure the money doesn't belong to the little man in the green pants?"

"I asked him how much was in the bag, and he didn't know. He's a common thief. He must have seen me find it, and now he wants to steal it."

"He followed us out of the Burg this morning," Briggs said. "Least, I think it was him. It was some little guy in a white Toyota."

I looked around. "Is he here?"

"I haven't seen him," Briggs said. "I lost him when I got into traffic after I turned off the parkway."

"I'm gonna go get some dessert," Grandma said. "And then I'm hitting the slots again."

"I'm skipping dessert and taking my money to the craps table," Lula said.

"Me, too," Connie said. "Only I'm playing blackjack."

Briggs handed the money out and sat tight, using the duffel bag like a booster chair.

TWO

My phone rang, and I saw my home number appear in the readout.

"It's feeling lonely here," Diesel said. "I'm not getting vibes on you or my target. Where are you?"

"Atlantic City. Grandma's here. She found some money, and she's having an adventure."

"Found?"

"Remember the bag I was searching for in her room? She has it here with her, and it's filled with money. She said she was walking home from the bakery yesterday, and she found it sitting on the curb."

"Green duffel bag with a yellow stripe?"

"Yeah."

"Oh man, what are the chances?" Diesel said. "How much money?"

"Around a million."

"I don't suppose there's a little guy with curly gray hair and green pants lurking somewhere?"

"A little guy in green pants attacked Grandma yesterday. And it's possible he followed her out of the Burg this morning."

"His name is Snuggy O'Connor. He's the guy I'm tracking, and the money in that bag is stolen. If you see him, grab him for me, but don't take your eyes off him or he'll evaporate into thin air."

"Really?"

"No. People don't just evaporate. Boy, you'll believe anything."

"You sort of evaporate. One minute, you're standing behind me, and then you're gone."

"Yeah, but that's me. And it's not easy."

Diesel disconnected, and I went back to my lunch. Macaroni and cheese, potato salad, turkey with gravy, macaroni and cheese, a dinner roll, three-bean salad, and more macaroni and cheese. I like macaroni and cheese.

A half hour later, Grandma was back at her video poker machine, and Briggs and I were standing guard. I was hoping Diesel would have a plan when he arrived, because I had no idea what to do with Grandma. It's not like I could put her in handcuffs and drag her home.

I caught a flash of fire-engine red in my peripheral vision and realized it was Lula's hair making its way across the casino floor.

"You're not gonna believe this," Lula said,

coming up to me. "I was rolling crap at the craps table . . ."

"Easy come, easy go," Briggs said. "So much for the lucky money theory."

"Yeah, but turns out it *was* lucky. The guy standing next to me was some big-ass photographer on a photo shoot for some lingerie company, and he said they were looking for experienced plus-size models. He gave me his card, and he said I should just show up tomorrow first thing in the morning. I almost peed my pants right there. This here's my opportunity. I always wanted to be a supermodel. And a supermodel's just one step away from being a celebrity."

"Just what the world needs," Briggs said. "One more big fat celebrity."

Lula narrowed her eyes at him. "Did you just say I was fat? Is that what I just heard? Because my ears better be wrong, or I'll grind you into midget dust."

"*Little* person," Briggs said. "I'm a *little person*."

"Hunh," Lula said. "If it was me, I'd rather be a midget. It's got a good sound to it. 'Little person' sounds like you should be in kindergarten."

Briggs was hands on hips, leaning forward. "How'd you like a punch in the nose?"

Lula looked down at him. "How'd you like my thumb in your eye?"

"I didn't know you had experience modeling lingerie," Grandma said to Lula.

"Not modeling, exactly. I got more general experience. When I was a 'ho, I was famous for accessorizing with lingerie. Everybody knew if you wanted a 'ho in nice undies, you go to Lula's corner. And another thing, I'm always reading them fashion magazines. I know how to stand. And I got a beautiful smile."

Lula smiled for us.

Grandma squinted at Lula. "Look at that. You got a gold tooth in the front. It's all sparkly under the lights. I never noticed before."

"I got it last week," Lula said. "It's got a diamond chip in it. That's what makes it sparkle."

"So if the modeling doesn't work out, you could be a pirate," Briggs said.

"It's for when I sing with Sally Sweet and his band," Lula said. "We changed our focus to rap. Sally's breakin' new ground. He's like the premier drag rapper."

Sally Sweet drives a school bus in Trenton during the day and does bar gigs on weekends. He looks like Howard Stern, and he dresses like Madonna. I had a mental picture of Sally rapping in drag, and it wasn't pretty.

"How are you doing at the video poker?" Lula asked Grandma.

"I'm not doing so good," Grandma said. "Maybe I just got to get warmed up."

"That's the way it works," Lula said. "First you got bad luck, and then you got the good luck."

My cell phone buzzed in my pocket. It was my mother.

"Where are you?" she asked.

"I'm at Daffy's in Atlantic City."

"Did you find your grandmother?"

"Yes. She's playing the slots."

"Do *not* leave her side. And do *not* put her on the bus to come home. God knows where she could end up."

"Right," I said to my mother. "No bus."

"Call me when you get on the road so I know when to expect you and your grandmother."

"Sure."

I disconnected and looked at Grandma hunched on her seat, back to punching the PLAY button, and wondered if it was a felony if you kidnapped your own grandmother. I suspected it would be the only way I'd get her to go home.

"I'm going shopping," Lula said. "I gotta look good tomorrow morning for my supermodel debut. And I know this is plus-size lingerie, but maybe I should go to the gym and try to lose ten or fifteen pounds. I bet I could do it if I put my mind to it."

I looked past Lula and locked eyes with the little man in the green pants. He was openly staring, watching us from the other side of the casino floor. I crooked my finger at him in a *come here* gesture, and he sidestepped behind a row of slots and disappeared. I took off across the room but couldn't find him.

Lula was gone when I got back. Briggs was asleep on top of the duffel bag. And Grandma was staring at the poker machine.

"I'm not feeling so good," Grandma said. "My button finger is all swollen, and I'm sort of dizzy. I can't take the lights flashing at me anymore."

"We should go home."

"I can't go home. I gotta stay here and wait for my luck to get good. I got myself one of them high roller rooms this morning. I'm gonna take a nap."

I toed Briggs, and he jumped off the bag, eyes wide open, ready to be the wolverine.

"What?" he asked.

"Grandma wants to go to her room."

Ten minutes later, I had Grandma locked in her room with the money and Briggs standing guard outside her door.

"I'm going to check on Connie," I told Briggs. "Call me on my cell when Grandma gets up."

I walked down the hall, took the elevator to the casino floor, and found Connie still at the blackjack table. She had fifteen dollars in chips in front of her.

"This is *not* lucky money," Connie said. "I haven't won once . . . and I broke a nail."

The guy sitting next to her looked like he bludgeoned people for a living. Not that this would bother Connie, since half her family looked like this . . . and some for good reason.

"It was real ugly when she broke the nail," the guy said. "She used words I haven't heard since I was in the army." He leaned close to Connie. "If you want to get lucky, I could help you out."

"I don't need to get lucky that bad," Connie said.

"Just offering. No need to get mean," he said.

I wandered the casino looking for the little man in the green pants. I patrolled the gambling floor, browsed through a couple shops, checked out the bar and the café. No little man in green pants. Truth is, I was relieved. I mean, what the heck would I do with him if I found him? I had no legal right to apprehend him. And it seemed to me Grandma had sort of stolen his money. What would I say if he demanded it back?

I found a machine that I liked, took a seat, and slid a dollar into the money-sucker slot. Forty-five seconds later, my dollar was history and the machine went silent. I felt no compulsion to insert a second dollar. I love the casinos, but gambling isn't my passion. I like the neon and the noise and the optimism. I love that people come here with unrealistic hope. The energy is palpable. Okay, so sometimes it's fueled by greed and sloth and addiction. And sometimes the energy dissipates into despair. The way I see it, it's a little like driving the turnpike through Newark. The turnpike will get you to your destination faster, but there's always the possibility that you'll crash and die. It's the Jersey way, right? Take a chance. Act like a moron.

I felt all the little hairs stand up at the back of my neck and suspected Diesel had invaded my air space. I swiveled in my seat and found him standing behind me.

"How's it going?" he asked.

"I lost."

"I can fix that."

He fed a dollar into the machine and bells dinged and bonged, lights flashed, and the machine paid out four hundred and twenty dollars.

I rolled my eyes at him, and he grinned down at me.

"This is nothing," he said. "You should see me shoot craps."

"I saw your little man in the green pants."

"Here?"

"Yep. I ran after him, but he disappeared."

"What was he doing?" Diesel asked.

"Watching Grandma."

Two older women in velour running suits paused on their way through the slots to appreciate Diesel. They looked him up and down and smiled.

"Ladies," Diesel said, returning their smiles.

One of the women winked at him, and they moved on.

Diesel mashed the PAYOUT button and the machine printed a chit for the money. He tucked the chit into my sweatshirt pocket and pulled me off the stool. "Let's go on a Snuggy hunt."

"Why is he called Snuggy?"

"He gets into snug places . . . like bank vaults. Where's Grandma?"

"Taking a nap in her room. Briggs is in front of her door standing guard."

Diesel was holding my hand, walking us through the casino, and I could feel heat radiating up my arm. When the heat hit my shoulder and started to head south, I was going to disengage.

Daffy barked two o'clock and laser beams shot out of his eyes and danced across the casino ceiling. The old folks were lethargic after stuffing themselves at the lunch buffet and barely noticed. The dog barked "Yankee Doodle," and casino-wide, people self-medicated for acid reflux and irritable bowel. The day was already winding down. The senior buses would begin loading at four, and by five, the casino would be a graveyard. At six, the night-timers would start arriving. They'd drink more and spend more and wear tighter clothes. The men would have more hair and the women would have bigger boobs. Or at least the boobs would sit higher.

"How do you expect to catch Snuggy?" I asked Diesel.

"I thought I'd drag you around the casino for an hour or two hoping to run into him. And if that doesn't work, I'll use Grandma as bait."

We meandered through the rows of slot machines and patrolled the gaming tables . . . roulette, craps, blackjack. We checked out the bar and the café and the shops. We left the hotel and stood on the Boardwalk. A low cloud cover had moved in and the wind had picked up. The ocean was gray and foamy in front of us. Some rollers and choppy waves. No one on the beach. There was some Boardwalk foot traffic, but heads were down and sweatshirts were zipped.

Diesel looked like he belonged here. Sin City behind him and the wild, untamable sea in front of him. I had a hunch I looked like I belonged in Macy's shoe department.

"Now what?" I said to him.

"Call Briggs and see if Grandma's up and ready to play."

"She's sleeping," Briggs said, answering on the second ring. "I can hear her snoring. Probably half the hotel can hear her snoring. She sounds like she's trying to suck her face into her nose. It's giving me a headache. And I hafta go to the can. I need a break here."

Diesel and I went back into the hotel and rode the elevator to Grandma's floor. Randy Briggs took off, and Diesel and I sat on the carpeted floor with our backs to the wall.

"Tell me about Snuggy," I said to Diesel.

Diesel had one knee bent and one long leg stretched out in front of him. "Snuggy gives me a cramp in my ass. This is the second time I've had to chase him down. The first time, I found him in a goat tent halfway up Everest. And I am *not* an Everest kind of guy. Everest is cold. And when you get tired of looking at rock, you can look at more rock." Diesel closed his eyes. "I'm more a tropical breezes and palm trees swaying man."

"What about Trenton? Do you like Trenton?"

"Does it have palm trees?"

"No."

"There's your answer," Diesel said.

"Are you after Snuggy because he stole the money?"

"No. I was after him before that. He stole a horse

and was recognized leaving the scene. I was asked to put him on ice until the mess could get cleaned up. Problem is, Snuggy's like smoke. Hard to hang on to."

"And he doesn't want to be put on ice?"

"He claims it'll interfere with his life's work."

"Which is?"

"Apparently, it's stealing shit," Diesel said.

"Not many people steal horses these days."

"Guess he likes horses. He used to be a jockey. He'd win the race by some odd stroke of fate and then fall off the horse after it crossed the finish line. That's his M.O. He's unbelievably lucky, but he bungles everything. Yesterday, he stole close to a million dollars from Lou Delvina, got caught on Delvina's security tape, and managed to leave the money sitting on the curb for your grandmother to find."

Lou Delvina was a local mobster and a very scary guy. Diesel and I had a run-in with him not too long ago, and I wasn't thrilled about the idea that I was indirectly involved with him again.

"So your target is lucky, rides horses, likes green pants, and isn't smart. Anything else?" I asked Diesel.

"He talks to animals. Two-way conversations," Diesel said.

"Like the horse whisperer and the pet psychic on television."

"Whatever."

"Can you talk to animals?" I asked him.

"Honey, I can barely talk to humans."

THREE

The elevator door opened toward the end of the hall-way, and Snuggy stepped out. His eyes locked onto Diesel and me sitting on the floor and widened. "You!" Snuggy said.

Diesel got to his feet. "Surprise."

Snuggy turned and punched the DOWN button and clawed at the closed elevator doors.

"Cripes, that's so pathetic," Diesel said. "Stop clawing at the elevator and come over here."

"Faith and begorrah, I can't. My sainted mother is dying. I need to go to her bedside."

Diesel cut his eyes to me. "Add fake Irish accent and pathological liar to the list."

"That cuts to the quick," Snuggy said.

"I have a file on you," Diesel said. "Your birth name is Zigmond Kulakowski, you were born in Staten Island, and your mother died ten years ago."

"I *feel* Irish," Snuggy said. "I'm pretty sure I'm a leprechaun."

Diesel was hands on hips, looking like he'd heard this before. "It doesn't say leprechaun in your file. And here's some bad news—a closet full of green pants doesn't make you a leprechaun."

"I'm Unmentionably lucky."

"Yeah, and I'm Unmentionably randy, but that doesn't make me a goat."

I stood and moved next to Diesel. "I want to know about the money my grandmother found. The money that belonged to Lou Delvina."

Snuggy slumped a little. "I needed cash, and I heard Delvina had a safe filled with numbers money. I mean, if you have to steal something, steal something that's already dirty, right? I know Delvina works his operation out of a car wash on Hamilton and Beacon Street, so I went to the car wash just as it was getting ready to open for business. And here's the lucky part. Everyone, including Delvina, was around back, looking at a broken water valve. The door to the office was wide open. I went in, saw the duffel bag sitting all by itself on the front desk, looked inside, saw the money, and walked out with it. I set the bag on the car roof while I looked for my keys, and then I forgot about it and drove away. I guess the bag slid off when I turned the corner. I came back and saw the old lady dragging it down the street. I tell you, some people have no scruples. I was perfectly nice, explaining to her how I lost the bag, and she told me to kiss off. And then she called me some rude names!"

"She said you couldn't identify the amount of money in the bag."

"I hadn't counted it. I didn't know how much there was. I'd only just stole it. Faith and begorrah."

"You say 'faith and begorrah' again, and I'm going to hit you," Diesel said.

"You can't hit me," Snuggy said. "I'm old, and I'm half your size."

"Yeah, it'd be embarrassing," Diesel said, "but I think I could force myself to do it."

Snuggy shuffled foot to foot. "Well, anyway, the money's mine. And I want it back."

"I think it might be finders keepers, losers weepers," I told Snuggy. "And besides, Grandma's spent a lot of it."

Snuggy went bug-eyed and a red scald started to creep from his neck to the top of his head. "What? No way! I need that money. It's a matter of life or death. They'll kill Doug!"

Oh boy. "Who's Doug?"

"He's a horse. Douglas Iron Man III. We've known each other for years. He was a four-year-old when I retired. He was really something back then. He won the Preakness. Anyway, times have been hard for him lately. I ran into him last week when I went to visit a friend in Rumson. They had

Doug in a stall, waiting to get put down. He had a sore on his leg, and they'd decided it'd be too costly to treat."

"That's so sad."

"It's more than sad. It's criminal. Poor Doug. He was really depressed. He could hardly pick his head up. He looked at me with those big brown eyes, and I knew I had to do something. So I returned that night, and I sneaked him out and drove him to Trenton. My cousin has a house on Mulberry Street, and he let me put Doug in his garage until I could make arrangements for his leg operation. There's a real good equine veterinary hospital in Pennsylvania. Problem was, I had to get the money to pay for Doug's care. When I heard about Delvina, I thought it was perfect. It's not like he earned the money and deserved it. I figured it was better spent on Doug."

I nodded. "Makes perfect sense."

"It didn't make perfect sense to the guy who owned the horse," Diesel said. "He woke up missing a horse. And he wasn't happy."

"I left a note," Snuggy said. "I even offered to buy Doug."

"We have people working to smooth things over," Diesel said. "Until that happens, you and Doug need to keep a low profile. Doug can't stay in a garage in Trenton."

"It's worse than you think," Snuggy said. "Delvina followed me to the garage last night and took Doug. Now he's holding him for ransom. Delvina wants his money. All of it. Or else he'll do something terrible to Doug."

"Great," Diesel said. "It wasn't bad enough that I had to find a guy who thinks he's a leprechaun, now I have to rescue a horse."

"He's not just any old horse," Snuggy said. "He's very intelligent. And he's sensitive. It hurt his feelings when he found out they weren't going to fix his leg. He worked hard all those years to stay in shape so he could win races. And then he was put out to stud, and he worked night and day impregnating mares. And it's not like they were all love matches. Doug said sometimes they were downright cranky."

"Maybe Doug should have paid closer attention," I said. "*No* is *no*."

"It was his *job*," Snuggy said. "He was caught between a rock and a hard place."

Diesel gave a snort of laughter.

"You're supposed to help me," Snuggy said to Diesel.

"No," Diesel said. "I'm supposed to remove you from action so you don't do something stupid and end up on *Letterman* telling everyone you talk to animals."

"Jeez," I said. "I feel really bad about this. I can't just walk away and let Delvina kill Doug."

Diesel looked like he had another cramp in his ass. "You're not going all girly and gushy on me over this horse, are you?"

"I am absolutely *not* relegating some poor horse to the glue factory just because he has a sore on his leg. It's a horse! Horses are amazing."

"Have you ever seen one up close?" Diesel asked.

"Not lately. But they look wonderful on television. And I read all the Walter Farley books about the Black Stallion."

Diesel choked back a smile. He thought I was amusing. "Do you know where Delvina is keeping Doug?" he asked Snuggy.

"No."

"How do you get in touch with Delvina?"

"He calls me. He gave me until three o'clock tomorrow to return the money. He said if he didn't get it by three, he'd shoot Doug."

"That's plenty of time," I said. "We just get the money from Grandma and give it to Delvina. Probably he won't notice if there's a little missing. These things happen, right?"

I called Lula. "Don't spend any more of that money," I told her. "We need it."

"Too late," she said. "It's all gone. And I'm wearing everything I bought. I'm dressed in my supermodel clothes. And I was real lucky on account of I found that photographer at the craps table and he took pictures of me so I'd have a portfolio tomorrow morning."

"Uh-oh."

"What *uh-oh*? There's no *uh-oh*. It's all good. He spent a hour taking pictures, and he said they were the most fabulous he's ever done."

"Did you pay him to take the pictures?"

"Yeah. It was expensive, but it was worth the money. I tell you, he knows what he's doing."

"Where is he now?"

"I don't know. I just come back to the casino, and he didn't come with me. We took the pictures outside. It was cold, but he said the light was real good. Where are you?"

"I'm on the fourteenth floor. I'm waiting for Grandma to wake up. She wanted to take a nap."

"I'll come up there."

I disconnected and called Connie.

"Are you still at the blackjack table?"

"Yeah."

"I don't suppose you have any money left?"

"Nope. Lost every last cent."

"Maybe you'd better come up to the fourteenth floor. We have a situation."

Grandma's door opened, and Grandma stuck her head out. "What's going on?" She spotted Snuggy and sucked in some air. "It's the robber! I'd know him anywhere." She ducked into her room and, an instant later, was in the hall with a gun in her hand. She squeezed off a shot and took out a wall sconce before Diesel could disarm her.

"She's insane!" Snuggy said. "She's a crazy woman. Someone do something."

"Must be something wrong with that gun," Grandma said. "I don't usually miss by that much."

"He's lucky," I told Grandma.

"I'm pretty sure I'm a leprechaun," Snuggy said.

Grandma eyeballed him. "I guess that could explain it."

Diesel emptied the gun, pocketed the shells, and gave the gun back to Grandma. "Do you have any idea how much money you've spent?"

"No. I wasn't paying attention. Randy was keeping track of that." She looked around. "Where is he?"

"He went to the men's room."

"Maybe the leprechaun made him disappear," Grandma said. "Everybody knows you can't trust a leprechaun."

I told Grandma about Doug and Lou Delvina.

"Sounds like a lot of baloney," Grandma said.

"I've got pictures," Snuggy said, taking his phone out of his pocket. "I took pictures so I could send them to the vet in Pennsylvania."

We all looked over Snuggy's shoulder at the pictures of Doug.

"He looks real, all right," Grandma said. "And he's a beauty. He's got pretty eyes."

Lula stepped out of the elevator and made her way over to us. "What are we looking at?"

I filled her in on Doug and Delvina, and I checked out her new clothes. Spike-heeled gold Louboutins, metallic gold miniskirt, and a long black satin tuxedo jacket. She took the jacket off and she was wearing a gold bustier that wasn't nearly big enough to contain *the girls*.

Snuggy was eyeball-to-headlight with Lula, and he looked like he'd swallowed his tongue when she turned to face him. Diesel was rocked back on his heels, smiling. I'm solidly heterosexual, but I have to admit, I was mesmerized by the sight of all that boob spilling out over the gold top.

"Boy, you got some hooters in that getup," Grandma said to Lula. "I wouldn't mind having an outfit like that."

"I was worried it might not fit just right," Lula said.

"It looks good from down here," Snuggy said.

"I'm not complaining," Diesel told her.

The elevator *bing*ed and Connie stepped out. "What's going on?"

I repeated the Doug and Delvina story, and Connie got a look at the photo.

"We gotta rescue this horse," Lula said. "I can't take a chance on crappin' up my karma now that I'm gonna be a supermodel."

"What's with all this feng shui and karma stuff?" Connie asked Lula.

"I got my horoscope done, and it said I needed to be more spiritual. I looked into being a Catholic and it sounded like a real pain in the ass, so I'm going with Asian shit."

"I guess I wouldn't mind giving my money over to save Doug," Grandma said. "And I still got my RV, so I'm pretty lucky when you think about it."

We all trooped into Grandma's room and waited while Diesel counted the money.

"We have six hundred and forty thousand," Diesel said to Snuggy. "How much did Delvina say you stole?"

"Eight hundred and ninety thousand."

Diesel dumped the money back into the bag and zipped it closed. "We're short a quarter of a million."

"I went through ten," Connie said.

"I went through another ten," Lula said.

"I got a good price on the RV," Grandma said. "It was only thirty thousand. And I paid some to

Randy for guarding the money and driving the RV."

Diesel was smiling at Grandma. "You blew through almost two hundred thousand and you were playing dollar slots? That's impressive."

"Especially since some of that time I was winning," Grandma said.

"Twelve dollars?"

"Yep. I was on a roll."

"Delvina isn't going to be happy," Snuggy said. "He wanted *all* his money back."

"Delvina shouldn't get any of that money back," Diesel said. "Delvina's lucky he's still alive and walking upright."

"Yeah, but we gotta think about the horse," Lula said. "We gotta focus on the horse. How're we gonna get the horse safe and sound?"

"Why don't you do something lucky?" Grandma said to Snuggy. "You're the leprechaun. You're supposed to go around finding pots of gold."

"I could, except you need a rainbow to follow, and it was cloudy today. And I can't do it at night. And anyway, I'm a Polish/Irish leprechaun, so the pot of gold business might not work for me. Mostly, I find it's easier to steal the gold."

"I got a idea," Lula said. "Suppose we take the money we have left, and we let it ride on the craps table. Okay, so we got a half-assed leprechaun, but this is still lucky money, right? I got lucky with it. And Grandma got lucky with it."

I looked over at Diesel. I knew who had the ability to win at craps. I suspected Diesel could make the spots change on the dice if he put his mind to it.

"No," Diesel said.

"I didn't say anything."

"You didn't have to. I know what you were thinking."

"Now you're reading minds?"

"Cutie Pie, that thought flashed in neon across your forehead."

"I don't think it's a good idea to gamble with *all* the money," Snuggy said. "Maybe we should each take a small amount and see how it goes."

"It's your money and your horse," Diesel said. "How much do you want to hand out?"

"A thousand apiece," Snuggy said.

Diesel gave Lula, Connie, Grandma, and Snuggy a thousand and didn't take any for himself.

"Where's Randy?" Grandma asked. "I need him to guard my money while I get lucky."

I called Briggs on my cell phone.

"Yeah," Briggs said.

"Where are you?"

"I'm with a girl. She's twice my size and half my age and I'm busy. What do you want?"

"Grandma's awake and wants to go back to the casino."

"Jeez, give her a pill or something. I think I'm in love here."

"How long do you think this love will last?"

"Ten minutes. Twenty, tops."

I disconnected Briggs.

"Briggs is temporarily indisposed," I told Grandma. "I'll hold the bag for you."

"Okay, let's do it," Grandma said. "Let's kick some behind in this casino."

"What about you?" I asked Diesel.

"I'm babysitting the leprechaun."

"Was that sarcasm?" Snuggy asked.

Diesel held the door for him. "You have a problem with sarcasm?"

FOUR

We all piled into the elevator and took it to the casino level. Snuggy and Diesel walked off toward the blackjack tables. Lula headed for roulette. And Connie and I followed Grandma to her favorite video poker machine.

"I can feel a big payday coming up," Grandma said. "I was just getting warmed up before."

We got Grandma settled in, and Connie nudged me.

"Look across the aisle at the blackjack table closest to us," Connie said. "I think that's Billy Major in the striped shirt."

Billy Major has a stable of hookers who work the projects. To my knowledge, he's never been arrested for procuring. However, he has been arrested several times for possession of controlled substances, and the latest charge was outstanding. Billy Major was on my list of active skips. Major failed to appear for his court appearance, and until this moment, I hadn't been able to locate him. Probably because I was looking in Trenton, and he obviously was in Atlantic City.

I had a credit card and twenty dollars in my back pocket. My purse with all my bounty hunter paraphernalia was upstairs in Grandma's room. "I haven't got any equipment on me," I said to Connie.

Connie's purse was on her shoulder. She rooted around in it and came up with cuffs and a stun gun and a semi-automatic Smith & Wesson .45. I took the cuffs and stun gun and left her with the Smith & Wesson. Connie was a lot tougher than I was, but capturing felons was on my side of the division of labor.

I wedged the duffel bag with the remaining money between Grandma's stool and the poker machine. "I'll be right back," I told her. "In the meantime, keep your eye on the money."

I crossed the aisle and stood behind Major for a couple minutes, watching him play. I had the cuffs tucked into the back pocket of my jeans and the stun gun in my sweatshirt pocket. The dealer shuffled the cards, and I leaned over Major.

"Excuse me," I said, close to his ear. "Billy Major?"

"Yeah."

He turned and looked at me, and recognition registered. This wasn't the first time I'd apprehended him.

"Oh shit," Major said.

I clapped a cuff on him, and he yelped and jumped, knocking into the gaming table, sending chips flying. Everyone stood, the dealer called for security, overturned drinks dripped onto the carpet.

I struggled to get the second cuff on Major. "Bond enforcement. Hold still!"

"Fuck this," Major said, ripping the cuffs out of my hands, taking off for the exit on the far side of the room.

He had a head start, but he was hampered by high-heeled boots and forty pounds of gold chains hanging around his neck. He was plowing into people, but I was trying to be careful, dodging cocktail waitresses and casino guests. He crashed into an old woman with a walker and stumbled, and I took a flying leap and tackled him. My momentum took us to the ground.

I've never had formal martial arts training. Mostly, I rely on the fact that men tend to underestimate my desperation. I curled my fingers into Major's shirt, knowing casino security would help secure him if I could just hang on until they arrived. We were tumbling around, and I caught a flash of gold in my peripheral vision and realized it was Lula.

"Outta my way," Lula said.

I rolled off, and Lula sat down hard on Major. Major let out a *woof* of air, farted, and went inert.

An old man looked down at Major. "He's dead."

Lula got off Major, I attached the second cuff, and Major still didn't move. We all took a closer look.

"I might have seen him breathe just then," Lula said.

"I got a defibrillator on my Rascal," someone said. "You want to try to jump-start him?"

"I got oxygen," someone else said.

Lula got her foot under Major and turned him over. His eyes were open. His lips were pressed tight together.

"Christ," Major said through clenched teeth.

"He just got breathless," Lula said. "I have that effect on men on account of I'm a supermodel."

The security guys had arrived and were mixed in with the gawkers. The gawkers looked like they were enjoying themselves, but security didn't look happy.

Connie pushed her way through the crowd, corralled the senior rent-a-cop, showed him her documentation, and vouched for me as her representative. The gawkers began to disperse, and two tables down, I could see Diesel smiling at me. I flipped him the bird, and the smile widened.

"What are we gonna do with this fool?" Lula wanted to know. "I'd take him back, but I got my photo shoot tomorrow morning. I'm sleeping here so I wake up fresh as a daisy. Grandma said I could bunk with her. She's got that big ol' suite with a pull-out couch."

"I'll take him," Connie said. "I haven't got my gambling mojo going today. Let me borrow your Firebird, and I'll give you my thousand."

"Deal," Lula said. "I'm feeling hot. I probably don't need the extra thousand, but I'll take it just in case."

We dragged Major to his feet and walked him out of the casino into the parking garage. We got shackles out of the trunk of Lula's car, trussed Major up, and put him into the backseat. Connie got behind the wheel, and we watched her drive away.

"That was lucky," Lula said. "We caught a scumbag. And we didn't even kill him."

The casino was relatively empty when we returned to the gaming floor. The day-players were settling themselves into their buses. The night-timers were sitting in traffic on the Parkway. Attendants quietly swept carpets and collected empty glasses. The big Daffy Dog was silent.

"I'm going to the café for a burger," Lula said. "How about you?"

"I need to get back to Grandma. I left her alone with the money."

I hustled back to the gaming floor, and I saw Briggs before I saw Grandma. He was standing behind her, as always, but he wasn't guarding the duffel bag. Grandma was playing the poker machine, and Briggs was back on his heels, looking bored. And the duffel bag was missing.

"Where's the money?" I asked him.

"I put it in the hotel vault," Briggs said.

"It's not like I could spend it," Grandma said, punching the PLAY button. "I figured I might as well put it away where it was safe. Then Randy don't have to carry that big heavy bag around. We're almost done here anyway. It's amazing how fast you can go through a thousand dollars when you got the knack for it."

"Have you won anything?"

"Not a darn nickel. It's just as good, though, on account of I want to get back to the room to watch some television. Starting at seven o'clock, there's reruns of *Dancing with the Stars*."

I left Grandma and Briggs and walked over to Snuggy and Diesel. Snuggy was playing blackjack, and Diesel was standing behind him.

"How's it going?" I asked Diesel.

"I don't think it looks good for the horse."

"Snuggy hasn't got a lot of chips in front of him."

"He consistently gets great cards, but he's the worst blackjack player ever."

"Why don't you want to play?" I asked Diesel.

"Can't. I've won here too many times. If I sit down, I'll be asked to leave."

"They can do that?"

"They think I cheat," Diesel said.

"Do you?"

"Yeah." Diesel smiled down at me. "I liked the tag team wrestling exhibition."

"You could have helped!"

"You were doing okay without me. Who was the guy you took down?"

"Billy Major. He's a Trenton pimp who got caught in a drug sting. Vinnie bonded him out, and then Major failed to appear for a court appearance. It was dumb luck that Connie spotted him."

Snuggy was fidgeting in his seat and cracking his knuckles. Nervous. Knowing he was screwing up. He had only a few chips left.

"This is painful," I said to Diesel. "He should be playing something that's pure chance."

"There are decisions to be made with all the games," Diesel said. "Even with slots. And he's incapable of making a good decision."

Lula huffed up to us, clearly on a rant, hands waving in the air. "This place is fixed," Lula said. "I guess I know when I'm hot. And I was hot. And I lost. How could that be? I got a mind to report this to someone." She looked over at Snuggy. "Don't look like he's doing too good, either. I tell you, this place is rigged. Where's Grandma?"

"She went back to her room to watch a *Dancing with the Stars* retrospective."

"No kidding? I love that show. Maybe I should go watch with her. I think I got high blood pressure from losing all that money. I got a headache. What kind of headache do you get from high blood pressure? Is it on the top of your head? Is it behind your left eyeball? Does it go down the back of your neck? I got all of those. Maybe I'm having a stroke. Is anything sagging on me?"

"Not that I can see," I told her. Thanks to the miracle of spandex.

Lula left, and I cut my eyes to Diesel.

"Don't give me that look," Diesel said. "She asked about sagging, and I didn't say anything."

"You were thinking."

"Now you're a mind reader?"

"It was flashing in neon across your forehead."

Diesel grabbed me and hugged me to him. "Cute."

The night crowd was beginning to filter into the

casino. Young singles coming directly from work. Older couples in that awkward age, caught between assisted living and the family home in suburbia. Hard-core addicted gamblers who had spent all day sleeping off a hangover and were now ready to repeat the last night's disaster. The noise level rose and dealers notched up the action.

"That's it," Snuggy said, pushing back from the table. "I'm done. I lost all my money. I feel terrible."

A cocktail waitress sidled up to Diesel. "Can I get you something? *Anything?*"

"No," Diesel said, "but thanks for asking."

I did an eye roll, and the waitress sashayed away.

"How are we going to get the money for Doug?" Snuggy asked. "We only have until three o'clock tomorrow."

"I know we all like Doug," Diesel said. "But maybe it's his time."

Snuggy looked horrified, and I smacked Diesel on the back of his head.

"He's a horse," Diesel said. "Do you know how many horses you could buy for a quarter of a million? Lots. And they could be under the hood of a car."

"There are a bunch of casinos here," I said. "Surely one of them would let you play."

"Sorry, sugar. I'm persona non grata. These casinos put me through M.I.T."

I was speechless. "You graduated from M.I.T.?" I finally managed.

"Just because I'm big doesn't mean I'm stupid."

"You look like a street person."

"I like to be comfortable. Anyway, lots of women think I'm sexy like this." He smiled and ruffled my hair. "Not you, maybe, but lots of other women."

I did another eye roll.

"You keep doing that and you're gonna shake something loose in there," Diesel said.

"So you haven't always chased after bad guys?"

"I started doing this in my teens. Mostly part-time."

"Like Buffy the Vampire Slayer?"

"Yeah, except I don't mess with vampires. And I think Buffy might not be real."

"And you're real?"

"As real as a guy could get."

"Okay, great. Now we've established we're all real," Snuggy said. "Could we get back to the Doug problem?"

"I need an off-site poker game," Diesel said. "Private. High-stakes party."

Snuggy pumped his fist into the air. "Yes! I knew you'd come through. You guys stay here and I'll find a game. I'll ask around."

"You aren't going to take off on me, are you?"

Diesel asked Snuggy. "Because I'd track you down and find you, and the rest wouldn't be pretty."

"You got my word."

"Your word isn't worth squat," Diesel said. "Just remember my promise. Make sure no one in the game knows me. And find out if they're checking guns at the door."

"Okay, got that," Snuggy said. "Why do you want to know about the guns? Are you packing?"

"No. I don't want to get shot when I win. It hurts. We're going to the café. You can catch me there or you can call Stephanie on her cell."

Snuggy wandered away and Diesel stuck his hand into my sweatshirt pocket.

"Hey!" I said.

"I'm looking for your voucher."

"I bet."

"I need the receipt I gave you when I cashed out the slot."

"I put it in my jeans pocket. I didn't want to lose it."

"Even better."

I stepped back from him. "I can get it!"

"You're not a whole lot of fun," Diesel said.

"I have a boyfriend."

"And?"

I pulled the receipt out of my pocket and gave it to Diesel. "And I don't mess around."

FIVE

We were finishing burgers and fries when Snuggy rolled into the café.

"I got you into a game," Snuggy said. "It's at Caesars, but it's not got anything to do with the hotel. Strictly private party. Lots of money involved. Starts at ten." He gave Diesel a slip of paper. "Here's the room number, and the guy's name. You ask for him, and they'll let you in. You gotta have ten thousand to start."

I looked over at Diesel. "Do you have ten thousand?"

"Not yet."

"How are you going to get it?"

"I'll take it out of the money in the duffel bag."

Snuggy looked over his shoulder, back at the entrance to the café.

"Is there a problem?" Diesel asked.

Snuggy dragged his attention back to us. "No. Everything's good."

"Admirable but boring." Diesel took the receipt and towed me across the room to the cashier. "It wouldn't kill you to flirt a little, so I don't remember this assignment as totally sucking. I'm baby-sitting a guy who thinks he's a leprechaun, and I'm rescuing a has-been horse. The least you could do is grab my ass once in a while."

"Suppose I just *think* about grabbing your ass?"

"Better than nothing."

Diesel gave his receipt to the cashier and collected his winnings. "This is burger money," Diesel said, draping an arm across my shoulders, moving me toward the café.

A half hour later, we were knocking on Grandma's door.

"You're just in time," Lula said, letting us in, trotting back to the couch and wedging herself in between Grandma and Briggs. "This here's the beginning of that show where they made what's-her-name cry 'cause she wasn't hot enough. And then after that one is the time the fat chick wore the ugly blue dress."

Diesel had his mouth to my ear. "She's kidding, right?"

"Don't you watch television?"

"Yeah. Ball games, boxing, hockey."

"This isn't any of those," I told him.

Grandma had a two-room suite. The bedroom had a king-size bed, bureau, and two boudoir chairs. The sitting room had a large couch, a desk and chair, a comfy club chair and ottoman. The walls were butter yellow, dotted with pictures of beagles. The carpet was yellow with black dog paw prints. The draperies, couch, and chairs were done up in a yellow, orange, and white floral-print fabric. It was like the Snoopy Room at the insane asylum.

"What do you think of the room?" Grandma asked. "Don't you think it's cheery?"

"Yep," I said. "Very cheery."

Diesel was back at my ear. "If I stay in here too long, I'll have a seizure."

"We came to get some money from the bag," I said. "Diesel needs it."

"You have to wait," Briggs said. "I don't want to miss this part. The money's all the way down in the vault. You have to go to the desk, and they take you down two flights, where they've got safety deposit boxes for hotel guests. It's a whole big deal. It'll take a half hour, and I'll miss the rest of the show."

"Can *I* get the money?" Diesel asked.

"No. I put the money in, and I'm the only one who can get the money out. You need a picture ID, and they do a fingerprint scan. It's like Fort Knox."

"What kind of show is this?" Diesel asked. "They're dancing."

"Dancing with the Stars," I told him. *"Dancing with the Stars."*

"I'd jump off a cliff if I had to watch this every week."

"Suppose you got to eat birthday cake while you watched it?"

"That would help," Diesel said, "but it wouldn't close the deal."

"This is over at nine o'clock," Briggs said. "Can you wait until then?"

"I guess," Diesel said.

"I'm staying here," Snuggy said. "I like this show."

I pushed in next to Grandma. "Me, too."

"Do these dancers ever hit each other?" Diesel asked.

"No."

"Then I'm gonna pass. I'll be back at nine."

It was nine o'clock and Briggs was ready to go. Grandma was asleep in her bedroom. Lula and Snuggy were watching SPEED channel.

Diesel knocked once and opened the door.

"Why do you knock here, but you just pop into my apartment unannounced?" I asked him.

"I don't want to chance seeing some of these people naked. You're not one of them."

"Let's move," Briggs said. "I got a date tonight. I don't want to be late."

Diesel draped an arm across my shoulders. "I have a plan."

That was good since I didn't have any plans of my own. I was tired of watching television and tired of hanging out in the casino. I didn't have a room. I didn't have a way to get home. I didn't have any money. I'd called Morelli to tell him I didn't know when I'd be back in Trenton, and I'd gotten his phone service. That meant either he was called out on a case or the Rangers were playing and the game was televised.

"You're going to make me look civilized," Diesel said.

"How much time do I have?"

"Not enough. I just want you to come with me. I checked out the players and they're all older, and I doubt anyone's going to be wearing torn jeans. If I go by myself, I'll look like a hustler. If you come along, we can role-play." He turned to Snuggy. "You are *not* to leave the room. If you leave the room, I'll send Lula out to get you. And you saw what she did to that guy in the casino."

Snuggy gasped and gave an involuntary shiver.

"Yep," Lula said to Snuggy. "I'd squash you like a bug if I had to."

Diesel, Briggs, and I took the elevator and walked across the casino floor to the front desk. Briggs flashed his ID and asked to see his safety deposit box. He was ushered into a back room, and the door closed behind him.

My cell phone buzzed in my pocket. I hauled it out and looked at the number display. Blocked. Most likely Morelli or Ranger.

"Yep?" I said into the phone.

"Your car's at the bonds office, and the electronics in your purse tell me you're in Atlantic City. Are you okay?"

It was Ranger. Ranger's former Special Forces, now turned security expert. Our history together isn't all that long, and it's hard to say how our future relationship will go. Ranger's personality and skin tone run several shades darker than Morelli's. He's a little bigger, got a little more bulk to his muscle. His hair is brown and currently cut short, and his eyes are black. And with or without clothes, he's a heart-stopper.

In the past, I've gotten myself into some precarious situations, and Ranger now feels compelled to monitor me. Since I have no control over Ranger, and because sometimes I actually like having him watch over me, I go with it.

"I'm here with Grandma, and Lula, and Randy Briggs, and a guy who thinks he's a leprechaun . . . and Diesel."

"Babe," Ranger said.

"And I'm fine."

"Stay that way," Ranger said. And he disconnected.

Diesel had his thumbs hooked into his pockets. "I'm guessing that wasn't your mother."

"It was Ranger."

"Doing a bed check?"

"He likes to know his family is safe."

"And the boyfriend, Morelli?"

"I called him earlier."

I've known Joe Morelli all my life. I know his family, his friends, his history. I know his sexual tastes, his favorite sports teams, his shoe size, his pizza preferences, his iPod playlist.

I've had to judge Ranger and Diesel on actions and attitude, and touch. Ranger's touch is firm. He feels comfortable assuming authority. Diesel's touch is surprisingly gentle. I think Diesel is afraid he'll leave a bruise.

"Can you make a quarter of a million on this game?" I asked him.

Diesel shrugged. "Hard to predict how a game will go. I'd have preferred something with higher stakes, but this is what Snuggy found for me so I'll do the best I can."

The door behind the registration desk opened, and Briggs walked out with an envelope in his hand. He gave the envelope to Diesel and answered his cell phone.

"I'm on my way," Briggs said into his phone. He listened to something said on the other end, and he giggled. "Gotta go," he told us. "Don't wait up."

Caesars Hotel & Casino was a couple blocks north. The Boardwalk was lit, but beyond it was black ocean and sky. The surf surged onto the beach and whooshed away, sight unseen, and mist swirled around overhead lights. I found an elastic scrunchie in my bag and tied my hair back into a ponytail before it frizzed out of control.

"The game is in a high roller suite," Diesel said. "The suite was occupied this afternoon, so I wasn't able to get in, but it probably has a living room area where you can hang out. Stay away from the poker table and stay awake. I'll be John Diesel, so remember to call me John."

"I thought you were just Diesel?"

"Not everyone is comfortable playing cards with a guy who has only one name."

The casino and shopping pier were in front of us. Professionally illuminated palaces of hope and recreation. Diesel steered me toward the shopping pier.

"We need to glam you up a little," he said. "The jeans are okay. The sweatshirt and sweater have to go."

"How about you? Are we going to glam you up?"

"No. I'm the hedge fund guy who's so rich he can wear whatever the hell he wants."

"And I'm . . ."

"You're the bimbo."

Fortunately, since I was born and raised in Trenton, I'm good at selecting bimbo clothes. I found a little white T-shirt that had SWEET THING written in sparkly pink glitter across the boobs. It was a size too small and was cut low on the top and sat an inch above my jeans to show maximum skin. I covered it with a black leather jacket that coordinated with my black-and-white Converse sneakers. I added some extra eyeliner and mascara, and I was ready to rock and roll.

Diesel smiled when I walked out of the dressing room. "If I didn't have to save a horse, I'd marry you."

"I'm not surprised. I always had you pegged for the bimbo type."

"Saves time," Diesel said.

We left the shops and crossed the Boardwalk to the casino. The gaming floor was similar to Daffy's. Substitute statue of Caesar for Big Brass Dog. Even on a weekday in March, it was packed. Colored neon pulsed around the room. Slot machines clanged and dinged. We went directly to the bank of elevators.

Minutes later, we were in the suite. The guy who answered the door was young. Early twenties. And big. Over six feet and bulked up with steroids. A rental goon hired to serve as doorman. The suite was luxurious, with an ocean view. Not much to see but black glass at this hour, but in the morning, it had to be spectacular. Five men were already seated around the poker table. They were all in their fifties. All overweight from booze and excess. They looked like carnivores. They studied us with mild curiosity.

Diesel nodded to them. "John Diesel."

"Diesel, like an engine. Are you a train engine or a truck engine?" one of the guys asked.

Diesel just smiled. Diesel heard that a lot.

"I'm Rocky," the guy said. "Who's the lady?"

"Stephanie," Diesel said.

"Hedging your bets in case you drop out early?"

"Brought her along for luck," Diesel said.

He gave me a light kiss on the top of my head and took his seat at the table. I got a soda from the bar and got comfy on the sofa. It was a big over-stuffed affair with lots of throw pillows. Fresh flowers on the glass-topped coffee table. A plate of fresh fruit. There was a full buffet set out on the sideboard.

An hour later, I was still perched on the couch, watching the game. It had taken on a rhythm. Cards were dealt. Chips were moved. Not much was said. Diesel was looking pleasant, playing under the radar, staying in the game but not making a splash. I'd thought he'd be playing a role by now. Maybe drinking a lot or looking nervous. Instead, he'd chosen to almost disappear. It was a no-smoking room, but three of the men were smoking. One was smoking a cigar. No one objected. Diesel had a rum and Coke in front of him, but he'd only sipped at it.

Two of the six players had dropped out by midnight. Diesel and Rocky looked about even. The man to Diesel's left was sweating. His name was

Walter, and he'd lost beyond his comfort zone. He laid his cards down and was done. He stood and left. Didn't look at me.

From my distance, it was hard to tell how much money was involved. Diesel and Rocky were the only players still working from their original stake. All others had added. Some had added a lot.

Diesel looked around at me. "Are you doin' okay, sugar?"

"Yeah," I said. "I'm fine. Are you done soon?"

"Hard to say."

"Maybe we want to up the ante now that we've separated the men from the boys," Rocky said to Diesel. And he pushed his chips into the middle of the table.

The guy opposite Diesel scraped back in his chair and stood. "Too rich for me. I'm out."

Diesel counted his chips. Not enough. "This is too bad because I have a real good hand, but I'm short. I tell you what. I'll throw Stephanie into the pot and call you."

I jumped off the couch. "What?"

Rocky looked over at me. "I guess she's cute enough. What's the deal?"

Diesel leaned back in his chair. "What do you want? The night? Twenty-four hours?"

"The night. I'm flying out in the morning."

"Hey, wait a minute," I said. "You can't bet me in a poker game."

"I'll buy you a new car tomorrow," Diesel said.

"What kind?"

"What kind do you want?"

"I want a Ferrari," I told him.

"Forget it. I'll buy you a Camry."

"Lexus."

"A *used* Lexus."

"No way," I told him.

Diesel took another look at his hand and at the money on the table. "Okay, I'll get you a new Lexus."

I bit into my lower lip. I was pretty sure Diesel knew what he was doing. I mean, he cheats, right?

"How good is your hand?" I asked him.

Diesel shrugged.

"She's kind of a pain in the ass," Rocky said.

Diesel rocked back in his chair and studied me. "She grows on you. Anyway, she's the best I've got to offer right now unless you want to take a check."

"What the hell," Rocky said. "What have you got?"

Diesel laid his cards on the table. "Straight flush. Jack high."

"Beats me. Four of a kind. All kings." He gave

me the once-over for the second time. "Just as well. She'd probably give me a heart attack. She looks like a lot of work."

I narrowed my eyes at him. "Excuse me?"

"Don't get your panties in a bunch. I'm just saying."

I had my purse hung on my shoulder and my shopping bag in hand. I was ready to go. It was past my bedtime, and I was pissed off that everyone thought I wasn't such a great prize. All right, so I'm no Julia Roberts, but I had a nice nose, and I'd tweezed my eyebrows two days ago.

Diesel pocketed his winnings and moved to the door. "We should do this again sometime."

"I'm pretty sure you were cheating," Rocky said, "but I don't know how."

"I was lucky," Diesel said.

The rent-a-goon let us out and watched us walk to the elevator. We stepped in, and Diesel hit buttons for the fourth floor and the lobby. We got off at the fourth floor and took the stairs.

"Just in case," Diesel said. "Walter looked like he was going to shoot himself, but he might have changed his mind and decided it would be more satisfying to shoot me."

"How much did you win?"

"A hundred and ten thousand."

"That's a lot of money, but not enough."

"Delvina doesn't want to kill the horse. He wants his money, and I'm hoping he's smart enough to understand that half of something is better than all of nothing."

When we got to the second floor, Diesel took the service elevator to the ground level, and we exited through the kitchen. The staff didn't seem all that surprised. Probably people sneaked out like this all the time.

"Now what?" I asked Diesel.

"Now we go back to Daffy's and get a room."

"Two rooms."

I couldn't believe what I was hearing. "What do you mean there are no rooms?"

"There are four major conventions in town," the desk clerk said. "I've been calling around all night, trying to find rooms. If you want a room, you'll have to go off the Boardwalk."

It was almost one o'clock. Going off the Board-walk at this hour in Atlantic City didn't sound like a good idea.

"We can drive back to Trenton and be home by two-thirty," I told Diesel.

Diesel had his hand at my back, moving me away from the desk. "Do you have a car?"

"No. We came in Lula's car, and Connie borrowed it to take the FTA back. Don't you have a car? How did you get here?"

"You don't really want to know the answer to that question, do you?"

"Do you think we could rent a car?"

"Not at this hour, but I could *borrow* a car," Diesel said.

"You mean *steal* a car?"

"Stealing implies permanence."

"Grandma has a suite. We can crash there for the night and find a way to get back to Trenton in the morning."

We took the elevator to the fourteenth floor, stepped out into the hall, and saw Lula sprawled on the carpet in front of Grandma's suite. She was changed out of the fancy gold outfit, and she was wide awake, flat on her back with a pillow under her head.

"And?" I said to her.

"And I can't sleep, is what. I got my big photo shoot first thing in the morning. I need my beauty rest, and I can't sleep with your grandma snoring. I've never heard anything like it. It's not normal snoring. I tried to get my own room, but there's no rooms left."

"Where's Snuggy?" Diesel asked.

"He's still in there."

The door to the suite opened, and Snuggy lurched out. "I can't take it anymore. I need sleep."

Lula was on her feet. "Me, too. What are we gonna do?"

"Let's kill her," Snuggy said.

"Works for me," Lula said. "How you want to do it? Smother her with a pillow?"

The elevator *bing*ed, and Briggs hopped out. "What's everyone doing in the hall? And what's that disgusting sound? It sounds like King Kong with a sinus infection."

"It's Grandma snoring," I told him. "We haven't got any place to sleep. The hotel is full, and no one can sleep with Grandma. Where do you sleep?"

"I sleep in the RV. I just came back to make sure everything was okay here."

Lula's eyes opened wide. "I bet the RV has lots of room. It probably can sleep lots of people."

"Five," Briggs said.

"We're five," Lula said. "Imagine that. We'll just fit in that sucker. Where is it?"

"It's in a lot next to the garage."

"I'm there," Lula said. "Lead the way, and hurry up. I can feel bags growing under my eyes."

We followed Briggs to the lot and filed one by one after him into the RV.

"We can't turn too many lights on because no one's supposed to live here," Briggs said. "This is just a lot for hotel parking. I have a little battery-run lamp that I use."

Briggs switched the light on, and we all squinted into the dimly lit RV. It looked like at one time it had been a big, boxy Winnebago, but that was a while ago. It had been modified by exterior paint and patch and a complete interior retrofit.

"What the heck is this?" Lula said. "Everything's teeny tiny. Look at this itty-bitty chair. It looks like dollhouse furniture. How am I supposed to get my ass in this chair?"

"This RV was owned by a little person," Briggs said. "It fits me perfect."

"I feel like I'm in Barbie's camper," Lula said. "Where are we supposed to sleep?"

"There's the couch here in the front, and then there's two bunks in the middle of the RV, and there's a bedroom in the back with a double bed. That's where I sleep."

"The heck it is," Lula said. "Do you have a photo shoot in the morning? Hell, no. Get outta my way." Lula bustled into the bedroom and slammed the door shut.

Diesel looked at the bunks. "These are only four feet long."

"Plenty of room for me," Briggs said, rolling into the bottom bunk, pulling his curtain closed.

Snuggy looked at the top bunk. "I guess I could

just about fit." He climbed the ladder, settled in, and closed his curtain.

Diesel was hands on hips. "That leaves the couch for us, Sweet Thing."

"The couch is five feet long and maybe a foot and a half wide. Your shoulders are wider than that."

Diesel kicked his shoes off and stretched out on the couch, one knee bent, one foot on the floor. "You can have the top."

"You're kidding!"

"Do I look like I'm kidding?"

I shut the light off, got rid of the sneakers and leather jacket, and maneuvered myself onto Diesel, breast to chest, my knee wedged between his legs. "Am I squishing you?"

Diesel wrapped his arms around me. "No, but it'd be good if you don't make any fast moves with the knee."

"Oh, cripes," Briggs said from his bunk. "You two aren't gonna get romantic out there, are you? This is a family RV."

"If I thought there was a chance for romance, I wouldn't be worrying about her knee," Diesel said.

SIX

I was jolted out of a sound sleep. Without thinking, I tried to roll over, and Diesel and I fell off the couch and crashed to the floor.

Diesel was halfway on top of me. "Earthquake," he murmured. "Where am I? Thailand? Japan?"

"Atlantic City."

"Am I drunk?"

"No. You were holding on to me, and I rolled us off the couch."

The door to the bedroom burst open, and Lula stormed out in the gold supermodel outfit. "What time is it? Am I late? Did I oversleep?"

Diesel checked his watch. "It's six-thirty."

"I'm supposed to be at the photo shoot first thing in the morning. What does *first thing in the morning* mean?"

I dragged myself up to my feet and realized I was still in the little SWEET THING T-shirt, but I wasn't wearing a bra. "What the heck?" I said, looking down at myself.

Diesel pulled my bra out of his back pocket. "You were uncomfortable."

"How did my bra get off my body and into your back pocket?"

"One of my many special talents," Diesel said, handing the bra over to me.

"I gotta go," Lula said. "I got a room number where I'm supposed to show up, and I'm just gonna go wait."

Briggs stuck his head out of his bunk. "It's the middle of the night, for crissake. I'm trying to sleep here. Do you mind?"

Diesel sat on the couch to lace his boots. "I'm hungry. I'm going in search of breakfast."

"I'm going to get dressed and then check on Grandma," I said. "I'll meet you at the café."

I was back to wearing my sweatshirt and V-neck sweater, and I was in front of Grandma's door. Grandma was usually an early riser, but just in case, I'd taken the keycard from Briggs. I knocked once. No answer. I knocked again and was about to insert the keycard in the lock when the door opened. A guy reached out, grabbed me, and yanked me into the room.

I recognized the guy. Wheelman for Lou Delvina. I didn't know the guy's name, but he and Lou looked a lot alike. Early sixties and built like a fireplug. Lots of black hair and caterpillar eyebrows. He had the front of my sweatshirt in one hand and a gun in the other.

"This is good. Real convenient. Now we don't have to call you."

When something like this happens, adrenaline pours into your system. It's the whole fight-or-flight thing. It worked good back in caveman days because the smart choice was always flight, and you don't have to think a lot to run like hell. My reaction to the adrenaline is complete and utter panic. I break out in a sweat. My heart goes nuts. My mind freezes. Fortunately, it only lasts for a minute or two, and when the panic leaves, I go into survival mode.

"I can see you're real surprised," he said. "Probably you don't remember me. I'm Mickey. I work for Mr. Delvina. We had a run-in with you not so long ago."

"I remember."

"Then you must remember Mr. Delvina," Mickey said.

A gray blob of a creature hobbled in from the bedroom. "Well, well, Stephanie Plum," the creature said. The voice was deep and croaky. The face was puffed up, the bloated body oozed into the head so that no neck was visible. The eyes bulged.

"Lou Delvina?" I asked, not entirely successful at hiding the shock. Last I saw him he was an ordinary middle-aged Italian man. And now he was . . . a giant toad.

"Funny how things work out. I get money stolen from me, and it brings me *you*. Drops you right in my lap. How lucky is that? Bad luck brings good luck."

"Are you sure you're Lou Delvina?"

"Mr. Delvina hadda take steroids for a rash. He got some water retention," Mickey said.

"Where's Grandma?"

"She's in the other room. We were just getting ready to take her for a ride. We stopped in to see if she wanted to give us our money, but she said she didn't have it."

"It's in the hotel safe."

"That's just what she said. And she said she couldn't get it out of the safe."

"I hear you talking about me, you nitwit," Grandma yelled from the other room. "What part of *I can't get it out of the safe* don't you understand?"

"It's true," I said. "She can't get it out because she didn't put it in. I put it in."

"That's a big fib," Mickey said. "I called down

to the desk. Some guy named Randy Briggs put it in."

"He was a real A-hole when he called," Grandma said from the bedroom. "He told them I was senile and couldn't remember. He's gonna go straight to heck."

"In case you're wondering, we got her restrained in the bedroom," Mickey said. "She's a nasty one. She kicked me in the knee. We weren't even doing nothing to her."

"I was aiming for your privates," Grandma said, "but I couldn't get my leg up high enough."

"You see what I mean?" Mickey said. "How's that for an old lady to talk?"

Lou Delvina motioned for Mickey to bring Grandma out of the bedroom. "Bring her out," he said. "I got things to do. I gotta get back to Trenton. I'm due for my allergy shot."

Mickey trotted into the bedroom and wheeled Grandma out. They had her tied to a wheelchair and covered with a blanket.

"Pretty good, hunh?" Mickey said. "No one will know we're kidnapping her. Lots of old ladies getting rolled around this place."

Delvina shook his finger at Grandma. "You better be good when we get you out of this room. You make a fuss, and Mickey's gonna give you a blast with the stun gun, make you piss your pants."

"That don't scare me," Grandma said. "You get to be my age, and you do that all the time."

"Why are you kidnapping her?" I asked Delvina.

"I want my money."

"You already have a horse. How many hostages do you need?"

"As many as it takes."

"Take me instead of Grandma. I'll be more co-operative."

"You tricked me and Mickey last time we saw you," Delvina said. "I didn't like that. You and that train engine guy . . . Diesel." Some color came into Delvina's swollen, blotchy face. "I hate him. And you'll see, my time's gonna come. You don't mess with Lou Delvina. I got where I am today because I'm tough. I hold a grudge, and I get even. Everyone knows that. And now I got a plan. Ain't that right, Mickey?"

"Yeah, boss, you got a plan."

"What kind of plan?" I asked him.

"A *big* plan."

Oh boy. Besides looking like a toad, Lou Delvina had gone a little nutso.

"The first part of the plan is that I want my money," Delvina croaked. "Get the money to me, and you get your granny back."

"Why don't you wait here, and I'll get the money? I just have to find Briggs."

"What, do I look stupid?" Delvina said. "You'll come back with the cops. And besides, I gotta get my shot. And Mickey's gotta feed the horse."

Mickey was still holding his gun on me. He handed the gun to Delvina and took cuffs from his back pocket. "Gimme your wrist," Mickey said.

"No."

"Give it to me, or Lou's gonna shoot."

"I don't think he'll shoot me."

"You got that right," Delvina said. "I'll shoot the old lady. I'd *love* to shoot the old lady."

I blew out a sigh and held my hand out for Mickey to cuff. He snapped a cuff on, walked me into the bathroom, and attached the other bracelet to the towel bar.

Mickey left the bathroom, closing the door after him. Seconds later, I heard the faint sound of the door to the suite opening and closing.

On the surface, Lou Delvina and Mickey were clichéd, mid-level, bumbling bad guys right out of central casting for every Mob movie ever made. At least, they used to be before Delvina's cortisone issue. Problem was, Delvina was right about his reputation. Delvina had ruthlessly scratched and clawed his way up the crime ladder in Newark and finally had been rewarded with his own piece of real estate. That real estate was Trenton. In the old days, it would have been a prize, but the old days were gone and the Mob no longer exclusively ran Trenton. The Mob had to share the Trenton pie with Russian thugs, kid gangs, Asian triads, black and Hispanic gangstas. So Delvina was still scratching and clawing, and sometimes people who got in his way disappeared.

I sat on the edge of the tub and waited. Eventually, someone would show up. A maid. Diesel. Briggs. A half hour ground by and I heard my phone ringing in my purse in the other room. I prayed it wasn't my mother. My mother was going to freak. She sent me out to retrieve Grandma Mazur and now Grandma was kidnapped.

The phone stopped ringing and I waited some more. Ten minutes later, I heard someone enter the suite.

"Help!" I yelled. "I'm locked in the bathroom."

Diesel opened the door and looked in at me. "I'm not usually into bondage, but I'm getting turned on."

"Delvina and his pal Mickey were here. They kidnapped Grandma."

"Is that a bad thing?"

"Yes!"

Diesel pulled his keyring from his pocket, sorted through his keys, plugged one into the cuff, and the cuff opened.

"I thought you'd magically make the cuff fall off my wrist," I said to him.

"I could, but that would be showing off."

"Delvina is taking Grandma back to Trenton and holding her hostage for the money . . . along with the horse."

"Delvina's beginning to annoy me," Diesel said.

"Last time he annoyed you, you threatened to turn him into a toad. And now his voice is croaky and he's fat and blobby and has no neck."

"Imagine that."

"You didn't turn Delvina into a toad, did you?"

Diesel smiled. "He isn't really a toad. He's just toad-like."

"Sometimes you can be downright scary."

"Yeah, but I'm sexy and cuddly, so it's okay."

I hauled my cell phone out of my bag, and I called Briggs. It rang a bunch of times and went to his answering service.

"We need the money out of the vault," I said to Diesel. "I'm worried about Grandma Mazur. Delvina isn't a nice guy."

"Briggs is probably asleep," Diesel said. "We'll go to the RV and get him up."

I went through the suite and packed up Grandma's things so I could check her out when I got downstairs. I wanted to make sure she had no reason to come back.

*　*　*

Snuggy was at the built-in banquette when we entered the RV. He was eating cereal, and he was looking rumpled.

"This sucks," Snuggy said. "I haven't got any clean clothes. I haven't even got a toothbrush. And there's no milk for the cereal."

"Where's Briggs? Is he still asleep?" I asked.

"No. His phone rang right after you left, and he got up and went out. I think he's got a thing going with some girl."

"Did he say anything? Do you know anything about the girl?"

"Nope. Didn't say anything."

The door banged open, and Lula stormed in.

"I'm gonna kill him," Lula said. "I'm gonna find him and kill him. And then I'm gonna kick the crap out of him. I been sitting outside this hotel room, wondering when this photo shoot was gonna start, and along comes a maid and goes into the room. So I go in with her and what do you think I see? They're gone. There's no one in the friggin' room. So I go down to the desk and ask where they are, and turns out they took off in the middle of the night."

Snuggy tapped the cereal box with his spoon. "Want some cereal?"

"Yeah," Lula said. "I didn't have breakfast. I could eat a horse. Nothing personal."

"I bet it was a scam," Snuggy said. "You pay the photographer money to make a portfolio, and then he doesn't even have film in the camera. Happens all the time."

"How do you know?"

"It was on *Everybody Loves Raymond*. Ray's brother got scammed like that."

Lula dumped a load of cereal into a bowl and started shoveling it into her mouth. "Wait a minute," Lula said. "There's no milk in this cereal."

"We haven't got any milk," I told her.

"I'm so mad, I don't know what I'm eating. I'm beside myself. I gotta take a breath. I gotta calm down. I'm probably giving myself a stroke." She scarfed down some more cereal. "So what's happening around here? I miss anything while I was getting scammed?"

"Lou Delvina kidnapped Grandma."

"Get out! Why'd he want to do that?"

"He figured we didn't want the horse back bad enough, so he took another hostage."

"He took the wrong one," Lula said. "No offense. I like your grandma and all, but she's gonna make their life a living hell."

That was my fear. If Grandma got too cantankerous, Delvina might think she wasn't worth the effort and get rid of her . . . permanently.

Diesel was slouched on the couch. "How did Delvina find Grandma?" he asked Snuggy.

"It wasn't me," Snuggy said. "I swear."

Diesel kept looking at him. Not saying anything. Just looking.

Snuggy squirmed in his seat. "He must have followed me here."

Now we were all looking at Snuggy.

"Okay!" Snuggy said. "He *did* follow me. I saw him. I didn't have a choice. He was gonna kill Doug, and he had me by the short hairs. And I figured it didn't matter that he was here. I figured he was just watching me. And then he started pressuring me, calling me, so I told him I couldn't get my hands on the money because it was in the vault. I didn't know he'd kidnap Grandma. He had Doug. Who'd think he'd kidnap an old woman?"

"I don't want to be an alarmist or anything," I said to Diesel, "but we need to get Grandma back *now.*"

"We can bring the police in, but that would get messy for Snuggy and Doug. And Delvina might panic and make Grandma disappear."

I bit into my lower lip to keep from sniveling and told myself to get a grip. I didn't want Grandma to disappear.

"Looks like we'll have to get the money without Briggs," Diesel said.

"Oh boy," Lula said. "Are we gonna rob the vault?"

"No," Diesel said. "We're going to help them return our deposit."

We took the elevator and followed Daffy's footprints through the casino gaming floor to hotel reception.

"I want to know the safety deposit box routine," Diesel said. "Someone needs to go to the desk and ask to get walked through the process."

"I'll do it," Lula said. "Us supermodels are always carrying a shitload of jewelry. I'll tell them I need to know everything's okay before I hand over my valuables for safekeeping. And if they disrespect me, I'll scream discrimination. It's illegal to discriminate against a supermodel. We got rights like everyone else."

Lula strutted up to the desk, and we all watched while she talked to one of the clerks. The clerk turned Lula over to a manager, and the manager led Lula into a back room. Ten minutes later, Lula emerged, thanked the manager and clerk, and crossed the lobby to where we were waiting.

"You gotta get behind the desk and through the door," Lula said. "Once you're through the door, you walk down the hall and take a special service elevator two flights down. It opens into another hallway with a guard at a desk. You gotta show the guard your ID and do one of them fingerprint scans like at Disney World. If I was by myself, I wouldn't have got anywhere, but I was with the manager, so he took me halfway down the hall to a door marked GUESTS. That's the door that leads to the guest security boxes. There's other doors down there that lead to the money-counting room and all, but they're locked up tight. Once you get into the room with the security boxes, you can only open them with a key and a code. You get the code wrong, and the Marines come and cut your balls off. Oh yeah, and another thing, you're always on television," she said to Diesel, "so maybe you want to comb your hair."

"How do I know which box is mine?" Diesel asked.

"The guy at the desk with the fingerprint machine has a book with everyone's name and box number. Plus, did I tell you he's got a gun? A big one."

"The armed guard is a problem," Diesel said. "I can scramble television transmissions, and I can open locks. I can't make myself invisible."

"I got a stun gun," Lula said. "How about you jump out of the elevator and real quick you give him some jolts? You just gotta move fast before he shoots you. How fast can you move?"

"I can't move as fast as a bullet."

"I can get past the guard," Snuggy said. "I can be real sneaky when it comes to people. I have this thing. Take your eyes off me, and I disappear."

"I hear leprechauns can do that," Lula said.

"Exactly!" Snuggy said to her.

Diesel looked down at Snuggy. "You don't disappear. You have a knack for knowing when people are distracted."

"I'm almost positive I disappear," Snuggy said.

"If you're wrong, the Marines are gonna cut your balls off," Lula told him.

"I'd hate that," Snuggy said. "I'm attached to my balls."

Diesel scanned the lobby and looked beyond it into the gaming area. "I wish Briggs would show up."

I dialed Briggs, and we all waited while his phone rang. Finally, his service kicked in.

"Call me!" I said. *"Now."*

"Let's assume you can actually get past the guard," Diesel said to Snuggy. "Can you open the locked door to the safety deposit box room and get into the box?"

"Piece of cake. Problem is, I'll get caught by the security cameras. For some reason, television picks up my image."

"I can scramble the television," Diesel said, "but you can't waste time once you're out of the elevator. You'll only have a couple minutes before they send someone to investigate."

"I can do it," Snuggy said. "Doug is depending on me."

My phone rang, and I snatched it out of my pocket, hoping it was Briggs.

"Plum?"

It was Lou Delvina. Easy to recognize his croaky voice.

"You better be on the road with my money," Delvina said.

"Not yet, but I'm working on it."

"You have until three o'clock. First, I kill the horse, and then the old lady. And then I'll come get you. Or maybe I should go for your mother next. Or your sister. Or even better, one of your little nieces."

Delvina disconnected, and Diesel wrapped an arm around me. "Are you okay? Your face just went white."

"We need to get Delvina his money."

Diesel looked over at the registration desk and then at Snuggy. "I know I'm going to regret this," Diesel said.

"How do you want to do it?" Snuggy asked. "Do you want me to just slip behind the desk and go to the elevator?"

"No. I need to go to the elevator with you. That

means I need a diversion, so we're going to play some slots."

Ten minutes later, Lula had a bucket filled with quarters and nickels.

"I love when they have nickel slots," Lula said, two arms around the bucket. "I like seeing all that money drop into the tray. It don't matter that you only won eight dollars. It's the experience of the money coming out at you that counts. And I can't believe how lucky we were. I never was able to fill a bucket like this."

I cut my eyes to Diesel.

"I'm a lucky kind of guy," Diesel said.

"Maybe you're a leprechaun."

"It doesn't say leprechaun on my driver's license."

"Well, if anyone would know, it would be the DMV."

"Okay, let's do it," Diesel said. "This is how it's going to go down. Stephanie stays here, so we have someone to float bail if we all get arrested. Snuggy stays glued to my side until I get the communications scrambled. And Lula creates chaos, so Snuggy and I can get behind the desk."

"I get it," Lula said. "You want me to dump the bucket."

"Exactly," Diesel said. "Make sure all eyes are on you."

Lula shrugged out of the black jacket and handed it over. "Leave it to me. You have to be dead not to be looking at me do this. I'm gonna be the Queen of Chaos."

Lula minced up to the desk in her stiletto heels and skintight gold-sequined supermodel outfit. The skirt was three inches below her ass, and her boobs moved like Jell-O barely held in place by the bustier. She held the bucket of change at arm's length in front of her, not wanting to distract from her natural assets.

"Yoohoo!" she called to one of the men behind the registration desk. "I'm almost a supermodel, and I've got a bucket full of money. I'm thinking I might need some help protecting all this money. I'm thinking . . . whoops!" Lula stumbled, jerked the bucket, and the money shot out in all directions. "My money!" Lula shrieked.

Lula bent to retrieve her money, and her left boob fell out of the top and her skirt rode up past the full moon. She was wearing a matching gold thong, but most of the thong was lost in deep space. The entire hotel and casino gasped. It was as if all the air instantly got sucked in and, seconds later, got spewed out. Four guards rushed to the scene, and all six men behind the registration desk were mouths agape, eyes glued to Lula.

Lula stood and pushed her boob back into the

top of her dress and pulled her skirt down. Then she bent in another direction to get her money, and the boob fell out again, and the dress rode up. People were scrambling around her, trying to scoop up the change and return it to the bucket without unduly sticking their noses in Lula's business. And Lula kept spilling the money out of the bucket and bending over.

"My word," Lula exclaimed. "Mercy me! Lordy, Lordy, Lordy."

Diesel and Snuggy disappeared behind the door that led to the elevator, and Lula continued to create chaos. She was finally stopped by an assistant manager, who grabbed the bucket. Most of the change was returned to the bucket, and the manager asked Lula if she would like the change converted into paper money or Daffy Dollars.

"Do you think I should?" Lula asked him. "What would you do? Maybe I should just take this and keep playing. I think I'm hot. Don't I look hot?" Lula looked over at me. "What do you think I should do?"

I was watching the door behind the desk. Fifteen minutes had passed. Briggs had returned in ten when he got Diesel's poker stake.

"I think you should put it back in the machine," I said. "And save some for parking meters."

The door opened and Diesel ambled out. He was

stopped by one of the registration people. He swayed a little and smiled. Snatches of conversation carried across the floor.

"Lookin' for the can," Diesel said. "They said it was in there, but I couldn't find it. There should be signs, right? How'r people supposed to know?"

"Public restrooms are across the lobby," Diesel was told.

"Okay," Diesel said, and he wandered toward me, a little unsteady on his feet. He reached Lula, and the door behind the desk banged open, and Snuggy came flying out. Snuggy was moving so fast his legs were a green blur. The guard chasing after him was slow by comparison, overweight and breathing hard.

Diesel bumped into Lula and knocked the bucket out of her hands. For the second time, people scurried for the money like roaches on pie. The guard pulled up, unsure of Snuggy's direction, craning his neck, attempting to see around the gathering crowd.

"I'll give ya ten dollars to do me in the lot," Diesel said to Lula.

"I'm there," Lula said. "Excuse me," she said to the manager. "I got business."

We all power walked through the casino and broke into a run when we reached the lot. Snuggy was already in the RV with the engine cranked over when we tumbled in.

"Go," Diesel said to Snuggy. "And don't look back."

A half hour later, we were on the Garden State Parkway heading for Trenton, and my heart rate was almost normal.

"What the heck was that back there?" Lula wanted to know.

Diesel was sprawled on the couch. "I was able to scramble the feed, but just to be safe I went down in the elevator with Mr. Sneaky. What happened after that is classic Snuggy O'Connor.

"The elevator doors opened, Snuggy zipped out and went straight to the guard at the desk and started thumbing through the guy's logbook, looking for the box number. 'What the hell do you think you're doing?' the guard says. 'And where did you come from? Where's your ID?' So Snuggy says, 'You can't see me. I'm a leprechaun.' "

"I could have sworn I disappeared," Snuggy said, concentrating, keeping his eyes on the road while he drove.

"But he wasn't disappeared?" Lula guessed.

"Not even a little," Diesel said. "The guard pulled his gun and pointed it at Snuggy's forehead."

"I don't understand why it didn't work," Snuggy said. "It always worked before."

"Maybe it didn't work because you aren't a friggin' leprechaun," Diesel said.

"Did you get the money?" I asked.

"Yeah," Diesel said. "I persuaded the guard to go to sleep, and we got the money. And then Green Pants panicked when a second guard came in. He took off shrieking like a girl and ran all the hell over the building with the guard running after him."

My phone rang, and I grimaced at the number displayed. It was my mother.

"I'm calling the police," my mother said. "Where are you?"

"I'm on my way back to Trenton."

"Thank goodness. Let me talk to your grand-mother."

"She's sleeping."

"It's morning. How could she be sleeping?"

"I don't know, but I'm pretty sure she's sleeping."

"Will you be home soon?" my mother asked. "I have cold cuts for lunch. Should I make some po-tato salad? Maybe get some nice rolls."

"Grandma said she wanted to go shopping, so we won't be home for lunch. I'm going to take her to Quaker Bridge Mall." I made some static sounds. "I'm breaking up," I yelled into the phone. "Can't hear you. Gotta go." And I disconnected.

Diesel was smiling. "You're going straight to hell for lying to your mother."

"You never lied to your mother?"

"I'm a guy. It's expected."

"What's the plan when we hit Trenton?" Snuggy wanted to know. "Where am I supposed to park this monster?"

"Drop Lula and me at the bonds office on Hamilton, so we can get our cars. Then you can park this in the lot behind my apartment building," I said.

SEVEN

Lula and I watched the RV pull away from the curb and chug down Hamilton.

"This has been a strange couple days," Lula said. "Good luck and bad luck and good luck and bad luck. And then there's the stupid leprechaun. And now your grandma's been kidnapped. How often does that happen? 'Course, there was that time she got locked up in the casket and burned the funeral home down. I guess that counts for a kidnap."

I was fishing through my purse, searching for my car keys. "I'm worried about her. Delvina is a scary guy."

"Tell you the truth, I'm worried about her, too. Is there anything I can do?"

"No, but thanks. You were great today."

"I'm going inside to talk to Connie." She looked past me to the car pulling up to the curb. "You have a visitor. Mr. Tall, Hot, and Handsome is here."

Ranger parked his black Porsche Turbo and

angled out of the car. He was in his usual Rangeman black. Black boots, black cargo pants that fit
perfectly across his butt, black T-shirt under a black
windbreaker with RANGEMAN written in black on
the sleeve. He walked over and gave me a friendly,
lingering kiss on my temple, just above my ear.

"Babe."

Babe covered a lot of ground with Ranger. Depending on the inflection, it could be sexy, scold-
ing, or wistful. He said "babe" when I amused
him, astonished him, and exasperated him. Today,
it was mostly hello.

He gave my ponytail a playful tug. "You look
worried."

"I could use some help. Lou Delvina kidnapped
Grandma."

"When did this happen?"

"This morning. Two days ago, on St. Patrick's
Day, Grandma found a bag of money. She bought
an RV and hired Randy Briggs to drive her to Atlantic City. Turns out, the money belonged to this
little guy who thinks he's a leprechaun. And the
leprechaun stole the money from Delvina. So Delvina
kidnapped the leprechaun's horse and Grandma
until he gets his money. Problem is, we only have
some of his money."

"We?"

"Diesel and me."

Ranger covered his face with his hands, pressing his fingertips against his eyes. It was one of those gestures you do instead of jumping off a bridge or choking someone. "Diesel," Ranger said.

"He's not your favorite person?"

"We don't hang out together."

"I think he turned Delvina into a toad."

"Delvina only looks like a toad. Under the warts, he's still a middle-aged, mid-level mobster. And he's ruthless. And a little insane."

"Great. This makes me feel much better."

"You haven't gone to the police?"

"No."

"Morelli?"

"No. We were afraid Delvina would panic and make Grandma disappear."

"That's a genuine concern," Ranger said. "How can I help you?"

"For starters, you can get me Delvina's phone number."

Ranger called his office and asked for Delvina's number. Moments later, he gave it to me. "Now what?" he asked.

"Hopefully, this will do it. I'll give him his money, and he'll give me Grandma."

"Call me if there are complications. I have to run. I need to look in on a commercial account."

I immediately called Delvina. "Okay," I said, "I

have the money." Most of it. "How do you want to do this?"

"Put the duffel bag on the passenger seat of a car and take the car to the car wash at three o'clock. If the money's all there, you'll get your grandmother."

"Will she be at the car wash?"

"More or less. We'll deliver her to the car wash as soon as we count the money. You shouldn't worry about it. Trust me, the sooner we're rid of her, the better."

"I suppose I should tell you we're a little short."

"How short?"

"Roughly . . . a hundred and forty thousand, more or less."

"No deal. No way. I need all the money. At three o'clock, we shoot the horse, and then we shoot the old lady. I'm almost hoping you don't get the money. I really want to shoot the old lady."

I got into my piece-of-crap car and drove to my apartment building. By the time I got there, I'd sort of stopped crying. I ran up the stairs and took a minute to blow my nose and get myself under control before I opened the door.

Snuggy was on the couch, watching television. He was looking more like Dublin bum than leprechaun.

"Where do you keep all your green pants?" I asked him. "Do you live near here?"

"I have an apartment in Hamilton Township. By the pet cemetery."

That figured.

Diesel strolled out of my bedroom wearing his same clothes but looking fresh out of the shower. His hair was still damp and the stubble was gone.

"I used your razor and toothbrush," Diesel said. "I figured you wouldn't mind."

"You aren't diseased, are you?"

"I couldn't get a disease if I tried." He stood for a beat with his thumbs hooked into his pants pockets. "Are you okay?"

"Yes." A tear leaked out of my eye and streaked down my cheek.

"Oh, shit," Diesel said. "I'm not good at this. It's not the toothbrush, is it? I'll buy you a new one."

"It's Grandma. He's going to shoot her because we haven't got all the money. I talked to him, and he told me they were going to count the money, and if it wasn't all there, they were going to shoot Grandma and the horse."

"So we have to get more money," Snuggy said. "How hard can it be?"

"We're not talking about small change," Diesel said. "We need a hundred and forty thousand dollars."

"Maybe you could pop into a bank," Snuggy said to Diesel.

Diesel looked at his watch. "Delvina's keeping the horse and the woman somewhere. Let's see if we can find them. If we can't find them by two o'clock, we'll go to plan B."

"What's plan B?" I asked him.

"I don't actually have a plan B. I suppose plan B would involve the police. I'm going to have Flash take a look at Delvina's country house."

Flash works with Diesel. Or maybe Flash works *for* Diesel. Or maybe Flash is just Diesel's friend. Hard to tell where Flash fits in the big picture. He's slim and spikey-haired and a couple inches taller than me. He lives in Trenton. He has a girl-friend. He likes to ski. And he's a handy guy to have on your team. That's everything I know about Flash.

Diesel punched Flash's number into his phone. "I need you to check out Lou Delvina's house in Bucks County," he said when the connection was made. "He's holding a horse and Stephanie's grand-mother as hostages somewhere. I'm going to scope out his house in Trenton."

"Is there something I can do?" Snuggy asked.

"You can stay here and not make a move," Die-sel said. "When we leave, don't open the door to anyone. Don't order pizza. Don't buy Girl Scout cookies. Don't look out a window. Bolt the door and keep the television low." Diesel had his head in the refrigerator. "There's nothing in here. How can you live without food?"

"I have peanut butter in the cupboard and some crackers."

"I like peanut butter and crackers," Snuggy said.

"Knock yourself out," Diesel said. He wrapped an arm around me. "Let's hustle. I want to see the car wash, and then we'll snoop around Delvina's social club. He has a house in Cranbury, but I don't think he'd keep a horse and an old lady locked up with his wife."

I followed Diesel down the stairs, through the small lobby, and out the back door. We got to the car, and he took the keys from me.

"Excuse me?" I said.

"I'll drive."

"I don't think so. This is my car, and I drive."

"The guy drives. Everyone knows that."

"Only in Saudi Arabia."

He dangled the keys over my head. "Do you think you can get these keys from me?"

"Do you think you can walk after I kick you in the knee?"

"You can be a real pain in the ass," Diesel said.

Another tear slid down my cheek.

"You forced yourself to do that," Diesel said.

"I didn't. I'm feeling very emotional. I'm hungry and I need a shower and some awful toad man

is going to shoot my grandmother. And I'm tired.
I didn't get a lot of sleep last night."

"It was nice last night," Diesel said. "I liked
holding you."

"You're trying to soften me up."

"Is it working?"

I did some mental eye rolling and got into the
passenger side of the car.

The car wash wasn't far from my apartment. We
cruised past, made a U-turn, and drove by a second time. It was a little after eleven o'clock on a
Thursday, and the car wash was empty. Three Hispanic guys in car wash gear lounged in front of
the drive-through brushless system that was built
into a cement block tunnel. The waiting room and
Delvina's office were a couple feet away in a second cement block building. The waiting room was
glass-fronted, and I could see some vending machines and a counter with a cash register, but no
people. There were two junker cars in the lot. Nothing that looked like it would belong to Delvina.

Diesel drove around a couple blocks, getting the
lay of the land, looking for black Mafia staff cars.
We didn't see any Mafia cars, horse barns, hay
wagons, or men hobbling around holding their privates because Grandma finally managed to get her
leg up high enough to do damage.

"Delvina could have your grandmother stashed

anywhere," Diesel said. "The horse is a whole other thing. You don't ride a horse through downtown Trenton to get handed off for ransom. Delvina needs a horse van to move Doug around. So far, I'm not seeing any evidence of a horse or a van."

Diesel turned onto Roebling and slowed when he came to Delvina's social club. It was a dingy, redbrick, two-story row house. Two metal folding chairs from Lugio's Funeral Home had been placed beside the front stoop. This was Chambersburg patio furniture. Pottery Barn, eat your heart out. There was no visible activity in or around the club. No place to hide a horse.

Diesel took the alley behind the row houses. Each house had a small, narrow yard with a single-car garage at the rear. Diesel parked halfway down the alley, left the car, and walked. He looked in each of the garages and in all the yards.

"No sign of a horse," he said when he returned. "But I'm guessing a couple people are hijacking trucks. Do you need a toaster?"

I called Connie and asked if Delvina had any other properties.

"Hold on," Connie said. "I'll run him through some programs."

I listened to Connie tap onto her computer keyboard and waited while she read through information appearing on her screen.

"So far, I'm only showing his house in Cranbury and his house in Bucks County. Plus the car wash. I know he owns other properties, but they were probably bought through a holding company. I can run that down, but it'll take a while. I'll call you back."

"Thanks."

"We have time," Diesel said. "We might as well look at the house in Cranbury."

Cranbury is a pretty little town within shouting distance of Route 130. Delvina lived on a quiet, tree-lined street. His house was white clapboard with black shutters and a red door. It was two stories, with a two-car detached garage. The lot was maybe a quarter acre and filled with trees and flowerbeds and shrubs. Mrs. Delvina liked to garden.

"This all seems so benign, so normal," Diesel said, sitting in the car, looking across the street at the house.

"Maybe when Delvina is in this house he *is* sort of normal."

Diesel methodically drove up and down streets in Delvina's neighborhood. There were some rural areas around Cranbury where a horse could be kept without notice, but we didn't know where to begin.

I called Connie for a property update.

"I'm not finding anything local," Connie said.

"He's got real estate in the Caymans and a condo in Miami under LD Sons Import."

"Did you try his wife's maiden name?"

"Yeah. Nothing came up."

Diesel put the Monte Carlo into gear and headed out of town, back to Trenton. We were on Broad Street when Flash called. I gave Diesel raised eyebrows, and he shook his head no. No sign of Grandma or Doug in Bucks County.

"I could use a change of clothes," Diesel told Flash. "And check to see if the O'Connor mess has been resolved. If it hasn't been resolved and I need to keep him close, he's going to need clothes, too. And a toothbrush."

We stopped at Cluck-in-a-Bucket, got bags of food, and brought them back to my apartment.

Snuggy was still on the couch in front of the television. We dumped the food on the coffee table and we all dug in.

"I got an idea while you were gone," Snuggy said. "Delvina won't give us Grandma, because we don't have all the money, but maybe he'll take the money we've got in exchange for Doug. We can ask for another twenty-four hours to come up with the rest. And here's the best part. Once we get hold of Doug, I can ask him where Delvina is keeping Grandma."

Diesel was halfway into a second chicken

sandwich. "On the surface, that sounds like an okay idea. If it turns out you can't actually talk to that horse, I'll throw you off the Route 1 bridge into the Delaware River."

"You have trust issues," Snuggy said to Diesel. "I sense some passive-aggressive tendencies."

"I'm not passive-aggressive," Diesel said. "I'm actively aggressive. And I'd have to be an idiot to trust you. You're a nut."

"Should I call Delvina?" I asked Diesel.

"Yeah. At the very worst, it'll buy us some time."

I had the money in the duffel bag on the seat next to me. I eased the Monte Carlo up to the car wash and put it in park. I got out and a guy in a car wash uniform got in. The Monte was rolled through the car wash, and when it emerged on the opposite side, the guy got out holding the duffel bag. He walked over to me and gave me a piece of paper. "This is from Mr. Delvina. He said you'd know what to do."

Diesel and Snuggy were in the RV half a block away. I drove around the block and parked my clean Monte Carlo behind the RV. I got out, locked up, and climbed on board. Snuggy was at the wheel. He was the only one who could fit in the seat.

"Here's the address," I said to Snuggy. "It's south of town, off Broad. It's a light industrial park that's pretty much abandoned."

Ten minutes later, Snuggy maneuvered the RV into the parking lot of a small warehouse. Grass grew from cracks in the pavement and one of the front office windows was covered with a plywood slab. Diesel hopped out and stood still for a moment. I supposed he was taking some sort of cosmic temperature. He walked to a side door, and Snuggy and I hopped out of the RV and followed him.

Diesel opened the door, and we all peered into the dim interior. Something rustled in a far corner, and deep in shadow I could see the horse. He was tethered to a cinder block. He turned his head and looked at us and made a horse sound. Not a high-pitched whinny. This was more of a low snuffle.

"Doug!" Snuggy yelled. And he ran to the horse and threw his arms around the horse's neck.

Diesel and I approached the horse, and I could see why Snuggy was so taken. The animal was beautiful. His mane and tail were black and his coat was chestnut. He had large, soulful brown eyes and long lashes. And he was massive. Even in the dark warehouse, you could sense his power. It was a lot like standing next to Diesel.

We cut the rope away from the cinder block and led Doug through the warehouse to the parking lot.

"Are you sure this is going to work?" I asked Snuggy.

"Sure, it'll work," Snuggy said. "Doug's a real trouper—right, Doug?"

Doug looked at Snuggy with his huge horse eye.

"Just exactly how do you talk to him?" I asked Snuggy.

"It's sort of telepathic."

"Can he understand me?"

"Yep. See, that's the mistake people make. Everyone thinks just because animals can't talk means they can't understand."

I thought about Morelli's dog, Bob. I was pretty sure Bob didn't understand a damn thing.

"Go ahead," Snuggy said to Doug. "Give her a sign that you understand."

Doug blinked.

"See?" Snuggy said. "Impressive, hunh?"

"That was it? A blink?"

"Oh man," Diesel said. "We are so fucked."

Doug moved to the side and stepped on Diesel's foot. Diesel gave him a shot to the shoulder and Doug moved over, off Diesel's foot.

"Okay," I said, "now that each of you has marked your territory on the fire hydrant, can we get on with it?"

"We brought the RV instead of your car because it has a tow hitch, but they didn't leave the horse trailer," Snuggy said. "I borrowed a horse trailer from a friend, and they took it when they took Doug, and it's not here."

"Maybe you can ride him back," Diesel said.

"I can't ride him back on the highway!" Snuggy said. "And anyway, he has a bad leg. It hurts when he walks on it too much."

We all looked down at Doug's leg. It had a bandage wrapped around it.

"Put him in the RV," Diesel said.

Snuggy and I did an openmouthed *What?*

Diesel was looking a quart down on patience. "Do you have any better ideas?"

Snuggy and I shook our heads. We didn't have any ideas.

"We're wasting time," Diesel said.

Snuggy took Doug's halter and led him over to the door of the RV. There were three steps going up, and the door opening looked maybe a half-inch wider than Doug's ass.

Doug planted his feet firm on the ground and gave Snuggy a look that I swear said *Are you insane?*

"Up you go," Snuggy said. "Into the RV."

Doug didn't budge.

Snuggy went into telepathic mode, nodding his head, looking sympathetic.

"I understand your concern," Snuggy said to Doug, "but you have nothing to worry about. You have to make a tight turn when you first get in, but then you'll have plenty of room."

More telepathy.

"*I'm* driving," Snuggy said to Doug.

Doug still didn't move.

"What are you talking about?" Snuggy said. "I'm a good driver. I brought you around the track to win at Freehold."

Doug rolled his eyes.

"I fell off *after* we won," Snuggy said. "And it had nothing to do with my driving. It was one of those freak things."

"How about this?" Diesel said to Doug. "You get into the RV, or we leave you in the parking lot and don't come back."

Snuggy went in first, pulling on Doug's halter, and Diesel put his shoulder to Doug's butt. After a lot of swearing on Diesel's part, and a lot of nervous foot stamping on Doug's part, Doug got himself into the RV.

"Jeez," Snuggy said to Doug. "Quit your complaining. Look at Diesel. He doesn't fit in here, either, but he's making the best of it."

Doug turned his horse eye on Diesel, and I didn't think it looked friendly.

"Maybe you want to give Doug some room," I said to Diesel. "Maybe you want to go up front and hang with Snuggy."

EIGHT

It was four o'clock when we cruised into the lot to my building and parked the RV in the back, next to the Dumpster.

"We should get Doug out of the RV for a couple minutes," Snuggy said. "Let him stretch his legs and go potty."

The possibility that Doug might have to go potty got us all on our feet. We maneuvered Doug into the back bedroom, turned him around, and managed to get him out the door and down the steps. Snuggy walked Doug around in the lot, but apparently Doug didn't feel the need to do anything. I wasn't all that unhappy, because I didn't know how I was going to explain a load of horse shit in the parking lot.

"Ask him about Grandma," I said to Snuggy. "Does he know where she is?"

Here's the thing. I didn't entirely buy into the whole horse talk business, but a part of me wanted to believe. Not only did I want to believe for Grandma's sake, but I liked the idea that communication was possible between species. I also liked the idea that reindeer could fly, there was such a thing as the birthday cake diet, and, most of all, I wanted to go to heaven.

"What about it?" Snuggy said to Doug. "Unhunh, un-hunh, un-hunh."

I looked up at Diesel. "Are you getting anything?"

"Yeah, a real strong desire to quit my job and go to bartending school."

"Doug says before they drove him to the warehouse, they had him outside, in a yard, and he was tied to a thing in the ground, like a dog. He said it was humiliating. He doesn't know exactly where it was, but he might be able to spot it if you drive him around."

"That's a little vague," Diesel said.

"Doug thinks they might have Grandma there because he heard a lot of yelling, and then they pulled the shades down, so he couldn't see in the window. And he thinks he might have heard a gunshot."

"No!" I had my hand to my heart. "When?"

"Just before they loaded him into the horse trailer."

I whipped my phone out and dialed Delvina.

"What?" Delvina said.

"Is my grandmother all right?"

"Was she ever all right?"

"I want to talk to her," I told him.

"No way. We got her locked in the crapper, and I'm not opening that door until I get a cattle prod. Do you have the rest of my money?"

"Not yet, but I'm working on it."

Delvina disconnected.

"Doug says he's hungry," Snuggy said. "He said he had to eat grass, and there wasn't hardly any. He says he thinks he could be more helpful if he wasn't hungry."

Diesel dialed Flash. "I need horse food," he said to Flash. He listened a minute and studied his shoe. "I don't know what horses eat. Just go to a horse food store and let them figure it out. And bring some beer and pizza with the horse food."

"What are you going to do with Doug?" I asked Snuggy. "He needs a barn or a stable or something."

"I have him scheduled for surgery next week, and after that, I have a place for him to live in Hunterdon County. I just don't have anything for him right now. And I guess I'm in a bind with the surgery. I lost the money I was going to use."

I called my mother.

"Do you know anything about Lou Delvina?"

"You aren't involved with him, are you? He's a

terrible person. If your cousin gave Delvina to you to find, you give him back. Let someone else look for him."

"He's not one of my cases. This is something else."

"Well, I hear he's sick. And something happened with him and his wife, because he's not living at the Cranbury house anymore."

"Do you know where he *is* living?"

"No, but I ran into Louise Kulach at church last week, and she said twice she saw Delvina getting cold cuts at the deli on Cherry Street. She said he looked terrible. She said you wouldn't recognize him, except the butcher told her who it was. Where's your grandmother?"

"She's in the bathroom."

"What should I do about supper? I have a pot of spaghetti sauce on the stove."

"Grandma wants to eat at the mall."

"I guess that's okay, but don't let her eat from that Chinese place. It always gives her the runs."

I put my phone back into my pocket. "North Trenton," I said to Diesel. "Delvina's been seen at the deli on Cherry Street."

"Never underestimate the value of gossip," Diesel said. "Let's roll before it gets dark."

"What about the horse food?" Snuggy asked.

"We'll stop at Cluck-in-a-Bucket," Diesel said.

"Doug doesn't eat burgers," Snuggy said. "Horses are vegetarians."

"Whatever," Diesel said. "We'll stop at a supermarket and get him a head of lettuce. Just get him into the RV."

Snuggy rolled the RV slowly down Cherry Street. Doug was in the aisle between the dinette table and the couch, looking out the big front window, eating an apple. It was his fourth apple, and half the apple fell out of his mouth while he chewed. Turns out it's hard to eat an apple efficiently without opposable thumbs. We'd been driving a grid pattern through north Trenton, and this was our second pass down Cherry.

Diesel was perched on the seat next to Snuggy. "You'd better not be blowing smoke up my skirt with this horse," Diesel said to Snuggy.

Doug reached forward and bit Diesel on the shoulder. Not hard enough to draw blood, but hard enough to leave a dent and apple slobber on Diesel's shirt.

"This is the reason I don't carry a gun," Diesel said. "It'd be satisfying to shoot him, but I'd probably regret it . . . eventually."

Snuggy turned off Cherry, drove a couple blocks,

and stopped in the middle of the road. "Doug says the neighborhood didn't look like this. He said the house was by itself."

"Was it in the woods? In the middle of a field?" I asked.

"No. It was just by itself," Snuggy said. "And it was noisy. He could hear cars all night long."

"Route 1," I said to Diesel. "The house was at the end of a street that backed up to Route 1."

The sun was setting, and I could see a rosy glow in the sky in front of us.

"Pretty sunset," I said.

"That's not a sunset," Diesel said. "The sun is behind us. That's a fire."

A cop car raced past us, and I heard sirens in the distance. Snuggy moved to the side of the road to allow a fire truck to get through.

"I've got a bad feeling about this," Diesel said. "Follow the truck."

Snuggy eased the RV down the street and parked a block from the fire. Cop cars and fire trucks were angled in front of the burning house. The house was at the end of a cul-de-sac. The lot was large. There was a two-car garage attached to the house. The garage doors were open and whatever was in the garage was on fire. Firemen were running hoses and shouting instructions to each other. There were large trees to the side and behind the house. The rumble of the fire trucks drowned out all other noise, but I knew on a quieter night you could hear the Route 1 traffic from here.

Diesel was on his feet. "Stay here," he said. "I'm going to look around."

"No way," I said. "I'm coming with you."

"Every cop and fireman in the county knows you," Diesel said. "Morelli will get a phone call, and we'll have the police involved in this."

"Maybe the police *should* be involved."

"Let me scope it out before we jump to conclusions. I'll be right back."

I sat on the couch and dialed Delvina. My hands were shaking, and I had to dial twice to get the right number. Delvina didn't answer.

My next call was to Connie. "Are you at the office or has this been forwarded?" I asked her.

"I'm still here. I'm trying to clear out some backed-up paperwork."

"I need you to run an address for me."

Moments later, she was back on the line. "The house is owned by Mickey Wallens, Delvina's wheelman."

I disconnected and clamped my teeth down into my lower lip. Snuggy and Doug were silent, watching out the front window with me. The three of us barely breathing. Diesel appeared from behind a fire truck and jogged back to the RV.

"It looks like the fire was started in a second-floor bathroom. The firefighters haven't determined if anyone was in the house, but I think the house was empty. One of the garage bays was empty. There was a horse trailer in the other. The horse trailer is toast."

"Now what?" Snuggy asked.

"Take us back to Stephanie's apartment," Diesel said.

"Drive by the car wash on the way," I told him. "I want to get my car."

Snuggy parked the RV in his spot by the Dumpster, and I parked one row up, making sure I could drive straight out. I got out of my car and tried Delvina one more time. The phone rang twice and he answered.

"Sonovabitch," he said.

"I want to talk to my grandmother."

"She's in the trunk. Don't worry about her. She's got a quilt and a pillow, and she's curled up next to the spare tire. It's a big trunk."

"She's old. That's awful!"

"I'll tell you what's awful. She burned Mickey's house down. She said it smelled like poop in the bathroom, so Mickey slid some matches to her under the door."

I could hear Mickey next to Delvina. "I was trying to be helpful."

"How many times I have to tell you?" Delvina said to Mickey. "No guns, sharp objects, or matches to hostages."

"We never had a old lady hostage before," Mickey said. "I didn't know the rules was the same."

Delvina came back on the line to me. "So Sir Walter Raleigh here gives your grandma matches, and she uses them to set off the smoke detector. Then somehow the curtains got caught on fire. We're lucky we didn't die, for crissake. Now we're riding around like some homeless people. I gotta go. I think we're lost."

Delvina disconnected.

"Well?" Diesel said.

"They're lost."

"I know the feeling," Diesel said. "I'm going upstairs, where I hope there's some pizza and beer waiting for me."

We all walked over to the back door, and when I reached it, I realized Doug had followed us.

"What are we going to do with Doug?" I said.

"Doug can stay in the RV," Diesel said.

"Doug doesn't want to stay in the RV," Snuggy said. "He's freaked out from the fire. Doug wants to stay with us."

"Yeah, but this is an apartment building for people," I said.

"Doesn't it allow pets?"

"Not horses!"

"How do you know? Does it say that in your rental agreement? And anyway, you let Diesel stay here."

"Diesel is housebroken."

"So is Doug," Snuggy said.

Doug was standing with his head down, looking pathetic, not putting any weight on his bad leg.

"Oh, for goodness sakes," I said.

Snuggy, Diesel, Doug, and I got into the elevator, and I looked at the posted weight limit.

"How much does Doug weigh?" I asked Snuggy.

"About thirteen hundred pounds," Snug-gy said. "Don't anyone breathe. I'm going to push the button. We only have to go up one floor."

The elevator paused when it got to the second floor, and I prayed that the doors would open. I didn't want to get caught in an elevator with a horse. The doors opened after a long moment, and we all paraded down the hall to my apartment. Flash had left a sack of grain, two buckets, two six-packs of beer, three pizzas, and a duffel bag with Diesel's and Snuggy's clothes in front of my door.

We carried everything inside and closed and locked the door. Snuggy poured some grain into a bucket for Doug and filled the second bucket with water. Diesel took one of the pizza boxes and a beer and settled himself in front of the television.

Some people can't eat when they're under stress. I get hungry when I'm nervous. I eat to fill the hollow feeling in my stomach. I sat next to Diesel and wolfed down pizza. I looked at the box and saw that it was empty.

"Are you going to eat the cardboard, too?" Diesel asked.

"Did I eat pizza?"

"Four pieces."

"I don't remember."

"Take a deep breath," Diesel said. He put his hands on my shoulders and kneaded. "Keep breathing," he told me. "Try to relax. Your grandma's going to be okay. We're going to find her."

I was warming under Diesel's touch. The heat was working its way up my neck and down my spine. It wasn't sexual. It was sensual and soothing. I could feel myself going soft inside. I could feel my heartbeat slowing.

"You have terrific hands," I said to Diesel. "I always get warm when you touch me."

"I've been told it has something to do with sympathetic body chemistry and shared electrical energy. The person who told me that was full of mushrooms, but I thought it sounded cool. The other explanation is that my body temperature runs higher than normal, and I like touching you."

I didn't know I'd fallen asleep until I woke up. I was snuggled against Diesel, and he was watching a basketball game. Snuggy was watching, too. He was in his new clothes, which looked exactly like his old clothes, except the wrinkles and knee bags and ketchup stains were missing. Doug was in the kitchen with the light off. Guess Doug wasn't a Knicks fan.

It was nine o'clock and my mother was probably pacing the floor, waiting for me to bring Grandma home. I tapped her number into my phone and imagined her jumping at the first ring.

"Where are you?"

"I'm home."

"Where's your grandmother?"

"I sort of lost her."

"What?"

"Remember how, in the beginning, she took off on a road trip? It's a little like that. But I don't think she's gone too far this time."

"How could this happen?"

"She's very wily."

"I don't understand. She has a nice home here. Why would she do this?"

"I think she needs to have an adventure once in a while. And she's overly curious."

"You get that from her," my mother said. "You're a lot like your grandmother."

Sort of a scary thought, but I knew it was true. Even at this moment, I had a horse in my kitchen.

"Don't worry," I said to my mother. "She's fine. I'll find her and bring her home tomorrow."

Diesel pulled himself away from the game when I disconnected. "How did that go?"

"As well as could be expected. I would have gotten grounded if she didn't need me to find my grandmother."

"I bet you got grounded a lot when you were a kid."

I laughed out loud, remembering. "I used to climb out the bathroom window."

"Was Morelli waiting for you at the bottom?"

"No. I only had a couple isolated experiences with Morelli back then. He was one of those hit-and-run guys."

"And now?"

"Now he's waiting for me at the bottom." I did some mental knuckle-cracking. "I feel like I should be doing something. I hate sitting here knowing Grandma is locked in Delvina's trunk."

My cell phone rang and for a moment the number displayed didn't register. Then it hit me. Briggs. I'd totally forgotten about him.

"Yes?" I said.

"Where is everybody?"

"We're back in Trenton. Where are you?"

"I'm in Atlantic City. I'm on a roll. I'm shooting craps with my lucky Edna money and I can't lose. Why'd everyone leave?"

"Lou Delvina kidnapped Grandma."

"Get out!"

"I think it's safe to assume you're unemployed."

"Jeez. Did you get her back yet?"

"No. We're working on it. We need a hundred and forty thousand dollars to ransom her. How much have you won?"

"Not that much."

"Keep rolling," I said. And I disconnected.

NINE

I slapped the alarm button on my bedside clock, but the ringing continued.

"Phone," Diesel murmured against my ear.

I fumbled for the phone and mumbled hello.

"I just got off a triple shift," Morelli said. "Gang fight in the projects. Two dead. Do you want to meet me for breakfast before I crash?"

"What time is it?"

"Six-thirty."

"I've got a full house here. I think I should stay and keep my eye on things."

"Who's there?"

"Diesel and Snuggy O'Connor and Doug."

"Snuggy O'Connor," Morelli said. "I know that name from somewhere."

"He was a jockey. He's here with Doug."

"And Doug is who?"

"Doug's a horse."

There was a long moment of silence.

"They're not all in your apartment, are they?" Morelli asked.

"Yep."

"Is Doug a *little* horse?"

"No. Doug is a big horse. It's complicated."

"It always is," Morelli said. "I'm really tired. Probably I'm hallucinating this whole conversation. I'll call in a day or two when I wake up."

Diesel was in the bed with me, fully clothed except for shoes. I'd also fallen asleep in my clothes . . . minus my bra. The bra was dangling from the door-knob. I didn't want to dwell on how it got there.

"What are you doing in my bed?" I asked Diesel.

"You fell asleep watching television, so I carried you in here and figured you wouldn't mind if I joined you. I don't fit on your couch, and I'm not in love with sleeping on the floor. Did you put in for a wake-up call?"

"That was Morelli coming off a triple shift. Checking in."

I got up and peeked into the living room. No horse. No Snuggy. I went to the bedroom window and pulled the curtain aside. Snuggy and Doug were on a patch of grass at the back of my parking lot. Doug limped when he walked.

"Doug's leg is bothering him," I said to Diesel.

"It makes me feel sad to see him limping. I bet he was a sight when he was young and healthy."

"He'll be okay," Diesel said. "We'll find a way to get him healed."

I nodded and blinked to keep from tearing up. Between Doug and Grandma, I had a lot of painful emotions clogging my throat.

"I'm going to take a shower," I said to Diesel.

"Would you like company?"

"No, but thanks for offering."

"The least I could do," Diesel said.

I got clean clothes, locked myself in the bathroom, and stepped into the shower. When I got out, I felt reenergized.

"I got an idea while you were in the shower," Diesel said. "We need money, right? Who has money sitting around? Delvina. I watched the duffel bag get carried into the car wash, and I didn't see it come out. I'm guessing Delvina has the money in the car wash safe."

"And?"

"And we steal the money from Delvina. Then we can give it back to him to get Grandma. I swear, sometimes I'm so brilliant I can hardly stand it."

"Only problem is, how do we steal the money without getting caught?"

"We need a diversion."

"Oh boy. Been there, done that."

"It's going to have to be a much better diversion. Something clever. Let me jump in the shower and change my clothes and we'll go do some recon."

Snuggy, Diesel, and I sat in my car across from the car wash and watched the action. Friday was senior citizen discount day, and at eight o'clock, business was already jumping.

"This is going to be tough," I said to Diesel. "Too many people. We should have done this last night, when it was dark."

"I didn't think of it last night. Let's get out and walk around. Get a different perspective. See if we can come up with an angle."

Diesel crossed the street, walked half a block down, and then doubled back, coming up behind the building. Snuggy and I walked in the opposite direction on the other side of the street.

A Doberman was sitting in a small front yard, watching traffic. He was wearing a collar with a little box attached.

"Invisible fence," Snuggy said. "There's a wire buried under the ground, and he gets zapped if he crosses it." He smiled at the dog. "How's it going?"

The dog looked at Snuggy.

"Wow, no kidding," Snuggy said.

"What?" I asked.

"He says he ate a sock, and he's waiting to crap it out. That's why he's outside. Ordinarily, he's inside at this time of the day."

The Doberman stood, concentrated for a moment, and sat back down. Guess the sock wasn't ready to leave.

"We're doing surveillance," Snuggy said to the dog. "I'm a leprechaun and the guy who owns the car wash has my lucky money locked up in his safe."

The dog's eyes widened ever so slightly. Either he was impressed with the leprechaun thing or else the sock was moving south.

"Swear to God," Snuggy said. "I'd just pop over there and take it, but I'm having trouble with my leprechaun invisibility."

The Doberman looked Snuggy up and down.

"Really? Are you sure?" Snuggy said.

"Tell me," I said. "What? *What?*"

Snuggy thunked the heel of his hand against his forehead. "Of course. Why didn't I think of that? It's so obvious."

"What's obvious? What didn't you think of?"

"No time to explain, but I know what went wrong. Tell Diesel not to worry. I'll take care of everything. You guys get in the car and pick me up when I come out of the office."

"Wait! We should discuss this. What did the dog say to you?"

"He said it was my clothes! You see, it all makes sense. I was invisible, but my clothes weren't. It was probably the new laundry detergent I used. All I have to do is take my clothes off, and then I can go in and open the safe and take the money, and no one will see me."

"No, no, no, no. Bad idea."

Snuggy shrugged out of his jacket and shirt and kicked his shoes off. I frantically waved at Diesel, but he was making his way around the building and didn't see me. I made a grab for Snuggy and missed.

"Trust me. This will work," Snuggy said, dancing away, unzipping his green pants.

Snuggy had tighty whities under the green pants, and in an instant, they were on the ground and Snuggy was running across the street.

"Eeek!" I said. And I clapped my hands over my eyes. When I took my hands away, I saw Snuggy's lily-white leprechaun ass hop the curb and sprint for the car wash office door.

The office door opened and a big Sasquatch-type uniformed car wash guy looked out at Snuggy. "What the fuck?"

Diesel was on the sidewalk, rooted to the spot. He looked at Snuggy in amazement and then he looked across the street at me.

I shrugged and made an *I don't know, but it's not my fault* gesture.

Snuggy danced around in front of the car wash guy. "'Tis invisible I be, and lucky fer you or t'wud be the wrath o' me shillelagh ye'd be feelin'."

"Your shillelagh don't look like anything to worry about," the guy said.

A couple more uniformed guys stopped work and looked over at Snuggy.

"What's with him?" one of them said.

"He thinks he's a leprechaun," Sasquatch told him.

"No way," the guy said. "Leprechauns got red hair down there."

Everyone stared at Snuggy's thatch and exposed plumbing, including Snuggy.

"Cripes, I've smoked fatter joints than that," one of the guys said. "I didn't know they came that small."

"I'm supposed to be invisible," Snuggy said.

Several cars were lined up to take advantage of senior discount day. The drivers honked their horns at Snuggy and yelled at him out of their windows.

"You're holding up the line."

"Get out of the way. You think I have all day to do this?"

"Pervert!"

"Somebody shoot him."

"You should come nice and peaceful with us,"

Sasquatch said. "We'll take you to the hospital. They got a special room set aside for leprechauns."

Sasquatch reached for Snuggy, and Snuggy yelped and jumped away. The men ran after Snuggy, and Snuggy took off in blind panic, running around the cars that were waiting in line. Two more uniformed car wash attendants joined the chase, and the sheer number of people running after Snuggy added to his confusion. The seniors kept honking their horns and everyone was yelling.

"Catch him!"

"Cut him off on the other side."

"Go left."

"Go right."

It probably only took a couple minutes, but it seemed like it went on for hours, with Snuggy shrieking like a girl, waving his arms in the air as he ran. He dodged two guys, sprinted straight into the car wash tunnel, and disappeared from view behind a curtain of water.

"Eeeeeeeeyiiii!" Snuggy squealed inside the tunnel.

The car wash guys ran in after Snuggy, but Snuggy was the only one who ran out. He was soaking wet and clumped with soapsuds, and he was moving at light speed. Sasquatch crawled out on his hands and knees, and two more men wind-milled out and fell on their asses in the soapy water.

Diesel came from out of nowhere, grabbed the back of my sweatshirt, and yanked me toward the car. "Get in!" Diesel yelled at me.

I jumped in next to Diesel, and he rocketed away from the curb. Snuggy was running down the street in front of us, knees high, arms pumping, not looking back. Diesel honked the horn at him and pulled alongside. Snuggy ripped the door open and threw himself in.

"Damn Doberman," Snuggy said. "I should have known better than to trust a Doberman. They're all practical jokers."

I was facing forward, not wanting to look at Snuggy naked in my backseat. Snuggy naked wasn't an inspiring sight.

"You've had this happen before with a Doberman?" I asked him.

"I never learn," Snuggy said. "I'm too trusting. Are these my clothes?"

"Yeah. I picked them up off the ground and put them in the car. I figured sooner or later you'd get cold."

"Thanks," Snuggy said. "That was real nice of you."

I looked down at my feet and realized that I was sharing space with the duffel bag. "How'd this get here?"

"No one was paying attention to the office," Diesel

said. "Everyone was chasing Snuggy. So I scrambled the security system, walked in, opened the safe, and took the money."

I opened the bag and counted the money. It was all there. "Woohoo! Did anyone see you?"

"No. I went in and out through a back door. The office was empty."

Snuggy was dressed by the time we got back to my apartment. He still had some suds in his hair, but aside from that, he looked okay. I opened the door to my apartment, and Doug was stomping around in my kitchen.

"Doug has to go," Snuggy said.

"Go where?"

"Out! Hold the elevator."

I ran to the elevator and punched the button. The doors opened, Snuggy and Doug trotted down the hall, and we got into the elevator. Doug was dancing around, looking frantic. He lifted his tail, there was the sound of air escaping from a balloon, and the elevator filled with horse fart.

"Holy crap!" I said.

"Doug says he's sorry. He says it slipped out."

The doors opened, and we all rushed into the lobby and out into the parking lot. Doug took a wide stance and whizzed for about fifteen minutes. He walked around a little and dropped a load of road apples. We had a pooper-scooper law in Trenton, but I wasn't sure it applied to horse shit. I'd need a snow shovel and a twenty-gallon garbage bag to pooper-scooper what Doug dropped.

"Maybe an apartment isn't the best place for Doug," I said to Snuggy.

"He's too cramped in the RV. I don't know where else to put him."

"I have a friend who owns a building with a parking garage. It's very secure and the garage is well lit and really clean." Actually, cleaner than my apartment.

"That might be okay," Snuggy said. "He'd have room to walk around in a parking garage. And maybe I could bring some straw in for him to stand on just for a couple days until his surgery."

I dialed Ranger.

"Yo," Ranger said.

"Yo yourself. I was wondering if I could park something in your garage for a couple days."

"Something?"

"A horse."

A moment of silence.

"Babe," Ranger said.

"He used to be a racehorse."

More silence.

"He's sort of a homeless horse," I said.

"I'm leaving for the airport in two seconds, and I won't be back for a couple days. You can put the horse in the garage, but I don't want that horse in my apartment."

"Who would put a horse in an apartment? That's dumb."

"Where's the horse staying now?"

"My apartment."

"I can always count on you to brighten my day," Ranger said. And he disconnected.

I ran upstairs to tell Diesel and to get my purse.

"Snuggy can stay with Doug as long as he promises not to leave Rangeman property," Diesel said.

"I'm going to ride over with Snuggy. I'll be back as soon as I get them settled in. I thought I'd call Delvina before I go."

Diesel was foraging in the refrigerator. He found the leftover pizza and dug in. "If he lets you choose the exchange site, ask for the car wash again."

I called Delvina and told him we had the money.

"I'll get back to you," Delvina said. "I gotta make arrangements."

"The car wash was good last time," I told him. "Why don't we do the car wash again?"

"The car wash won't work for this," Delvina said. "I'll find someplace better and call you back."

We had enough overhead clearance to drive the RV into the underground Rangeman garage. We parked to one side and we off-loaded Doug.

The elevator doors opened and Hal stepped out. Hal was Rangeman muscle, with a body like a stegosaurus. He was dressed in Rangeman black, his blond hair had been freshly buzzed, and his face was brightened by a smile.

"This is a horse," Hal said, looking like an eight-year-old on Christmas morning.

"Ranger told me I could park him here for a couple days."

The smile got wider. "He's big."

"He was a racehorse."

"No kidding? Wow. I'm supposed to get you whatever you need."

"A couple bales of straw would be perfect," Snuggy said.

"Sure. And we have a bay over on the other side where we wash the cars. You can get water there. Just give me a holler if you need anything else."

"I could use a ride home," I said to Hal. "I'm going to leave the RV here."

Snuggy and I hauled Doug's food and buckets out of the RV, and Snuggy looked at the hose on the far wall.

"I'd like to clean up the sore on Doug's leg and rewrap it with a fresh bandage," Snuggy said. "I found some gauze bandages in the bathroom, but there's not enough soap."

I had a gizmo on my keychain that got me into

the Rangeman garage and Ranger's private apartment. I rode the elevator to the seventh floor, let myself into Ranger's lair, and went straight to his bathroom. I grabbed a bottle of shower gel and returned to the garage. It was Ranger's Bulgari Green, and I'd probably get a rush every time I smelled Doug, but it was the fastest solution.

"I have to go," I said to Snuggy. "If there's a problem, you can call Hal or me. I'll have someone drop food and clean clothes off for you. Diesel says you're not to leave the Rangeman building."

I parked the RV against the wall, and Hal pulled alongside in a black Explorer. We drove past the car wash on the way to my apartment. It was all business as usual. No one was running around looking like a robbery had just been committed. Fingers crossed that they wouldn't open the safe and freak. I didn't want anything to go wrong. I was excited about getting my hands on Grandma.

I thanked Hal and hurried into the lobby. Dillon Ruddick, the building super, and a couple tenants were milling around in front of the open elevator.

"I've never smelled anything like it," Mrs. Ruiz said. "I got out of the elevator, and it wouldn't go away. It's stuck in my clothes."

"It's a horse fart," Mr. Klein said. "There's manure in the parking lot, and the elevator smells like a horse fart. Someone's keeping a horse in this building."

"That's ridiculous," Mrs. Ruiz said. "Who would do such a thing?"

Everyone turned and looked at me.

"Do you smell it?" Mr. Klein asked.

"What?"

"Horse fart."

"I thought that was the guy in 3C."

Dillon snorted and grinned at me. Not a lot got by Dillon, but he was a good guy, and you could buy him with a six-pack. I ducked into the stairs and ran up a flight.

Diesel was at the dining room table, working at my computer. "Delvina called," Diesel said. "He wanted to make the exchange in an abandoned factory at the end of Stark Street. I told him that didn't work for us. He won't do it at the car wash again. I don't think he knows the money is missing, but he's uncomfortable. He's kidnapped an old lady. That's different from a horse. That's a trip to the big house."

"Did you settle on a location?"

"I wanted it someplace public. He wanted it someplace isolated. He's afraid the police are involved. It's a reasonable fear. We agreed to meet in the multiplex parking lot."

"Which multiplex?"

"Hamilton Township."

"That theater went bankrupt. It's boarded up."

"Yeah, I would have preferred to have more people around. I'm going to make the exchange. I don't trust Delvina. He's too nervous. I want you on the roof with a rifle."

"I'm not actually a gun person. If you want a sharpshooter, that would be Connie."

"Then get Connie. The exchange is set to take place at noon. I need to have you and Connie on the roof at least an hour ahead. The front of the parking lot is wide open. The back is up against an alley that gives access to the Dumpsters. To the other side of the alley is a greenbelt. So you should be able to sneak in the back door and get up on the roof. I'll make sure all the doors are open for you. I've been pulling up aerial shots of the area on your computer, and I think this will work."

TEN

"**We have the** money to ransom Grandma," I told Connie and Lula when I got to the bonds office. "The exchange is going to take place at noon in the parking lot of the bankrupt multiplex in Hamilton Township."

"Where'd you get that kind of money?" Lula asked.

"Diesel picked it up."

"He's the man," Lula said.

"He needs a sharpshooter on the roof, covering his back," I said to Connie. "Can you take a couple hours off today?"

"Sure," Connie said. "I'll pick out something nice from the back room."

The back room to the bonds office contained a mess of confiscated items ranging from toaster ovens to Harleys to computers and televisions. It also housed an arsenal. Connie had a crate of handcuffs bought at a fire sale, boxes of ammunition for just about every gun in the universe, handguns, shotguns, rifles, machine guns, knives, a couple Tasers, and a rocket launcher.

"I'm not exactly chopped liver with a gun," Lula said. "I'll come, too."

Lula was only a marginally better shot than me. The difference between Lula and me was that Lula was willing to shoot at most anything.

A half hour later, Lula parked her Firebird on the far side of the greenbelt, and we bushwhacked our way through the vegetation to the alley. The alley was empty and the back door to the theater was unlocked. Connie had a sniper rifle equipped with a high-powered scope and laser, plus a purse filled with assorted toys. Lula had chosen an assault rifle. And I was elected to carry the ammo and the rocket launcher.

"I really don't think we need a rocket launcher," I said to Lula.

"Better safe than sorry," Lula said. "And anyways, I always wanted to fire off one of them rockets."

Connie went in first, and we all followed the beam from her flashlight through the dark theater and up the fire stairs to the door that led to the roof. The door was unlocked, as promised. The roof was flat and tarred. The sun was weak in a gray sky, heavy with clouds and the threat of rain. I was wearing a sweatshirt under a windbreaker, and I felt the chill creeping through the layers.

I could see why Diesel had chosen this particular building. We were able to hide behind an elaborate stucco false front and still see everything in the lot below. Lula and Connie found positions they liked. I found a place where I could see the action and not get in the way.

"I feel just like a SWAT guy," Lula said. "If I'd known, I'd have dressed appropriately."

As it was, Lula was in four-inch stilettos, a short black spandex skirt that almost fit her, an orange spandex T-shirt, and a matching orange faux fur jacket.

We hunkered in to wait for the exchange, and at eleven-thirty, we heard a car pull up to the back of the building. We ran to the back and looked down at a black Lincoln Town Car. Two men got out and tried the door. We'd locked the door after we'd entered, so they went to the trunk of the Town Car, got a tire iron, beat the crap out of the door, and pried it open. They went back to the trunk, got a couple rifles, and disappeared into the building.

"I bet they're Delvina guys," Lula said. "They're probably coming up to the roof."

Connie nodded in agreement.

"Well, tough tooties," Lula said. "We were here first. We got dibs on the roof."

"I think we need to ice them," Connie said. "Anybody bring cuffs?"

"I got some," Lula said. She stuck her head in her purse and, after some rooting around, came up with two pair.

Connie and Lula stood on either side of the door and waited for the men. The door opened, the men appeared, and Connie raised her rifle.

"Freeze," Connie said. "Drop your weapons. Hands in the air."

They both turned and looked at her.

"What the fuck?" the one guy said.

They were middle-aged thugs, dressed in bowling shirts and Sansabelt slacks. Their hair was slicked back. Their shoes were scuffed and run down at the heel. Their guns weren't as big as ours.

"Guns on the ground," Connie said.

"And what if we don't do that? You girls gonna get tough?"

Connie shot a hole in his foot. Actually, it was mostly just a chunk taken off the side of his shoe, but from the way he dropped his gun and started jumping around, you could assume she'd nicked his little toe.

"Fuck, fuck, fuck!" he yelled. "What the fuck!"

There were a bunch of pipes running along the roof that attached to air-conditioning units. Lula patted both men down and cuffed them to one of the pipes.

"What about my foot?" the one guy asked. "Look at it. It's bleeding. I need a doctor."

"If either of you makes a single sound, I'm going to shoot you in the other foot," Connie said.

We went back to our positions in the front of the building and watched the lot. At exactly noon, two cars slowly drove into view. One was a black Town Car. The other was my Monte Carlo. The cars parked a good distance apart and sat at idle. The driver's side door to the Town Car opened and Mickey got out. Diesel got out of the Monte and ambled over. Surfer dude meets the Mob.

They stood talking for a moment, Diesel with his hands loose at his sides and a black canvas messenger bag hung on his shoulder. Diesel handed the messenger bag to Mickey. Mickey turned to leave, and Diesel wrapped his hand around the bag's shoulder strap.

"Not so fast. I want Grandma."

His voice was soft, but it carried up to us.

"Sure," Mickey said. "She's in the car. I'll go get her."

"I'll keep the bag until you come back," Diesel said.

Mickey shook his finger at him. "You have trust issues."

"People keep telling me that."

Mickey walked to the car and opened the back door. Grandma lurched out, gave Mickey the finger, and harrumphed over to Diesel. Diesel passed the messenger bag to Mickey and took possession of Grandma.

I almost collapsed with relief. I had to hold on to the wall to keep from sinking to my knees.

"Hold on," Lula said. "There's another car coming."

It was black, and it was moving fast. Diesel glanced at the car, grabbed Grandma's hand, and pulled her toward the Monte Carlo. The black car slid to a stop in front of the Monte and four men jumped out with guns drawn. Diesel changed direction and ran to the movie entrance with Grandma.

One of the men took aim, Connie picked him off, and everyone looked up to the roof. A second guy fired two shots at us, and Lula let loose with the assault rifle. It was like *war*. The three remaining men ducked behind their car and returned Lula's fire. Mickey and Delvina were out and shooting. And Diesel and Grandma scooted into the theater.

"This is bullshit," Lula said. "This here's the United States. We don't go around blasting the shit out of people here. Well, okay, maybe in the projects, but hell, this here's the friggin' multiplex.

There's things you don't do in the multiplex. Gimme that rocket launcher. I'll fix their ass."

"Do you know how to work it?" I asked.

"What's to know? It's point and shoot, right? They give these suckers to pinheads who join the army. How hard could it be? Just prop this big boy up for me, and I'll do the rest."

I covered my ears and closed my eyes and *phuunf!* The bird was away. We all looked over the edge of the building and *BANG*. The rocket blew up my car.

"Must be something wrong with the sight," Lula said. "At least you don't have to drive a car that's got no reverse."

The Monte was a fireball.

"You got insurance, right?" Lula asked.

Delvina and his men stood in openmouthed shock for a beat. Then they all dove into their cars and drove away. Diesel opened the door and looked out at my car. He was hands on hips, and from my perch high above him, I could see he was smiling. You want to make a man smile . . . just blow up a car with a rocket.

Rain had started misting down on us. I packed up the ammo, and Lula and Connie shouldered their rifles.

"Hey," the guy with the shot-off toe said. "What about us?"

"Someone will come up here looking for you . . . probably," Connie said.

"Yeah, but it's raining. I'm gonna get a cold."

"Hold on," Lula said, peering over the edge of the building. "The one black car is coming back."

Connie and I ran to the edge and looked down. It was Delvina's car. It pulled up to the front door, and Delvina got out and stormed into the building.

"You guys stay here and make sure no one else goes in," I said. "I'm going downstairs to help Diesel."

"Here," Connie said. "Take my flashlight and this microwave stunner. It's new. Vinnie won it in a crap game last week. Just point it like a gun and pull the trigger. It doesn't do any permanent damage, but it makes your skin feel like it's on fire."

I took the stunner and ran down the stairs into the dark lobby. I stood and listened. There was a corridor to my left and a corridor to my right. Multiple movie theaters opened off the two corridors. I thought I heard movement in the right corridor. I crept along, hand to the wall, feeling my way in total blackness. I didn't want to give myself away by using the flashlight.

I stopped and listened again. I was at the entrance to one of the theaters, and I could hear the very faint murmur of voices. I held my breath and eased inside. I tiptoed up the ramp that led to the stadium seating and cautiously moved into the aisle.

Delvina, Diesel, and Grandma were about twenty rows in front of me. Grandma and Diesel were facing me, caught in the glare of Delvina's flashlight. I saw Diesel's eyes flick to me for a nanosecond and return to Delvina.

"You know how I found you in here?" Delvina said to Grandma and Diesel. "I got a nose for it. I didn't get where I am for no reason. I'm cagey. And I got a nose for danger. I see danger and I get rid of it. You know what I'm saying?"

"No," Grandma said. "You're a nut."

"I'm saying you're disturbing my comfort level," Delvina said. "So I'm gonna have to get rid of you. Both of you. I should have gotten rid of you last month when you gave me this rash," he said to Diesel. "I know it was you. And you said you were gonna turn me into a toad, and now look at me. It's happening."

I aimed the stunner at Delvina's neck and hit the GO button.

"Yow," Delvina said, slapping at his neck.

He still had the gun trained on Grandma, but he was hopping around, and I couldn't keep the microwave stunner on target.

"It's you," he said to Diesel. "You're sending bugs to bite me, right? Fire bugs. I know you're not normal. O'Connor even said so. He said you had these *skills*. You and that horse. You're in this together, aren't you? Putting thoughts in my head."

"What kind of thoughts?" Grandma wanted to know.

"Horse thoughts," Delvina said. "He talks to me. I hear him in my head. What kind of horse does that?"

"Maybe he's an alien horse," Grandma said. "I saw a television show once about how these aliens came down to this place in Arizona and were controlling people's minds and making them go on all these porno sites on the Internet."

Delvina stopped moving, and I aimed for the hand that was holding the gun. He yelped, dropped the gun, and grabbed his hand.

"Get him!" Grandma yelled.

Delvina grabbed her, shoved her into Diesel, and took off running. By the time Diesel had untangled himself from Grandma, Delvina was out of the theater. I ran after him, but he had a good head start. Surprising how fast he could move his bloated body on his skinny little toad legs.

I heard shots being fired from the roof and it sounded like shots were being returned from the theater entrance. I flicked the flashlight off so I wouldn't be an easy target, and I came to a dead stop in the dark. Diesel came up behind me, grabbed my hand, and pulled me along, the two of us running flat-out. Me in blind trust, and Diesel not having a problem seeing.

We turned into the lobby, partially lit from the glass entrance doors, and beyond the glass doors I saw the black car take off.

Diesel and I pushed through the doors and stood against the building, sheltered from the rain, and watched the black car race out of the lot. My Monte Carlo was burning out of control in front of us.

"This is a pip of a fire," Grandma said, coming up behind us with Lula and Connie.

"I was inside the theater, but I saw the Monte Carlo get hit," Diesel said. "Who shot the rocket off?"

"I might have done that," Lula said. "I'm pretty sure that launcher was defective."

"Are you okay?" I asked Grandma.

"I could use some lipstick."

Lula dropped Grandma, Diesel, and me at my apartment. We waved good-bye and walked into the small lobby. The elevator doors were locked into the open position and a fan had been placed inside the elevator. Behind the fan was a pop-up spring meadow air freshener.

"Someone must have left a stinker in there," Grandma said.

We took the stairs and shuffled down the hall. There was a slight scent of horse when we entered my apartment, but it wasn't unpleasant.

"I know this is crazy, but I sort of feel sorry for Lou Delvina," Grandma said. "I heard him talking, and he was saying how his wife left him on account of Diesel giving him the rash and making him all swell up. That's why Delvina wants his money back. So he can buy a big fancy house for his wife. He figures that would get her back." Grandma slid her dentures around a little. "I tell you, that Delvina's only got one oar dipped in the water. It's a real sad thing to see. He used to be a respected mobster. And now he's nutso cuckoo."

I called my mother.

"I have Grandma here in my apartment," I said. "I'll bring her home in a little while."

"Why can't you bring her home now?"

"I'm having car issues."

"I'll send your father for her."

I got Grandma spruced up as best I could, and she was ready to go when my father knocked on my door.

"There's a fat guy who looks like a toad out in your parking lot," my father said. "He's talking to himself, and I think he's making a Molotov cocktail."

We all went to my window and looked out. Lou Delvina was in the lot, standing in the rain, trying to light a rag he'd crammed into a wine bottle. I opened the window and stuck my head out.

"Hey," I said. "What are you doing?"

"I'm doing what I have to do," Delvina yelled up at me.

He lit the rag and heaved the bottle. It crashed through the top pane of my living room window and rolled on the floor. Some of the carpet got singed, but the bottle didn't break. Diesel grabbed the bottle and threw it back out the window. It smashed on the pavement next to Delvina's black Town Car, and the Town Car was almost instantly consumed by flames.

"Eeek!" Delvina shrieked, jumping away from the fire. "Alien voodoo! Someone call the National Guard, Homeland Security, Men in Black." He looked up at Diesel and shook his fist. "You're not gonna get me. I know how it is with you aliens. I know what you do to people. This is a fight to the finish." And Delvina ran out of the lot and disappeared from view.

"Poor man," Grandma said. "Where do you suppose he got the idea Diesel is an alien?"

"As far as I'm concerned, none of this happened," my father said to me. "I didn't see anything. That's what I'm telling your mother."

I closed and locked the door when my father and grandmother left. Fire trucks screamed in the distance and black smoke billowed from the burning car. Diesel taped a plastic garbage bag to the broken window to keep the smoke and rain out of the apartment.

My phone rang and I saw from the display that it was Morelli.

"I hear there's a car burning in your parking lot," Morelli said.

"It's not mine. My car was blown up and burned at the multiplex."

Morelli absorbed this for a beat. "There was a time when I'd freak over that, but now it seems sort of normal. The car in your lot . . . did you set it on fire?"

"Nope."

"Do I need to know any gory details?"

"No. Everything's under control. Diesel taped a garbage bag over the broken window, and the firebomb only singed the carpet a little."

"Great," Morelli said. And he disconnected.

"He take that okay?" Diesel asked.

"I could hear him chewing Rolaids."

ELEVEN

The smoke stopped rolling past my windows and the unintelligible chatter and squawk of the police band was intermittent. One fire truck and one squad car remained. A tow truck was standing by to haul the remains of Delvina's car off to the auto graveyard. Most of my neighbors were back in their apartments, finding television to be more entertaining than the dismal charred carcass left in the lot.

Diesel and I were in the kitchen eating peanut butter sandwiches. Diesel stopped with a sandwich in hand and listened. "Now what?" he said. He went to the door, and the doorbell rang.

Diesel opened the door to Mickey.

"This is awkward," Mickey said.

Diesel and I looked past Mickey, down the hall. Mickey shook the rain off his umbrella and propped it up against the wall. "I'm alone. Can I come in?"

"Do you have a bomb?" I asked.

"No. What I got is a headache."

"What's up?"

"I'm looking for Mr. Delvina, and I couldn't help noticing you have a freshly cooked car in your lot that might be the same size as Mr. Delvina's car."

I spread peanut butter on a slice of bread and added some potato chips and olives. "It is, in fact, Mr. Delvina's car," I told Mickey.

"Was Mr. Delvina in it when it got cooked?"

"Unfortunately, no."

"Mr. Delvina isn't a well man," Mickey said.

"No kidding."

"He isn't himself these days. Between you and me, he doesn't have a rash no more, but he likes the medicine. He's been taking more and more of it, and I think it's making him funny in the head."

I finished constructing the sandwich and offered it to Mickey.

"Thank you. I didn't get no lunch. Mr. Delvina was anxious to get to the multiplex. He needs the money to get the missus back, but personally I think he's spending the money on his medicine. Now he's got this idea that Diesel is an alien. It's crazy. It's just crazy."

Mickey took a bite of the sandwich and chewed. "This is delicious," he said. "I don't usually like peanut butter, but this sandwich got everything in it."

"You don't think Diesel is an alien?"

"Of course not. Everyone knows aliens don't look like that. Aliens got them big heads with the big eyes and skinny bodies. They look like what's-his-name . . . Gumby."

"There you have it," I said to Diesel. "You don't look like an alien."

"Good to know," Diesel said.

"Anyways, after Mr. Delvina went goofy at the multiplex, we had a difference of opinion, and he kicked me out of the car and drove away. Mr. Delvina wanted to firebomb this apartment because he thinks you two are doing knicky-knacky here and trying to breed the spawn of the alien devil." Mickey stopped eating and thought about that for a moment. "How did Mr. Delvina's car get cooked?" he asked.

"Firebomb," I told him.

Mickey shook his head. "He never could get the hang of a good firebomb. I always had to make them. It's important to use the right kind of bottle. People think just anyone can make a firebomb, but that isn't so."

"It's a skill," Diesel said.

"Exactly," Mickey said. "We all got special skills, right? Like the boss. He used to be real good at sizing up people. He had instincts." Mickey gave his head a shake. "I feel bad that the boss is wacko. I think I've been one of them enablers. I've been going out and getting him the medicine. I shouldn't have been doing that." Mickey washed his sandwich down with a diet soda. "You should be careful. Mr. Delvina don't give up on something once he gets an idea in his head. Even now that he's screwy." Mickey wrote his phone number on a piece of paper and gave it to me. "Call me if you see Mr. Delvina, and I'll come try to catch him."

Diesel closed the door after Mickey and grinned at me. "People think we're doing knicky-knacky up here."

"Don't get any ideas."

"Too late. I have lots of ideas."

"Are any of them about Lou Delvina?"

"Not right now," Diesel said.

"Delvina's not going to be happy when he opens his safe to deposit the money he got today."

Diesel screwed the top onto the peanut butter jar and put his knife in the dishwasher. "I hate to say this, but we're going to have to find Delvina and neutralize him somehow before he figures out how to build a better bomb."

"Neutralize," I said. "That's very civilized."

"Yeah, I'd feel like a real tough guy if I said I was going to *whack* Delvina, but it wouldn't be true. I'm not a killer."

I went to the window and looked out. The fire truck and police car were gone. Delvina's car was slowly being towed away on a flatbed. Probably there was a cop somewhere in the building going door to door asking questions. I thought it best if we left before he got to the second floor.

I zipped an all-weather jacket over my sweatshirt and hung my purse on my shoulder. "Delvina is on foot. He can steal a car, call a friend, or he can walk to the car wash. I'm betting on the car wash."

We locked the apartment and took the stairs to the lobby. We pushed through the lobby doors and stopped. We didn't have a car.

"Crap," I said. "No car."

Diesel surveyed the cars in the lot. "Pick one."

"You don't kill people, but you steal cars?"

"Yep."

I hauled my cell phone out and I called Lula. "I need a ride to my parents' house."

My father was out running errands and my mother and grandmother were in the kitchen yelling at each other.

"You're grounded," my mother said to my grandmother. "You are not to leave this house."

"Blow it out your ear," my grandmother said.

My mother looked at me when I walked in. "What am I supposed to do with her?"

"I think you should make a deal."

"What kind of deal?"

"How about you buy her a television for her room if she promises not to go off like that ever again."

"I like that deal," Grandma said. "I could use a television in my room. I could watch whatever I wanted if I had my own television."

Everyone has a price.

"I guess that would be okay," my mother said. "We could get you a little flat screen that would sit on your bureau."

"I'm having car problems," I said. "I was wondering if I could borrow Uncle Sandor's Buick."

"Sure," my grandmother said. "Help yourself."

When my Great-Uncle Sandor went into the nursing home, he left his 1953 powder-blue-and-white Buick to Grandma Mazur. Grandma Leadfoot had her license revoked and isn't able to drive the car, but the car lives in my father's garage for emergency use.

"Sweet Thing, you've got a heck of a gene pool," Diesel said, following me out of the house. "Your grandmother is fearless. She's not even afraid of your mother."

"Grandma's philosophy is *now or never*."

I opened the garage door and Diesel's smile widened. "This is a *car*."

Actually, it only looked like a car. It drove like

a refrigerator on wheels. I gave Diesel the keys and climbed onto the passenger seat.

Diesel powered the car out of the Burg to Hamilton Avenue, and we cruised by the car wash. Not a lot going on in the rain. No sign of Delvina. We'd watched for him on the way over with Lula and hadn't seen him then, either.

"What will we do if we find Delvina?" I asked Diesel.

"Good question. If he was a normal person, we could sit on him and get him detoxed. Unfortunately, I don't think detoxing Delvina will entirely eliminate his desire to kill us."

We parked across the street half a block away, and I called Connie. "Tell me about Delvina's car wash. What does he do with it? Launder money? Run numbers? Pimp out hookers?"

"All of the above," Connie said. "I'm not sure about the laundering, but it's a cash operation, so it stands to reason he washes more than cars."

"How about employees? Would anyone have access to the safe besides Delvina?"

"So far as I know, he hires a bunch of dumb kids. If anyone else had access to the safe, I'd think it was his stooge, Mickey."

"Okay, here's what we've got," I said to Diesel. "He kidnapped Grandma and extorted Snuggy. He runs numbers out of the car wash, has a stable of hookers, and probably washes money. Surely we can get him sent away for at least one of those."

We'd sat there for a half hour and I was getting twitchy. Time was passing and Delvina was out there plotting God-knew-what.

My cell phone rang and I snatched it out of my purse.

"Delvina was here," Connie said. "He burst into the office like a crazy person, ranting and waving a gun around. He said he was looking for you and the alien. I'm guessing that would be Diesel. Clearly, neither of you was here, so he took off. He was rambling on about how you vacated your apartment, but he'd track you down. I think he might be going to your parents' house next. He said he knew where you lived."

"Stay here in the Buick and watch the car wash," Diesel said. "I'll go to your parents' house. If Delvina shows up, don't make a move. Just sit tight and call me."

"Take the Buick. It'll be faster."

He was out of the car. "I don't need the Buick."

"You aren't going to steal a car, are you?"

"Close your eyes and count to a hundred."

I closed my eyes and counted to twenty. I opened my eyes and Diesel was gone. I looked down the street. Was a car missing from the curb?

The rain had dropped back to a drizzle. It streaked the windshield and shimmered on the street. It was midafternoon and traffic was picking up. A black Town Car pulled into the car wash lot and parked behind the office. The rear quarter panel of the car was peppered with bullet holes. The headlights blinked off, and Mickey got out of the car and went into the office through the back door.

Minutes later, an armored truck rolled down the street, pulled into the lot, and parked beside the Town Car. Delvina got out of the armored truck and walked to the building, carrying the messenger bag. He was wearing a bulky raincoat, and his head was wrapped in aluminum foil.

I tapped Diesel's number into my cell phone and the number instantly went to voicemail. "Delvina's here," I said and disconnected.

I sat for a couple moments and ran out of patience. I got out of the car and ran across the street to the car wash. I crept around the building, hoping to see in a window, but had no luck. I very slowly and silently turned the knob to the back door and eased the door open just a crack.

The office was basically one large room with a front door opening into the car wash lobby and a back door opening to the parking lot. I peeked through the crack and saw Delvina and Mickey in front of the safe.

"You got a what?" Mickey asked.

"An armored car. I'm taking my money and I'm going to Kansas. I read where it's safer from aliens in the middle of the country."

"That's crazy. And what about the missus and her new house?"

"Screw the missus. I don't even want a new house. I don't know what was wrong with the old house. Anyway, this is serious. I'm gonna get rid of this alien, but there might be more. They travel in packs or pods or something." Delvina took a bottle out of his pocket and popped some pills into his mouth.

"You should go easy on those pills," Mickey said. "I think they might be making you goofy."

"I need these pills. I got a rash."

"I don't see no rash."

"That's because I'm taking the pills, stupid."

"What are you wearing on your head? Is that for the rain?"

"It's so they can't control my mind. You know how we use aluminum foil to scramble the GPS when we hijack a truck? It's the same with aliens. You wear this aluminum foil on your head, and they can't fuck with your mind."

"I guess that makes sense, but I'm not convinced they're aliens. They don't look like aliens."

"That's because they're shape-shifters. Remember when we used to watch *Star Trek*?"

"Yeah, them shape-shifters were nasty buggers."

"Anyway, I'm sorry I kicked you out of the car, and I didn't mean it when I fired you," Delvina said. "It's just you weren't making any sense."

"Maybe, but I don't see where we want to make trouble with that big guy Diesel and the Plum woman."

"It's us or them," Delvina said. "Anybody can see that."

Delvina set the black canvas messenger bag on the floor by the safe and spun the dial. He fed in the combination, pulled the door open, and gasped. No duffel bag in the safe.

"Where's the bag?" he asked Mickey. "Where's the money?"

"It's in the safe," Mickey said.

"The safe's friggin' empty."

"That's impossible. Only you and me's got the combination. How would the safe get empty? Maybe you took the money out and forgot."

Color was oozing into Delvina's face. "I got a mind like a steel trap. I don't forget nothing. I'm no dummy."

"Yeah, but boss, you been taking a lot of pills lately."

"Stop with the pills. I know what I'm doing. You're the one who don't know what he's doing." Delvina tapped his finger against the aluminum foil. "You're not protecting your brain like I am. And I'm smart enough to know who took the money."

"Who took it?" Mickey asked.

"You took it," Delvina said.

"I don't think so. I don't remember taking it."

"You took it because I fired you. Thought you'd get away with it."

"That's insulting. I wouldn't do something like that."

"I want my money," Delvina yelled at Mickey. "Give it to me."

"I don't got it. I swear."

Delvina grabbed a double-barreled shotgun from a gun rack on the wall. "This is your last chance."

Mickey's eyes looked like they were about to pop out of their sockets. "That's nuts."

Delvina raised the shotgun and Mickey took off for the back door. I jumped away and Mickey ran out of the building, slamming the door shut behind him. *BAM!* Delvina blasted a cantaloupe-size hole in the door. Mickey threw himself into the Town Car and cranked it over.

I looked down at my feet and told them to run, but they didn't do anything.

Delvina kicked the door open and aimed at the car, but the car was already skidding out of the lot. I was standing behind the door and would have been hidden except for the big hole in it.

"You!" Delvina said. And he turned the shotgun on me.

I was total deer in the headlights. I was open-mouthed, heart-thumping frozen.

"Get in the office," he said. "Go!"

I stumbled inside and tried to pull it together. I didn't think he'd shoot me if I didn't make any sudden moves. Diesel was the guy he really wanted. He'd use me to get Diesel.

Delvina took cuffs out of the top desk drawer. He dropped them on the desk and took a step back with the shotgun still trained on me. "Put them on."

I cuffed myself with my hands in front. If you're serious about restraining someone, you never do this. Hands are always cuffed behind, but Delvina didn't seem to care.

"Okay," he said. "Where is he?"

My mind was racing. I needed to get Delvina into a position where he'd be at a disadvantage. I was afraid if we stayed in the office, Diesel might walk in and get blown away. I decided my best chance at survival was to take Delvina to Range-man and have Ranger's crew come to my rescue.

"Diesel went to check on Snuggy and Doug,"

I said. "They're hidden in a parking garage down-town."

"Then that's where we're going." He motioned to the door with the shotgun. "Walk."

I squinted into the misting rain when I stepped outside. I didn't see Diesel. I didn't see Mickey returning with an attendant from the psychiatric ward at St. Francis. What I saw was an armored truck.

"Get in," Delvina said. "You're driving."

"That might not be a good idea," I said. "I've never driven an armored truck before."

"It's like any other truck. It's even automatic. Just get in before I shoot you. It's raining on my aluminum foil. It's real loud in my head. Like rain on a tin roof."

I hauled myself up onto the driver's seat and put my cuffed hands on the wheel. "You're going to have to turn the key and put it into reverse," I told Delvina.

I inched my way back, Delvina put it into drive, and I inched my way out of the lot. I had no rear visibility except for the side mirrors. Narrow bul-letproof windshield. My hands were cuffed to-gether, and the monster drove like a freight train. I was afraid I'd run over a Dodge Neon and never know.

"Where did you get this?" I asked Delvina.

"Borrowed it."

Oh boy.

I rolled over a couple curbs and took out a mailbox, but I kept going.

"Cripes," Delvina said. "You're the worst driver I've ever seen."

Obviously, he'd never driven with Grandma. Considering I couldn't see for shit and my hands were cuffed, I thought I was doing an okay job. I didn't mow down the crossing guard, and I'd stopped for most of the lights.

"Where are we going?" Delvina wanted to know.

"It's on the next block. It's the narrow building with the underground garage."

I crept down the street and eased the nose of the armored truck up to the garage security gate.

"Now what?" Delvina asked.

Now I was supposed to flash my key card, but my key card was in my purse and my purse was in the Buick.

"I forgot about the security gate," I said.

Delvina put the truck in reverse. "Back it up a couple feet."

I slowly moved the truck back.

Delvina put the truck in drive. "Now ram the gate."

"*What?* Are you crazy? I'm not going to ram the gate. It's not like it's plywood."

"This is a armored truck, for crissake. It's built like a tank."

Delvina leaned forward, mashed his foot down on the gas pedal, and the truck surged into the gate. There was a lot of noise and sparks, and the gate buckled, snapping off its hinges.

With the exception of the private apartments, every inch of Rangeman is monitored, including the pavement outside the gate. When I decided to bring Delvina to Rangeman, I hadn't counted on ramming the gate. Now I was worried about not only getting shot by Delvina but by Ranger's Merry Men.

Snuggy and Doug were backed into a corner. Snuggy's eyes were wide, and Doug's eyes were narrowed. Delvina lumbered from the truck with the shotgun still leveled on me and ordered me to get out. I swung down just as Tank and Hal stepped out of the stairwell. They looked at me in cuffs, and they looked at Delvina with the shotgun, and the expression in their eyes was *oh shit!* The elevator doors opened and two more Rangeman guys stepped out with guns drawn.

Delvina opened his raincoat. "See this?" he said. "I'm wired to explode. I'm loaded with plastique. Shoot me, and this whole building goes. So drop your guns."

Everyone threw their guns on the floor, and Delvina looked around. "Where is he?"

"Who?" I asked.

"You know who. Diesel."

"He isn't here," Snuggy said. "Why have you got aluminum foil on your head?"

"It's so the horse don't talk to me."

Snuggy looked up at Doug. "You talk to him?"

Doug sort of shrugged. Or maybe it was just a muscle twitch in his shoulder.

"This isn't working out," Delvina said to me, "and I'm getting real agitated. Every time you get involved in my business, it turns into a cluster fuck. I'll tell you what I'm gonna do. I'm gonna shoot you. And then I'm gonna shoot the horse. And then I'm gonna shoot all these guys in black. And then I'm gonna get the hell out of town." He scratched at his arm and at his neck. "Look at me. I'm itching again. It's the damn rash. I need more medicine."

"You can't shoot all of us with that shotgun," I said. "You can only shoot one of us."

"Yeah. I'm gonna shoot you with the shotgun. Then I'm gonna shoot everyone else with the Glock I got shoved in my pants."

"Ranger's gonna hate this," Tank said. "Better to get shot than to have to explain the gate. Bad enough I got a horse that smells like his shower gel."

I looked beyond Delvina and saw Diesel at the garage entrance.

"Hey, Delvina!" Diesel said. "Are you looking for me?"

Delvina turned to look at Diesel, and Doug lunged at Delvina, knocking him down. Tank and Hal rushed at Delvina and wrestled the guns from him.

"This isn't plastique taped to him," Tank said. "It's modeling clay."

"It was short notice," Delvina said. "I couldn't find any plastique."

Hal looked over at the armored truck. "Where'd that come from?"

"He borrowed it," I said.

Two police cars angled to a stop in front of the garage.

Diesel ambled over to me and released the handcuffs. "Are you okay?"

"Yep."

"Good thing I was here to rescue you."

Doug kicked Diesel in the leg, and Diesel went down to one knee.

"The horse says you're full of road apples," Delvina said to Diesel.

TWELVE

Lula pushed her way past the police. "Connie and me heard about this on the scanner, and we figured it had to be you," she said to me. "Where's Ranger? He still out of town?"

"Yep."

"I bet you can't wait to tell him how you drove a armored truck through his fancy-ass security gate."

Just thinking about it gave me creepy crawlies.

Delvina was going nuts in cuffs. "I itch everywhere," he said. "Someone scratch me. Scratch my nose. Am I breaking out? I need my medicine. I got a bottle in my pocket. Someone pop a pill in my mouth."

"I got big news," Lula said. "You'll never guess what came in the mail just now. Remember that photographer in Atlantic City? He sent me a letter. He said he was real sorry the photo shoot got moved, but he thought my pictures were hot, and he sold one of them to the tourist board, and they made it into a billboard. And he sent me this check for five thousand dollars and a picture of the billboard."

I looked at the photo. It was Lula in a red lace thong, and across her boobs was written WE CAN KEEP A SECRET IN ATLANTIC CITY—NO MATTER HOW BIG! Lula's left boob had to be about five feet wide on the billboard, and I couldn't even estimate the size of her ass.

"I gotta go to Atlantic City to see my billboard," Lula said. "This is so exciting. I know us supermodels aren't supposed to get excited about this shit, but I can't help it."

"Doug says he'd like to see your billboard, but we don't have a horse trailer anymore," Snuggy said.

"I talked it over with Stephanie's grandmother, and we've agreed that the Delvina money should go toward Doug's operation," Diesel said to Snuggy. "The money should more than cover the vet expenses and buy a horse trailer."

Snuggy's eyes got red and he swiped at his nose. "That's real nice of you. Doug says he's sorry he kicked you. And Doug just had a good idea. Maybe we can buy the RV from Grandma instead of a horse trailer, and then Doug and me can go on trips together."

"I'm sure Grandma would be happy to sell you the RV," I said.

"And I have more good news," Diesel said. "The issue with Doug's previous owner has been resolved, and Doug is officially in your care. I now pronounce you horse and leprechaun."

I walked outside with Diesel. "How did you know I was at Rangeman?"

"Lucky guess."

"I suppose this means you'll be moving on."

"Yeah, but I'll be back, Sweet Thing. Close your eyes and count to a hundred."

I counted to twenty and opened my eyes. Diesel was gone . . . and so was my bra.